Home Electrics

Home Electrics

A practical guide to understanding safe installation and maintenance

Edited by Julian Worthington

ORBIS PUBLISHING · London

Acknowledgments

Advertising Arts 113–5, 116–7, 118–9, 124–5, 126; Antiference Ltd 93 (centre); Arka Graphics 78–80 (artwork); British Broadcasting Corporation 93 (top & bottom); Alan Cheeseman 7, 11–12 (artwork), 25; Gordon Cramp Studios 17, 90–2 (artwork); Concord Lighting International Ltd 86; Electricity Council 1, 65, 74 (inset photo); GEC-Xpelair Limited 64, 70 (photo); Hayward Art Group 34–5, 46–9, 54–9, 70 (artwork), 72; MK Electric Ltd 81; Orbis/Langham Studios 10, 12–13 (photos); Orbis/Terry Trott 2, 14–15, 16, 21, 24, 29, 33, 36, 50–3 (photos), 60–3 (photos), 66–7 (photos), 74 (photos), 85, 90–2 (photos); W J Parry Domestic Products Ltd 98–9 (artwork); Power-Lectric Ltd 71; Redring Electric 78 (photo); Studio Briggs 18, 28, 30–2, 37, 38–41, 42–5, 50–3 (artwork), 60–3 (artwork), 66–9 (artwork), 73–7 (artwork), 82–4, 87–9, 96, 105–6, 107–9, 110–2, 120–1, 122–3; Mike Trier 97–9 (photos); Venner Artists 22–3, 26–7; Peter Weller 94–5, 100–2, 103–4; Garry Whitehead 8–9 (artwork).

We would like to thank the Electricity Council for their co-operation in the production of this book.

First published in Great Britain
by Orbis Publishing Limited, London 1981

Reprinted 1983, 1984

Printed in Czechoslovakia
ISBN: 0-85613-348-5
50142/4

Contents

Introduction

Every home is dependent on electricity as a means of power; in fact, few gadgets will work without it. It provides lighting and heating – even if you have gas or oil as your main source of fuel – and it powers virtually all those household appliances that have become an essential part of people's lives today.

Because we cannot see electricity we tend to fear it; the only reason we know it is there is when we operate a switch, or accidentally touch a live wire and get a nasty shock. But a basic understanding of what it is, how it works and where it runs through the home will go a long way to removing the apprehension. The key word is safety.

More than with any other work around the home, accuracy is all important. 'Nearly right' may be acceptable on some jobs, but this does not apply to electricity. Whatever job you do which involves working with or using this source of power, it must be 100 per cent right; there is no margin for error. That is why so much of this book is devoted to large, accurate diagrams on wiring and installation. If you follow the rules, check at every stage and double check at the end – and do not try to take short cuts – you will find that installing and repairing appliances, fittings and circuits is within the scope of the careful, competent worker.

There are of course many words of warning – and some are more obvious than others. For example, never work on any electrical fitting or appliance without first disconnecting it and – if necessary – switching off the power at the mains. This sounds very obvious, but it is amazing how many times people forget – and that is nearly always where the trouble starts. Always plan the work carefully before you begin. It may take that much longer to do what appears on the surface to be a perfectly simple job, but bear in mind that mistakes can be very costly to rectify – and you may not even be given that chance. When you disconnect or strip down any unit, always mark clearly each wire or terminal so that you connect up correctly when the job is completed.

Most of the electrical equipment and fittings are your property. But remember that the mains supply into your home, right up to and including the Electricity Board's meter, is not. This part of the circuit belongs to your regional Electricity Board and on no account should you ever try to tamper with or work on this part of the supply. Should you wish to isolate your consumer unit – if, for example, you want to fit a new, larger unit in order to run off it more circuits – you must get your regional Electricity Board to come and disconnect you and reconnect you when the work is finished. The Boards are required by law to isolate a consumer's installation from the mains on request during normal working hours.

On the whole, however, the work you will normally need to carry out can be done by turning off the main switch on your consumer unit or fuse box. This will isolate all circuits in the home and work can then be carried out in total safety. But remember that as soon as you turn the main supply back on it will activate all circuits again; so make sure you have finished all the jobs on the various circuits. Never leave a job unfinished, even though you may not wish to use that particular circuit immediately.

Although in this book you are given all the information needed for rewiring circuits or adding new ones, you may not want to tackle this type of work yourself. But there are many other smaller jobs which you can handle easily and safely and which will minimize the inconvenience of important fittings or appliances not working. The basic techniques of repairing fuses or wiring up plugs, stripping cable and flex and joining them, checking consumption and diagnosing faults are all covered in this book.

There are a lot of items you may want to fit yourself, such as light fittings and switches, dimmers and time switches, bells, buzzers, chimes, TV aerials and sockets, cookers and cooker hoods and the range of bathroom fittings. Within this book there are detailed instructions on how to carry out all these jobs, as well as the more major work of moving, adding and wiring up lights, switches and sockets, wiring a converted loft and wiring outside to a garage or greenhouse, for example, or putting lights in the garden.

One of the most inconvenient and costly types of electrical equipment when it goes wrong is the domestic appliance. One section in this book is devoted to the basic repairs you can safely carry out on some appliances – vacuum cleaner, iron, toaster, kettle, fire, hair dryer, tumble dryer, fridge, freezer, mixer, blender, washing machine and floor polisher. Major overhaul work should be left to the manufacturer or appointed repair specialists and models which differ in design from those illustrated should be left to specialists. There are individual parts of many appliances that you can replace yourself; but do not attempt to service any appliances contrary to manufacturers' instructions. Again a word of caution. Do not be tempted to buy cheap or reconditioned parts and always buy spare parts from a manufacturer's recommended outlets. Genuine spare parts may be that bit more expensive, but at least you know that you are getting the right part for the machine. There is another point you should bear in mind when considering doing your own repair work on an appliance. Check first whether you are covered by the terms of the manufacturer's guarantee. If you tackle certain jobs on a new machine yourself, you may well invalidate this guarantee, which could prove costly – and the manufacturer will not be sympathetic to any sob stories if this is the case.

The information contained in this book should not be regarded as an open invitation to tamper with electrical fittings and equipment. Initially it should be used to give you an understanding of electricity, where it goes, what it does and how it works. When you have grasped the principles, you can then look at the jobs you feel confident to tackle. And if you do not feel you have sufficient expertise to do the work yourself, you will save a lot of time and money just by being able to diagnose the faults and making sure any repair work is done correctly – and is necessary. Above all, take special note of all warnings. They are there for your safety and protection and you ignore them at your peril.

Electricity and the home

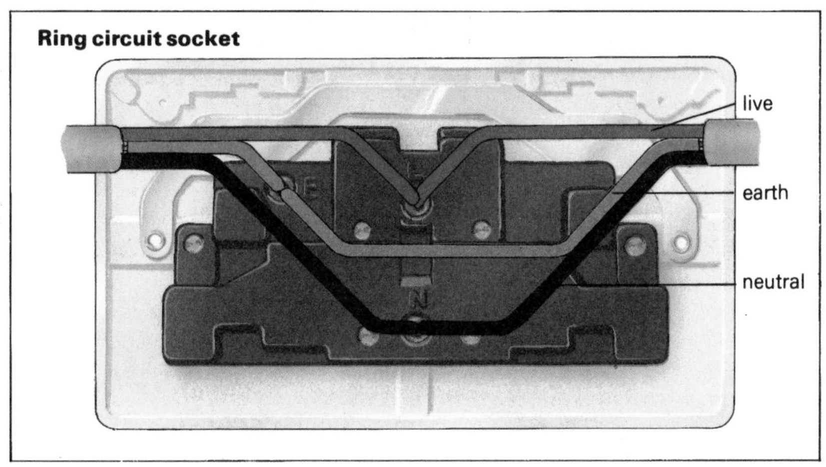

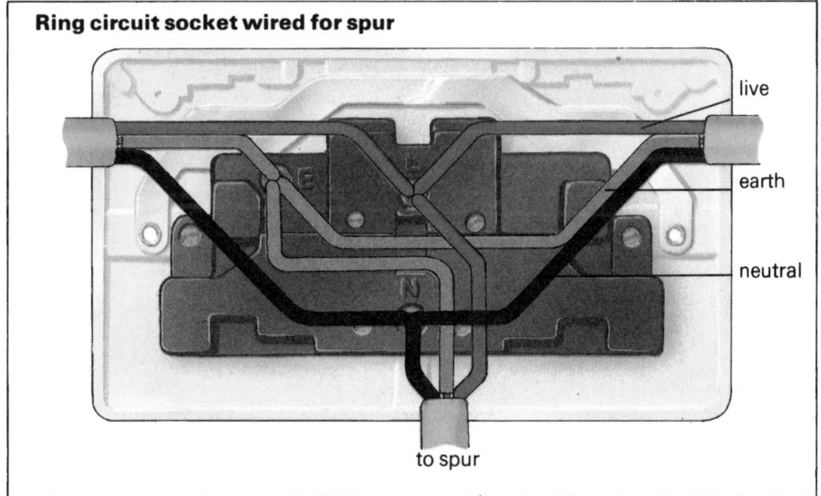

The first thing to learn about electricity in the home is how it works and what it does. Having grasped the basic principles, most of the work you may want to tackle will be that much easier to understand and carry out correctly. Find out where electricity comes from and where it goes and know the various types of cable and flex and what they are used for. Check your own consumption so you can work out where savings can be made. Save time and money by being able to diagnose the fault, whether you repair it yourself or call in the expert. And check on the major danger area of the home – the bathroom.

ABC of electricity

Electricity is the source of energy for heating, lighting and powering many appliances in your home. In knowing all about it, you can tackle all sorts of repairing and fitting jobs safely.

Rather like the water supply, electricity comes into most homes from some unknown outside source: but how does it arrive and what is it? Pushing down a switch gives immediate light and power to drive fans, cleaners and kitchen equipment; it also provides gradually increasing heat in kettles, cookers, fires, immersion heaters and central heating. But beyond this point electricity is to most people a mystery, and to many something to be feared. Some people even think that electricity leaks out of every power socket without a plug in it, or lampholder that does not have a bulb in it. An understanding of the simple principles of how electricity works can help to remove the fear.

Although it may help you to understand electricity by comparing it with the water supply, it is important to remember that this is only an analogy; the electricity supply is in some ways similar to the water supply, but it is quite wrong to suppose it will continue to behave like water in every respect. Electricity will only flow in a conductor; you can compare this to water flowing in a pipe. But while water will keep flowing out of a broken pipe, electricity will not continue flowing out of a broken wire unless there is some other conductor – a screwdriver, a hacksaw blade, some other metal or wet material – to conduct it away. The reason is that electricity does not really 'flow', it is much more like the hydraulic fluid that operates the brakes of a car or the big jacks used in constructional engineering.

Hydraulic fluid transmits pressure along a pipe from one place to another (**see 1**); and if the pipe is cracked, or there is not enough fluid, the system will not work. In the same way, electricity supplied to the home at a certain 'pressure' is used to do the work of driving motors, or making heat and light.

The earth will conduct electricity very easily. The human body will not conduct it so easily, but easily enough. If you touch the bare end of a 'live' wire, or the contacts in a lamp-holder when the switch is on, the electricity will be conducted through your body to the earth. If you are lucky, the electricity will make your arm muscles jerk away as soon as you touch the wire, and you will only suffer an electric 'shock'. If you are unlucky, the electricity will make your finger muscles clamp onto the wire so that you cannot let go. You may die by electrocution or at the least be badly burned and anyone who tries to help you by touching you will suffer the same. In this situation the helper must switch off the electricity or, failing this, try sharply jerking the afflicted person away with a rope, tea towel or scarf, or anything non-conducting (that is, not metal or a wet material) like a broom.

DC or AC

Electricity can be supplied in two ways in domestic circumstances: as direct current (DC) or as alternating current (AC). All batteries – the lead battery of a car, the 'dry cell' of an electric torch or transistor radio, or the rechargeable battery of certain pieces of portable electronic equipment – supply DC. So do many private domestic generators, such as used to be installed in houses and farms far away from public supplies. The national electricity grid now provides AC supply to all but the most remote areas of Great Britain. Light bulbs and simple heaters will work equally well on DC or AC supply, but most modern electrical equipment is made to operate on AC only, and needs special modification for DC supply.

1

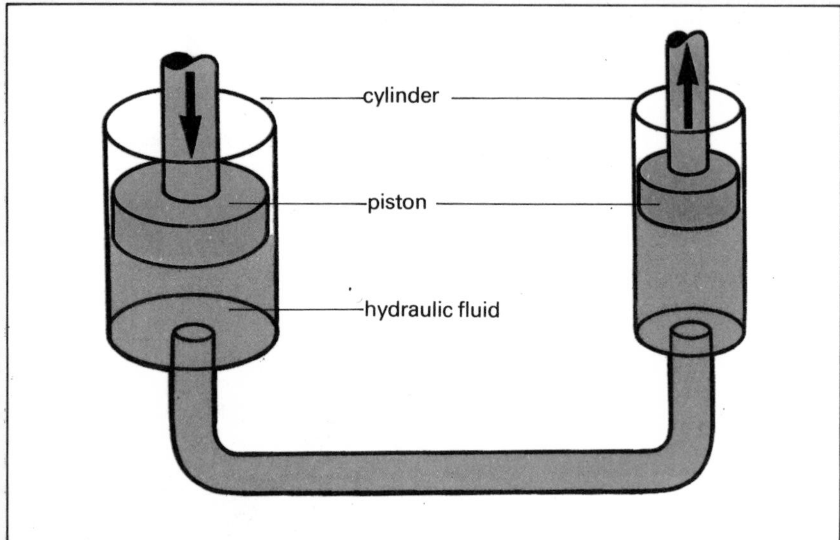

Voltage This term denotes the pressure exerted by the electricity supply. So a torch battery, at 1.5 volts, will give you no more than a tiny tingle if you put your wet tongue across the contacts; but don't try the same thing with your home supply at 240 volts!

It is easy to understand how the electricity from a DC source such as a battery can be imagined as exerting this pressure; but what about AC? In an AC supply the 'direction of flow' of electricity changes backwards and forwards, usually 50 times every second. The 'mains supply' enters your home as two wires: a 'live' wire (L) at a pressure of 240 volts, and a 'neutral' wire (N), which is connected to the earth. The live wire is coloured red and the neutral wire black.

The 'earth' wire

Why, then, is there a separate earth wire inside the home? The reason is that the neutral wire is only conducting to earth while everything is working properly. If a live wire works loose, or its insulation is worn away, it may touch the outside casing of an appliance; this is why any metal part of an appliance that can be touched, switch plates, lampholders etc. should be independently connected directly to earth by means of the earth wire.

Current and resistance

To understand a little more about electric current, you have to go back to comparing it with water flowing in a pipe (**see 2**). Suppose there is a pump A, which drives water through the pipe B. The ystem will only work if there is a complete circuit ack to A. The pump A can be thought of as the lectricity source, and it will only drive the turbine) if the tap C is open. So C is equivalent to a switch n an electrical circuit, and D is any appliance put nto the circuit (**see 3**).

The flow of the water round the pipe circuit is ike the 'flow' of electricity in an electrical circuit. As more water per second flows through D, so it vill do more work. In the same way, the greater the quantity of electricity flowing each second in the circuit, the more work it will do. The quantity of electricity per second, called current, is expressed in mperes (or amps for short). But here, once again, you must remember that electricity is not really like water. For instance, if you consider the statement 'more water is flowing per second', you think of it as flowing faster; but electricity always 'flows' at the same speed, and it is the amount of work it is capable of doing that changes. Imagine instead that the water is always flowing at the same pressure and the same speed, but being pumped through pipes of bigger bore.

You can also see that if the pipes were made narrower, it would become more and more difficult to get the water to flow, until eventually the pipe was so narrow that the pressure would not be sufficient to drive the water through at all. The narrow bore of the pipe is therefore exerting resistance. In the same way, part of an electrical circuit can be a resistance. In passing this resistance, the electricity does work. The work may consist of driving a motor or be in the form of heat or light. If there is no resistance to the electric current, electricity will flow through the circuit in such quantity that it is as if a pipe has burst: it can (almost literally) 'drain' the supply. This is why fuses are put into every part of the home electricity supply. If there is a 'short circuit', the large current flowing through the thin wire of the fuse heats it up and causes it to melt – breaking the circuit and stopping the flow.

Volts, amperes, ohms and watts

Resistance is measured in ohms. The relationship between volts, amperes and ohms is very easily expressed: volts = amperes × ohms.

As the domestic AC supply is at about 240 volts, and the safety limit for ordinary appliances is set at 13amps, you can calculate that the minimum resistance a circuit can offer is about 18 ohms.

The work that the electricity does is measured in watts. If you look at the manufacturer's plate on any electric appliance (**see 4**) you will see that it is rated at so many volts (220–240 volts, AC 50 cycles) and so many watts. The relationship between watts, volts and amperes is: volts × amperes = watts.

The pressure of the electricity supply – its voltage – does not normally change. The working appliance consumes electricity at a fixed rate. If the domestic supply is at 240 volts, and the appliance is rated at 960 watts, it will be consuming current at the rate of 4amps, which is within safe limits. If the total 'load' of appliances on any one domestic circuit adds up to more than 7200 watts, the current will exceed 30amps and the consumer unit fuse may 'blow'.

One thousand watts equal one kilowatt (kW) and electricity consumed over a period of one hour is called a kilowatt-hour (kWh), or one 'unit' of electricity. Electrical consumption is measured and charged for on this basis.

2

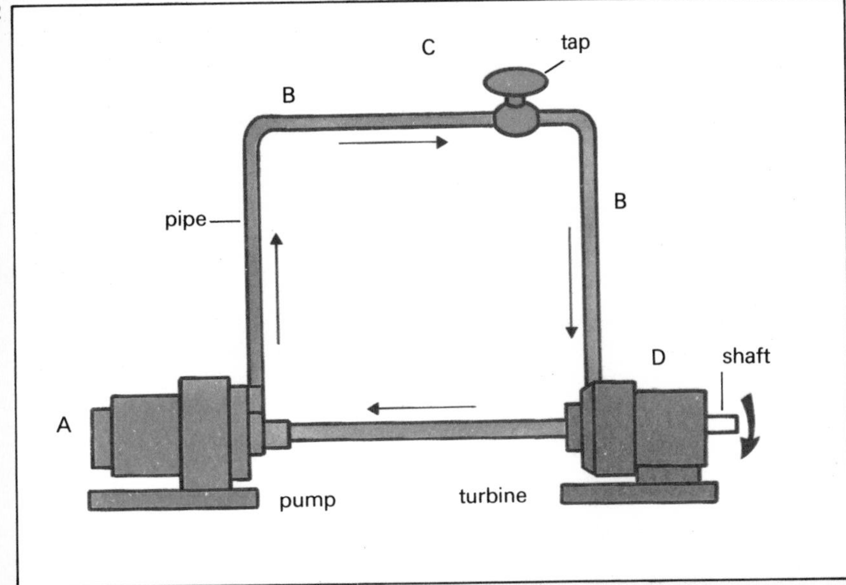

3

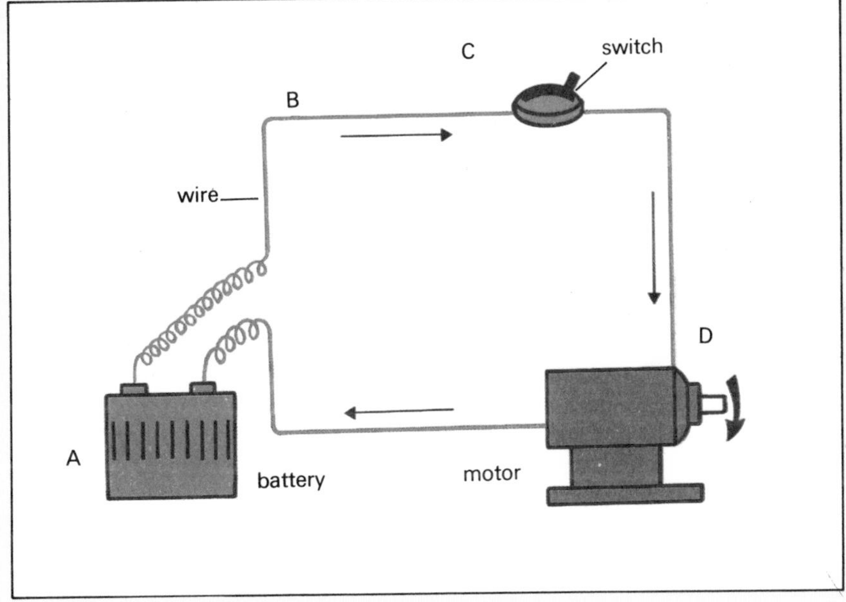

4

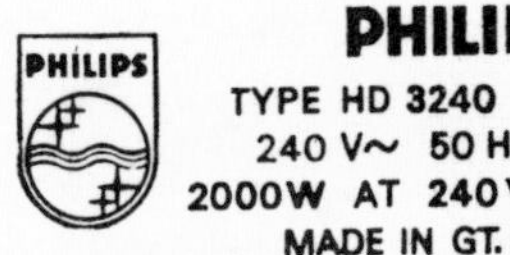

Earthing

When rewiring a plug make absolutely sure the earth wire (yellow/green or green) is properly connected. If it is not you run the risk of an electric shock should the metal casing of an appliance become accidentally live.

The only appliances which do not need earthing are double insulated ones supplied with two core flex and mains operated shavers which are intended for use with special shaver sockets.

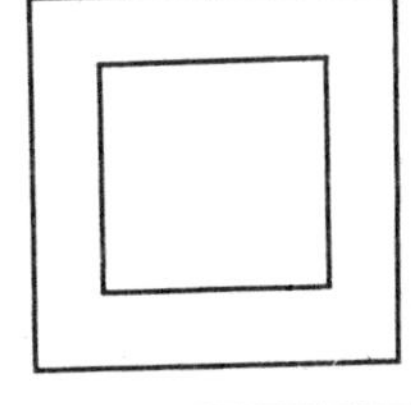

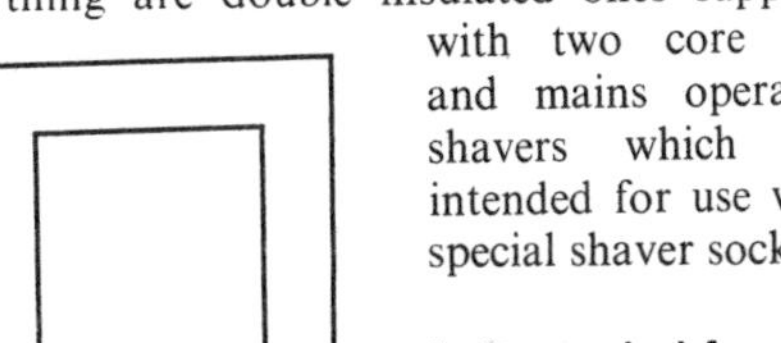

Left symbol for double insulation

Source of supply

The main electricity supply enters your home via an underground cable and normally appears at ground level; the system shown here is typical of many homes. On the left is the consumer unit (with a transformer underneath for the front door bell). To the right of the consumer unit is the black meter, which shows the consumption of electricity, and next to that is the sealed unit containing the Electricity Board fuse

When you turn on a switch you naturally expect the light to come on or a particular appliance to work. Circuits feed electricity all round the home, so you can use the power just where and when you want it.

Electricity is generated at a power station and conveyed across country by either underground cables or overhead cables strung between tall pylons. Its voltage is reduced by an enclosed transformer or sub-station in your locality and from there electricity is fed to your home at 240 volts.

Main supply

Cables which conduct electricity from the transformer to the consumer consist of insulated live (red) and neutral (black) conductors protected by an earthed metal sheath. The underground cable terminates in the house at ground level; in districts where there is overhead distribution, the supply is fed into the top of the house through a porcelain tube under the eaves.

In both cases the main supply cable terminates in a sealed unit which holds the service fuse. This fuse is designed to blow if there is a serious fault in the house which has failed to blow the fuse in the consumer unit (or fuse box), thus preventing the supply to neighbouring homes being affected. A 60 or 100amp fuse is connected to the live feed and the neutral conductor is connected to a brass terminal. There is another terminal on the outside of the sealed unit to which the household earth connection is made. The sealed unit containing the fuse belongs to the Electricity Board and must never be opened by the consumer; if the fuse does blow, you should call in the Electricity Board.

Two cables run from the service fuse to the meter, which measures the amount of electricity used. The meter is also the property of the Electricity Board and should never be tampered with by the consumer. The installation from the meter onwards is the consumer's responsibility and includes the two leads from the meter to the consumer unit.

Consumer unit

This contains a main switch and circuit fuses for the whole installation. Most houses have a lighting circuit for each floor so the whole house is not plunged into darkness in the event of a fuse blowing. A high wattage fixed appliance such as a cooker or immersion heater has its own sub-circuit. The cooker is wired directly to its own control switch – into which can be incorporated a power plug for use with other electrical kitchen gadgets. The control switch must be within two metres (or six feet) of the cooker, but separate from it. Make sure you have a long enough lead to the box so you can move the cooker out when cleaning.

Ring circuit

Socket outlets and small fixed appliances such as wall heaters and extractor fans are connected to a ring circuit, formed by a cable comprising a live (red) wire, a neutral (black) wire and a bare earth wire (which is encased in green PVC sleeving where it leaves the sheath). The cable used in domestic ring mains is 2.5sq mm twin core and earth, sheathed in PVC. This cable runs from a 30amp fuse in the consumer unit, serves each outlet and returns to the fuse, forming a ring.

The total load for a ring circuit is 30amps (7200 watts). So although it is possible to have, for example, twenty 13amp socket outlets on a ring, it is unlikely the number of domestic appliances being used at one time will exceed 30amps. If the circuit were overloaded, the 30amp fuse would blow and therefore maintain the safety requirements. However it is advisable to have a ring circuit for each floor in the house. If the kitchen has a large number of electrical appliances and/or a freezer, you should have a separate ring circuit in the kitchen to prevent overloading and ensure the freezer is not affected by a fault elsewhere.

Plugs used on a ring circuit have square pins and are fitted with 3 or 13amp fuses. The 3amp fuse covers all appliances up to a loading of 720 watts, which includes small appliances such as lamps. A 13amp fuse takes up to 3000 watts.

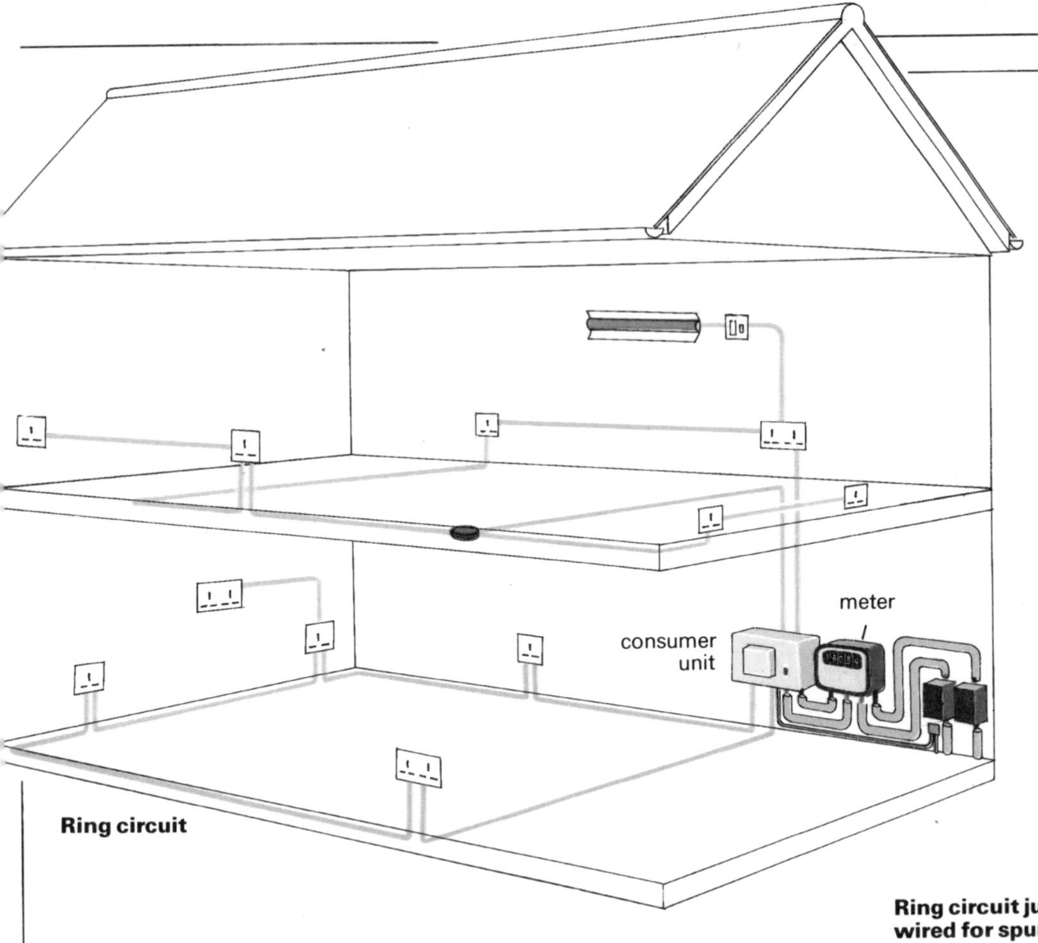

Ring circuit

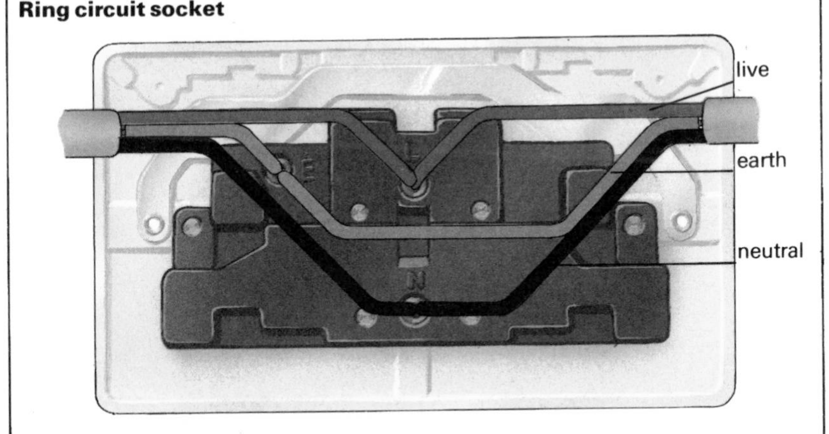

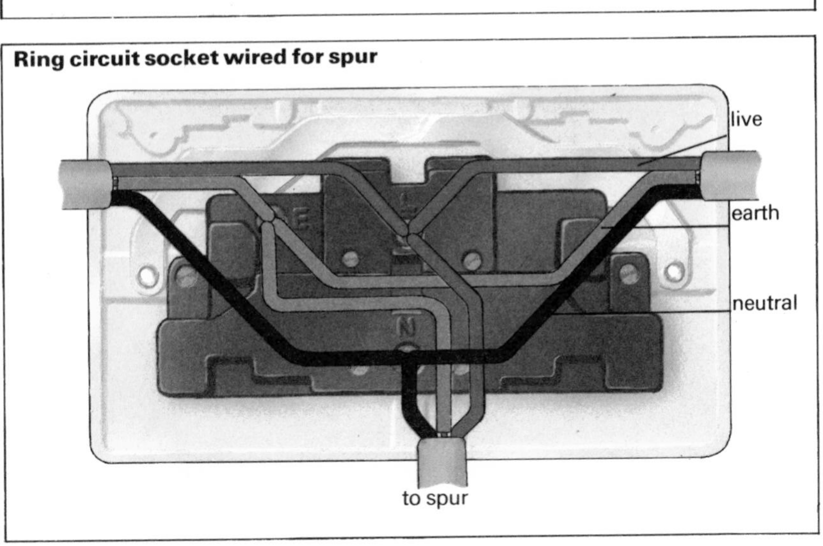

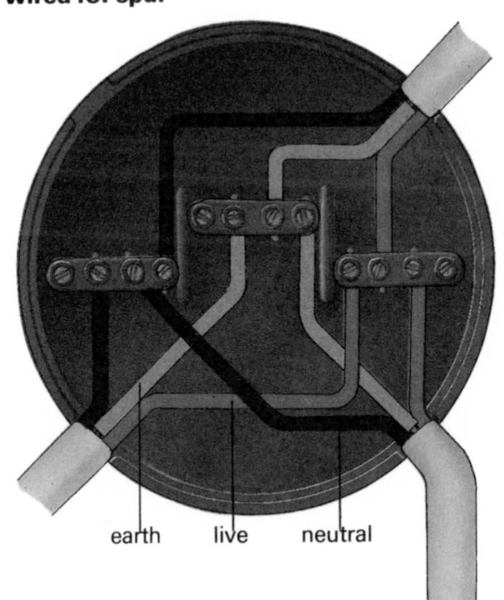

1

2

3

4

5

Lighting circuit

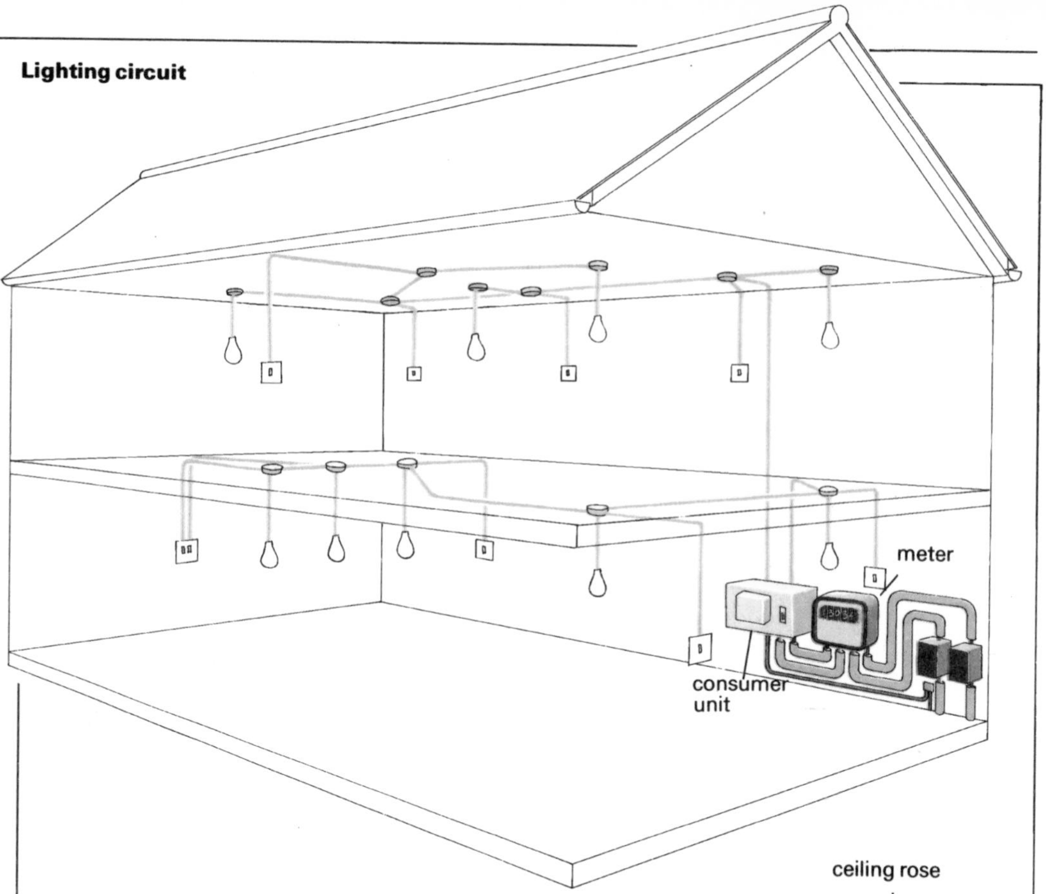

meter

consumer unit

Loop-in wiring

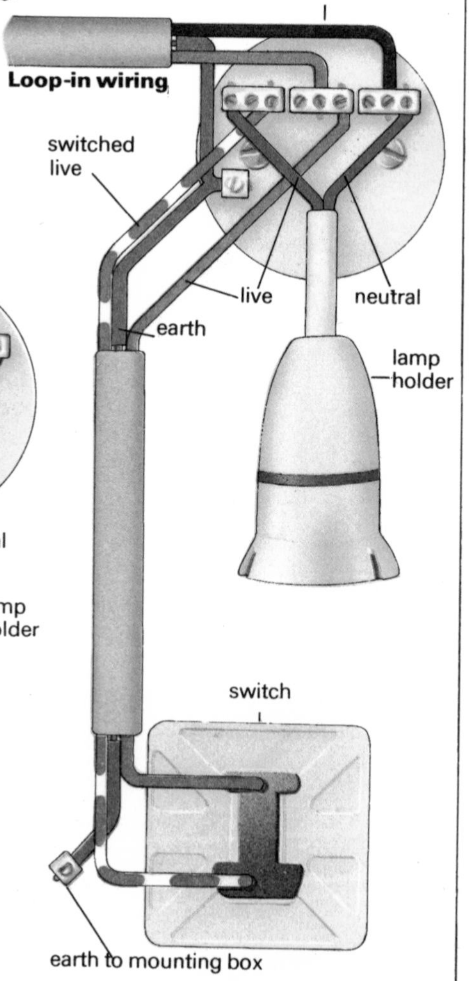

ceiling rose

switched live

live

neutral

earth

lamp holder

switch

earth to mounting box

Junction box wiring

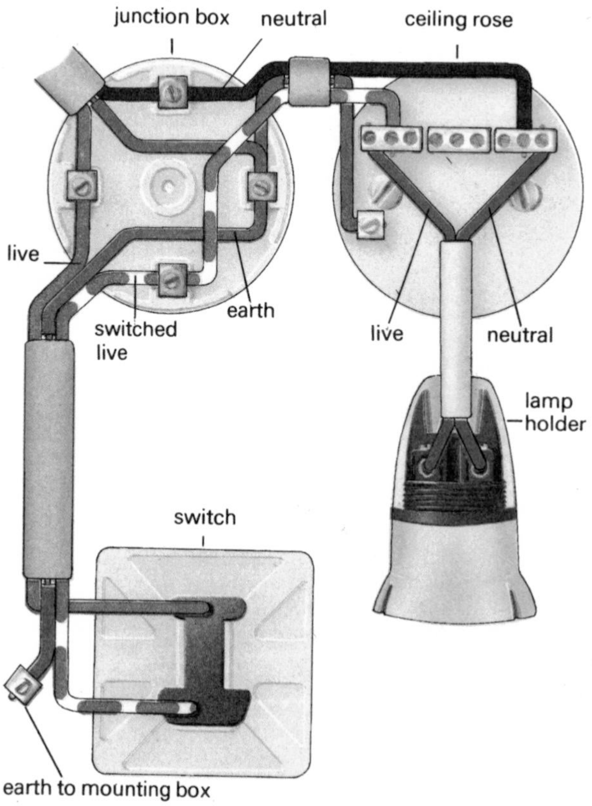

junction box

neutral

ceiling rose

live

switched live

earth

live

neutral

lamp holder

switch

earth to mounting box

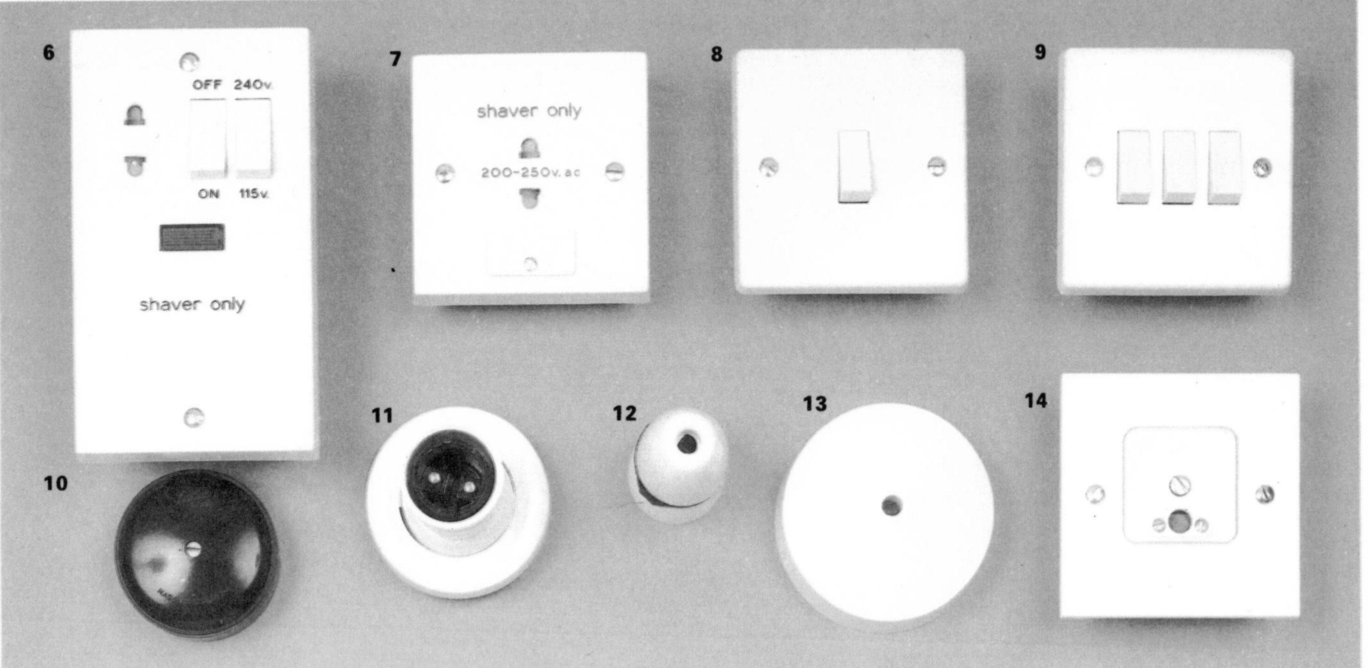

Opposite page Ring circuit fittings in the home
1 Unswitched single socket outlet
2 Switched single socket outlet
3 Unswitched fused connection unit
4 Switched fused connection unit with indicator light
5 30amp junction box

Above Lighting circuit fittings in the home
6 Switched shaver socket outlet (for bathrooms)
7 Unswitched shaver socket outlet (not for bathrooms)
8 Single lamp switch
9 Triple lamp switch
10 5amp junction box
11 Batten holder
12 Lamp holder
13 Ceiling rose
14 Clock connector

Additional socket outlets may be connected to a ring circuit, but the area served by the circuit should not exceed 100sq m (or 120sq yd).

Non-fused spur extensions

You can connect non-fused spur extensions to the circuit provided each spur supplies no more than two 13amp socket outlets or one fixed appliance and that the total number of spurs does not exceed the number of socket outlets on the main ring. No more than two spurs may be connected from each outlet on the ring; for this purpose a junction box wired into the ring can be classified as an outlet.

Fused connection units

These outlets, also used on a ring circuit, have the same fuse rating as plugs and are connected to a fixed appliance by a cable or flex. The unit may be switched or unswitched and fitted with an indicator light to show when the supply is connected to the outgoing flex or cable. Like socket outlets, the units can be flush or surface-mounted.

Flex outlets are simply a means of converting from a cable to a flex. A fused, switched connection unit, for example, outside a bathroom may supply a cable leading into the bathroom to feed a wall-mounted heater. Adjacent to the heater would be an outlet to feed the flex into the heater.

The clock connector is a similar type of unit, with a fuse fitted in a special plug into which the flex runs. The plug is retained in the socket by a knurled thumbscrew. Though called a clock connector, this is also suitable for small appliances such as window and wall extractor units.

Lighting circuits

Although lighting circuits are separate from the ring main or power circuit, there is nothing to prevent an individual light being taken from the ring. However, every home should have at least two lighting circuits protected by 5amp fuses. A 5amp fuse will carry up to twelve 100 watt lamps and it is usual, for example in a two-storey house, to plan one circuit for downstairs and another for upstairs. This will provide enough lighting points for decorative effects as well as general illumination.

Shaver units may also be connected to lighting circuits. For use in a bathroom, or room containing a shower, you must buy a unit which incorporates an isolating transformer. Here the socket is isolated from earth to remove the risk of an electric shock.

Lighting cable

Unlike the ring circuit, lighting cable does not return to the consumer unit. The cable now used is a 1sq mm PVC twin core and earth rated for up to 12amps. It is made up of a red insulated core for live, black insulated core for neutral and a bare earth conductor between them. The three conductors are laid side by side, surrounded by a PVC sheath.

The lighting cable travels from the consumer unit to a series of lighting points for ceiling roses or wall light fittings. It also connects to the switch or switches controlling the lamps and must do this in such a way that the individual switch, unless planned otherwise, does not affect other lights.

Two systems

There are two methods of wiring lights – by junction box or the loop-in ceiling rose. With the junction box system, cable is taken to a series of up to ten junction boxes. These are generally sited between ceiling joists or under floorboards close to where the cable is chanelled under the wall plaster to the switch. The loop-in system is more widely used and the ceiling rose incorporates the function of the junction box.

Extra lighting points may be added to an existing system by connecting cable from the junction box or ceiling rose to the new lighting point and switch.

Lamps may be controlled by switches in more than one place in a house – switches on the ground floor and first floor can both control a half-way or landing light. Or two lamps at different places – possibly in a large room – could be controlled by a double switch.

Cables and flexes

Cables and flex run all round your home – and it's important to know what each is for to make sure you use the right one for the right job.

Cable and flex are probably two of the most misused words when talking about electricity since, contrary to popular belief, they are not interchangeable. Cable is the main wiring carrying the supply to the many outlets in the home; flex is wiring that, for example, connects a lamp-holder to a ceiling rose or a vacuum cleaner to a socket.

Cables

Cables are not normally handled by the domestic consumer, since they have usually been built into the fabric of the house and make up the permanent wiring. Unlike flexes they are seldom moved during their working life; the expensive fine-wire construction of flex is not needed and many cables have single strand conductors running through them.

Cables connect the household electricity supply to flexes through suitable connection boxes such as ceiling roses or socket outlets. There are regulations to ensure cables are supported by clips at specific intervals depending on whether they run vertically or horizontally. PVC sheathed cable, for instance, can be buried in wall plaster without further protection.

Warning Cable should never be laid in grooves cut into joists because of the danger of floorboard nails penetrating the cable. It should pass through holes drilled at least 50mm (2in) below the tops of the joists.

Colour coding has not changed on cables. Red is live, black is neutral and green is earth, although in some types of domestic cable a bare uninsulated wire is the earth. Interior house cable can be single core (one conductor), twin core, twin core and earth, or three core and earth.

If there is a bare earth when cable is attached to a domestic connection box it should be covered with a short length of green PVC sleeving to insulate and identify it.

In some older houses you could well find the cable made up with a number of strands. This cable usually runs in metal conduit which acts as an earth conductor. In modern homes you will also find cable with conductors made of up to seven strands. This is for circuits which carry heavy current, such as for cookers. All modern cable has an outer covering of PVC which is proof against moisture and most common chemicals and acids so it can be safely buried in walls.

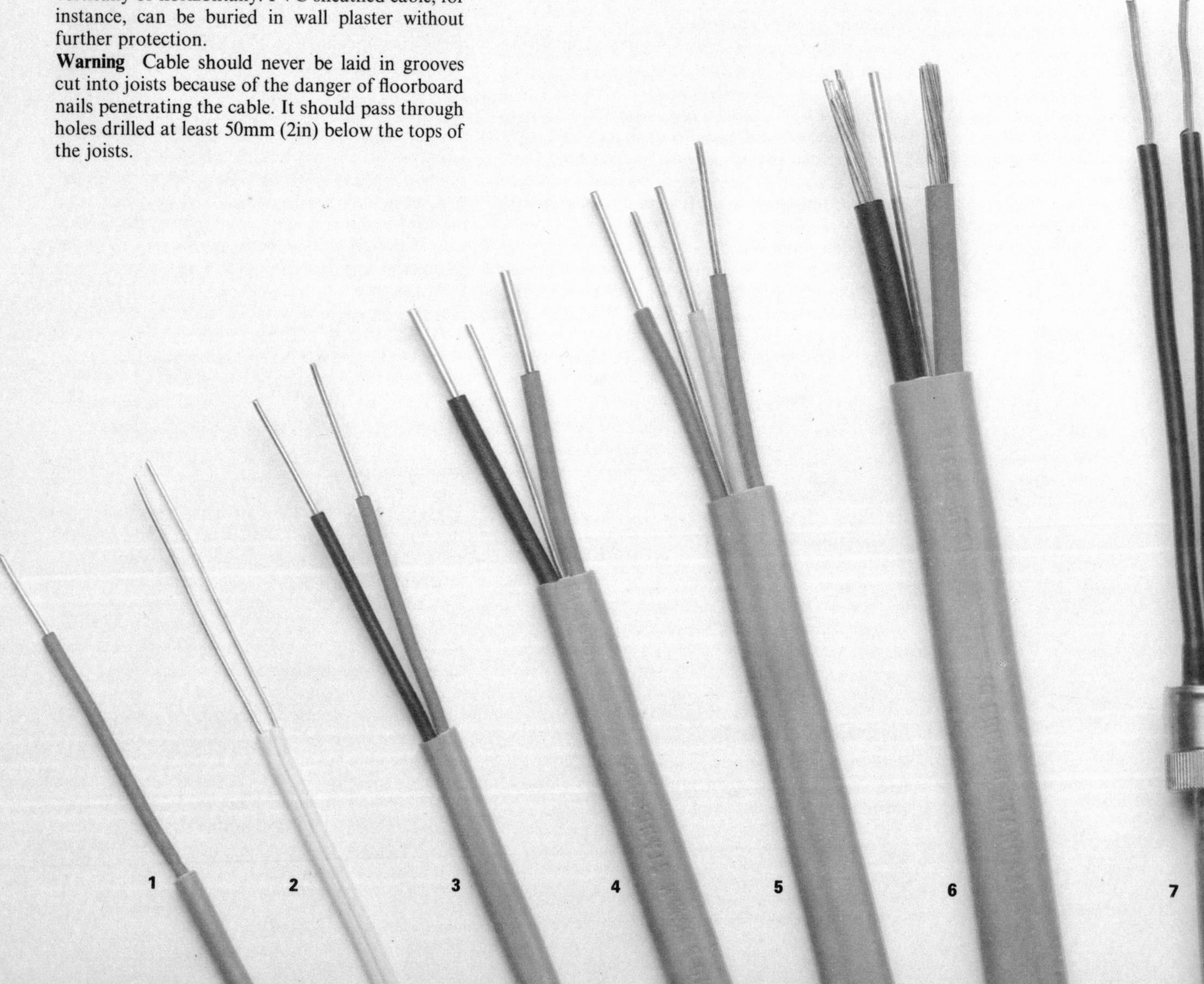

Below A selection of cables and flexes used for different installations in the home
1 Single core double-insulated cable
2 Twin core single-insulated cable
3 Twin core double-insulated cable
4 Twin core and earth double-insulated cable
5 Three core and earth cable
6 Twin core and earth double-insulated cable (conductors made up of seven copper strands)
7 Cooper-sheathed twin core cable insulated with chalk lining

8 Cloth-covered and rubber-insulated three core flex with old colour coding
9 Same flex with new coding
10 Rubber-covered and insulated flex with old colour coding
11 Same flex with new colour coding
12 PVC-covered and insulated three core flex with new colour coding
13 Same flex with old colour coding
14 Unearthed PVC-covered and insulated twin core flex with new colour coding

Flexes

Flex – or flexible cord – is a conductor of electricity which can be twisted and bent many times without breaking. It comprises metal conductors, each of which is made up of many strands of fine wire (rather than one thick one) encased in plastic or rubber. The finer the strands, the stronger the flex.

Flexes receive a lot of wear and tear, so it is very important they are connected properly and securely. In the case of a plug, the anchorage points must be secure enough to ensure any strain on the flex is taken by the tough outer covering (usually plastic or rubber) and not the metal conductors and the plug terminals. Similarly, connections to appliances must be through equally secure anchorage points to prevent strain at that end of the flex.

If the flex has to be lengthened at any time, it must be connected to another flex of the same type and joined by a proper connector.

Colour coding

Perhaps the most misunderstood aspect of flexes is the international colour code used for the PVC insulating covering. By law the three core flexes – whether sold separately or with an appliance – must have insulation coloured brown for the live wire, blue for the neutral wire and green-and-yellow bands for the earth. On older appliances you may find the live wire is red, the neutral black and the earth yellow.

There are, surprisingly, no regulations as yet covering two core flexes. You may buy an appliance with, for example, black and white plastic covering and no explanation about which is live and which is neutral. The reason is that here it does not matter which wire is connected to which plug terminal. Table and standard lamps are examples where, in most cases, plain two core flex can be used.

Different ratings

There are many variations in the types of flex and cables, although most have special uses in industry. For the domestic consumer flexes vary little. Cables are more varied; there are, for example, special cables with extra protection for outside lighting and garden use.

Cables and flexes are given a rating based on the area of the conductor's cross-section and are described by this area when ordered from a supplier. A cable for a ring circuit, for example, is described as 2.5sq mm (or $2.5mm^2$), representing the cross-sectional area of one of the conductors available for carrying the current. The other conductor carries the same current but in the opposite direction. The earth conductor is slightly smaller than the other conductors in the cable and carries current only when there is a fault.

Changing conditions Cable and flex ratings do vary according to installation conditions, but this is unlikely to affect the domestic consumer. In a very hot situation, such as in an industrial process, a cable could be rated much lower than a similar cable in a domestic location because the rating is based on the rise in temperature that occurs when a conductor carries a given amount of current.

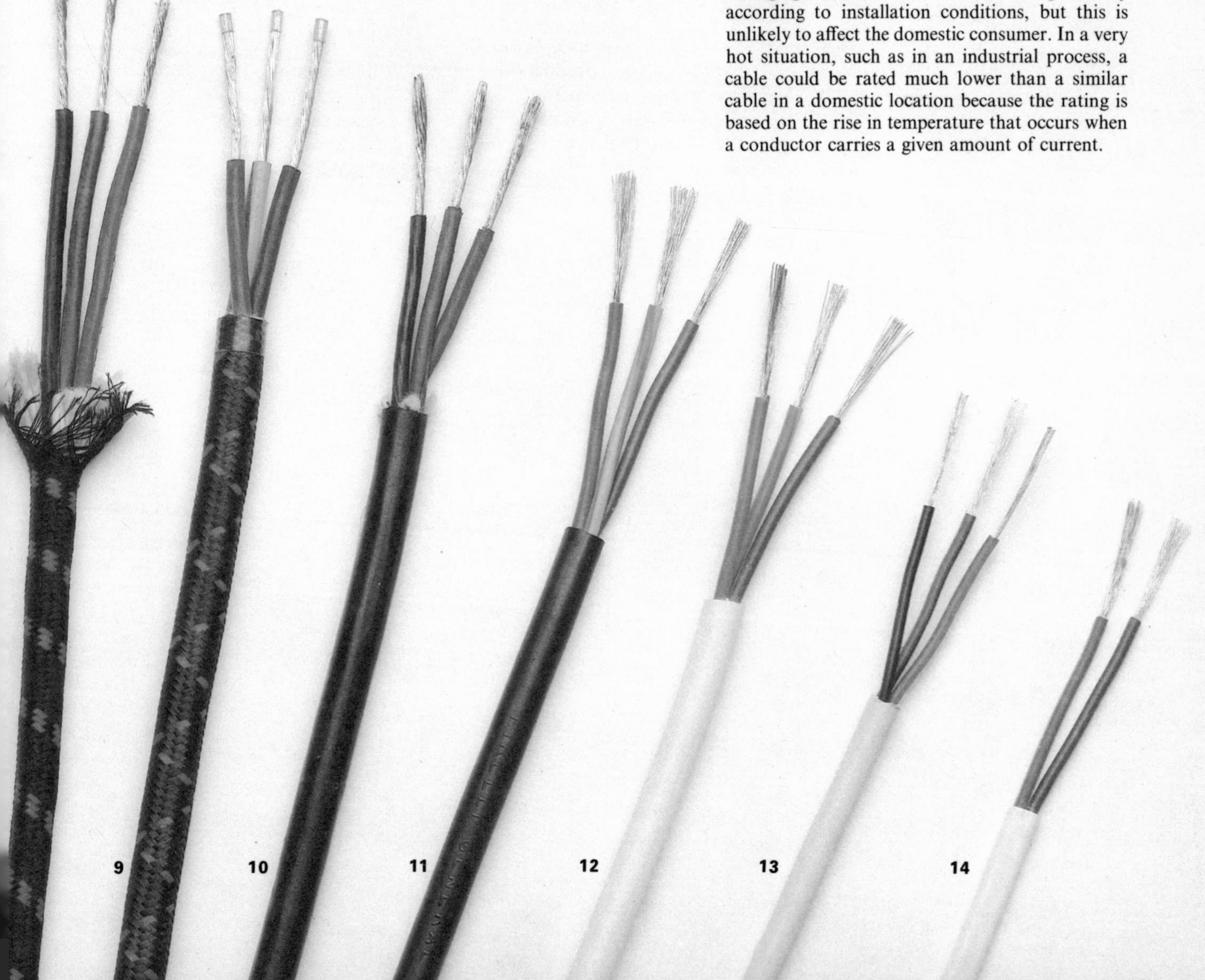

Safety in the bathroom

You can make your bathroom among the most comfortable rooms in the home if you choose the right materials and equipment – taking full advantage of all the electrical appliances that make life so much easier. But if you fail to follow the safety rules, you could be walking into danger whenever you use it.

Electrical appliances such as mirror lights, instant shower units, shaver sockets, heated towel rails, radiators and radiant heaters can add a touch of luxury as well as efficiency to any bathroom. But electricity can also make the bathroom potentially the most dangerous room in the house.

Socket outlets
It is against wiring regulations to install a socket outlet in a bathroom (or washroom), with the exception of purpose-made shaver units fitted with an isolating transformer which makes the units safe. Many striplights are available with combined shaver sockets, but unless these clearly state they have an isolating transformer they must not be installed in bathrooms.

Never use a mains voltage appliance in the bathroom by feeding it from a socket outlet from the landing or another room. However tempting it may be to trail a mains portable television in at bathtime, NEVER do it. Settle for a transistor radio if you are going to have a long soak. And never let other members of the family persuade you to let them use a hairdrier on the end of an extended lead.

Lights and switches
You must not have lights with open lampholders because this makes it possible to remove the lamp and use the lampholder as a socket for an appliance. All lights and appliances must be cord-operated or operated by switches outside the bathroom. Flexible cord should not be used to hang lampholders, which must always be fixed to the ceiling. Lampholders must also be beyond the reach of anyone showering or taking a bath and must be shrouded with an insulating material; or totally enclosed light fittings should be used. Mirror lights are specially designed, whether or not they have shaver units, to be safe in the bathroom.

Heaters
If you want an open reflector-type wall-mounted heater it must be installed out of reach of anyone using the bath or shower. It is also a good idea to have it operated by a switch outside the bathroom as well as by a cord inside the room; in the case of real emergency this means the appliance can be switched off even if the door is locked and quick access is difficult. This also applies to electrically heated towel rails and radiators. When installing a towel rail or radiator it is worth fixing a cord-operated ceiling switch that incorporates a pilot light. New rewiring regulations also state that any electrical equipment, like shower heater units or wall heaters or towel rails, must have an earth arrangement such as an ELCB.

Secure fittings
Make sure all fixtures are securely fitted and can only be removed by using the appropriate tools. This may sound fundamental but it is sometimes difficult to achieve in modern houses where plasterboard internal walls are used and do not always offer a strong anchorage point.

Warning There is always a danger of inheriting potential electrical hazards when you buy an older house. You must be especially careful where a scullery or bedroom has been converted to a bathroom without proper regard to safety. Always remove all socket outlets or old power points, move wall switches to outside the room and replace flex pendants with ceiling fittings.

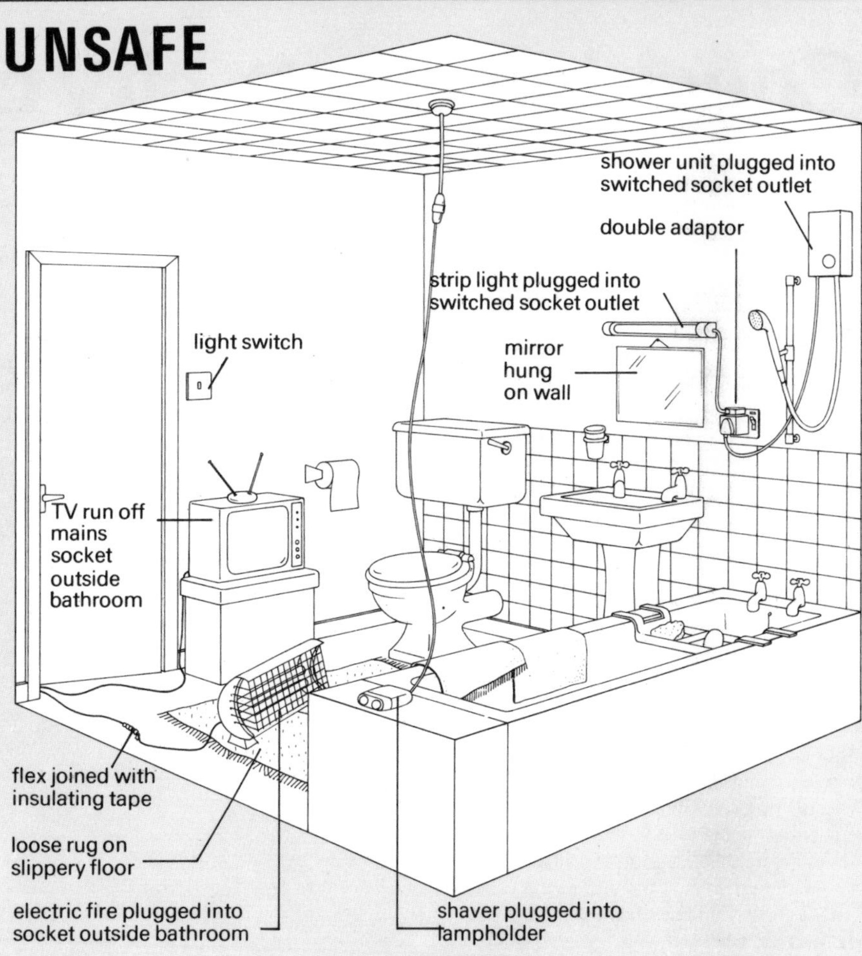

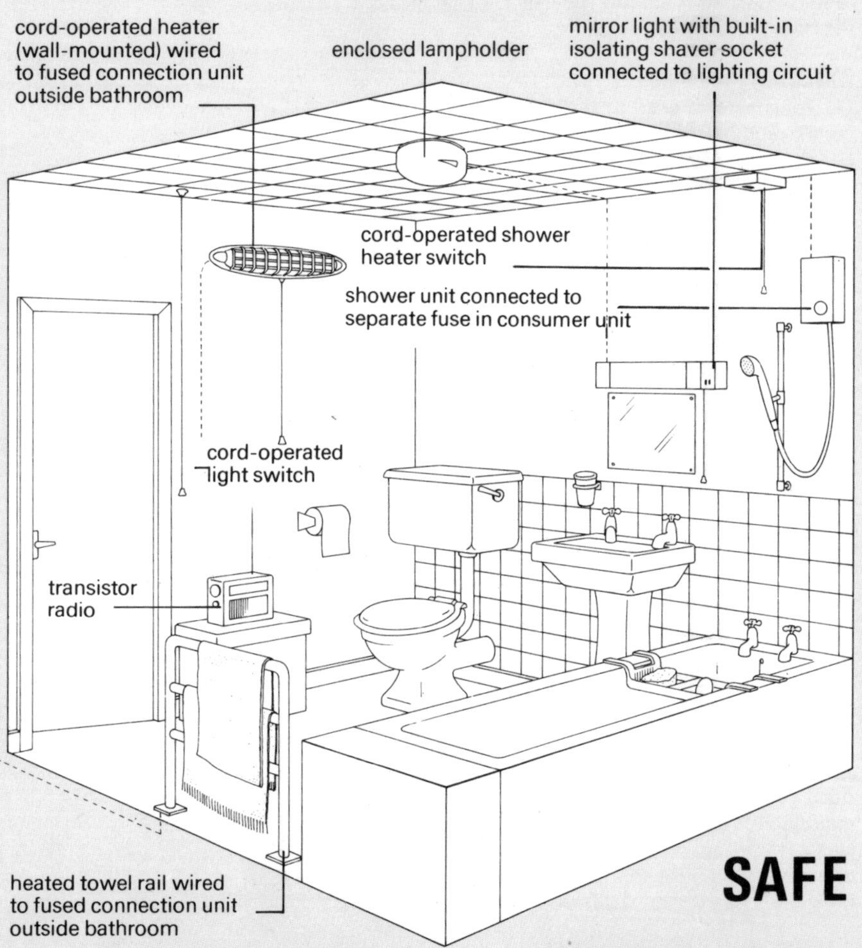

Checking electricity consumption

Increased electricity costs and the need to conserve energy make it even more desirable to keep a check on household consumption. To do this you must read your meter and check it is functioning correctly; you will also need to know how much power different appliances in the home consume; check this on our chart.

Reading your meter

The digital type of meter is similar to a distance meter in a car; you simply read the figures from left to right. The dial type which is probably the most common, requires more attention. It comprises five black dials and one red dial. Since the red dial measures tenths of a unit it can, for this purpose, be ignored.

The black dials show from left to right 10,000, 1000, 100, 10 and single units. Each dial is read in the opposite direction to its neighbour; the 10,000 unit dial is read clockwise, the 1000 dial is read anti-clockwise and so on. When the pointer of a dial is between two figures, always take the lower figure. For example, if the 100s pointer is between 1 and 2, it means that 100-plus units have been recorded. The 10s pointer will show the extra amount in 10s; if it is between 5 and 6, the number of units is 50-plus. The final figure is given by the single units dial which should always be read to the nearest unit.

By subtracting the previous week's reading from the current one, you can see how many units you have used in a week. Multiply this figure by the unit cost (shown on your bill) and you will have the price of the electricity, excluding the standing charge and the fuel cost adjustment.

Checking your meter

On your meter is a rotating disc which revolves a certain number of times for every kWh (kilowatt-hour) or unit of electricity consumed. The number of revolutions per kWh will be marked on the face of your meter. The disc is placed so you can see only the edge on which there is a black mark. You can count the revolutions by noting the number of times the black mark comes into view.

By a simple process you can check if your meter is registering correctly. If, for example, it is marked 500 revs/kWh, a total load of 1kW (for example, a one-bar electric fire or ten 100 watt lamps) will cause the disc to revolve 500 times in one hour. But there is no need for you to watch the disc for a whole hour. Switch off all the electrical equipment in the house and check the disc on the meter is stationary. Then switch on, for example, five 100 watt bulbs so you have a total test load of $\frac{1}{2}$kW. Count the number of times the black mark on the dial comes round in six minutes, using a stop-watch or a watch with a second hand for timing. Work out how many revolutions the disc should make in this time by using the following equation:

500 (revs/kWh) $\times \frac{1}{2}$(kW) $\times \frac{1}{10}$ (of an hour) $= 25$.

Compare this figure with the number of revolutions you counted. Allowing for variations in the manufacture of the lamps used, the disc should rotate to within a couple of revolutions of the calculated figure. But before you rush off to tell the Electricity Board that your meter is wrong, double check there is no other equipment switched on. To do this, switch off the test load – the disc should come to a complete standstill.

If you have an hour to spare, you need not count the revolutions. Instead, you can use the sixth (red) dial which measures one tenth of a unit. Since one complete revolution equals one whole unit, just note the position of the pointer at the beginning and end of one hour. If you use a total load of 1kW, the pointer of the dial should make one complete revolution.

Below Two types of electricity meter. The digital type (**top**) can be read in a moment; with the dial meter (**bottom**) read the bottom row – from left to right – first, adding the units indicated on the top right-hand dial. The red dial, showing tenths of units, need not be read

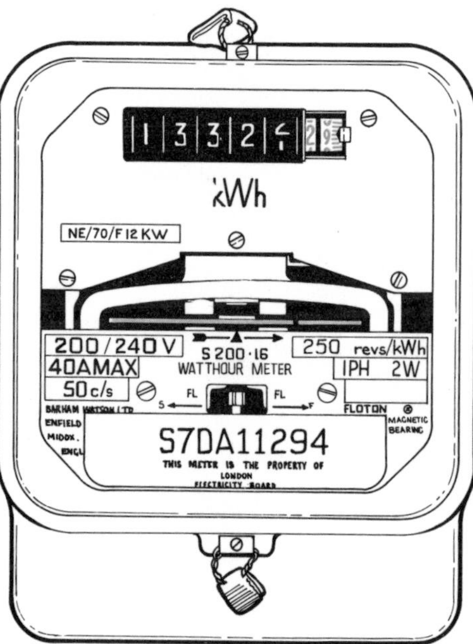

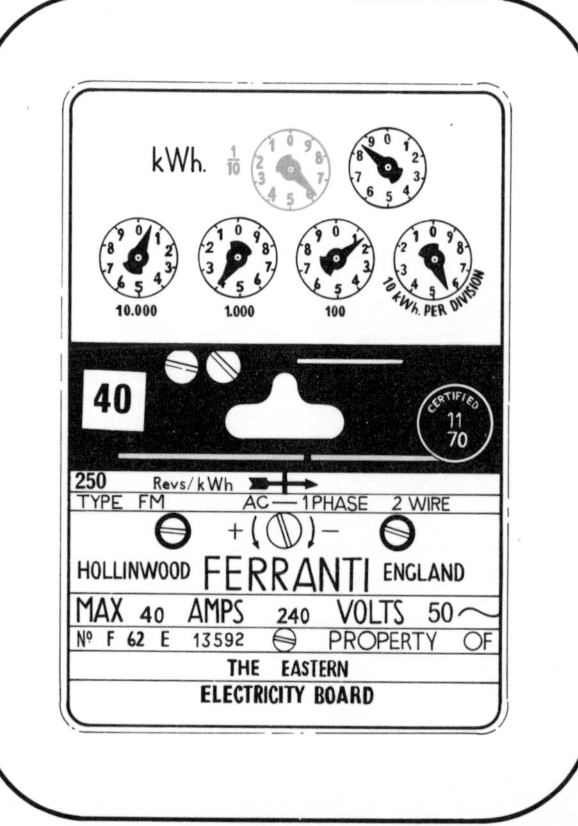

Unit consumption of domestic appliances

Appliance	Wattage	Use	Units used
Blanket (over)	120	All-night warmth for one week	about 6
Blanket (under)	60	Seven evenings	1
Blender	200	500 pints of soup	1
Coffee percolator	750	About 75 cups of coffee	1
Cooker	12000	Cooking for family of four for one week	20
Dishwasher	3000	Washing a family's dinner dishes	1
Extractor fan	75	12 hours' use	1
Food mixer (stand model)	400	Mixing 65 cakes	1
Freezer (chest model)	300	One week's running per litre of space (per cubic foot of space)	0.05 (1.4)
Freezer (upright model)	300	One week's running per litre of space (per cubic foot of space)	0.06 (1.7)
Hair dryer	350	Three hours' drying	1
Heater	2000	One hour's heat	2
Immersion heater	3000	Hot water for a family of four for one week	70
Iron	750–1250	More than two hours' ironing	1
Kettle	2500–3000	Boils about 7 litres (12 pints) water	1
Light (filament lamp)	100	Ten hours of light	1
Light (fluorescent tube) 1500mm (5ft)	80 (100W circuit rating)	Ten hours of light (gives four times as much light as 100W filament lamp)	1
Refrigerator (table top height)	100	One day's running	1
Shaver	16	1800 shaves	1
Spin dryer	300	Spins about five weeks' laundry	1
Stereo system	100–125	Eight to ten hours listening	1
Television (black and white)	150	About seven hours' viewing	1
Television (colour)	350	Three hours' viewing	1
Toaster	1000–1350	70 slices of toast	1
Tumble dryer	2500	One hour's drying	2
Vacuum cleaner	500	Two hours' cleaning	1
Washing machine (automatic)	2500	Weekly wash for a family of four (17kg/37lb) dry weight laundry	8–9
Washing machine (twin-tub)	2000	Weekly wash as above (one wash per fill; uses more water than automatic)	11–12
Waste disposal unit	250	Grinds 50kg (1cwt) of rubbish	1

Diagnosing electrical faults

Fault	Cause	Remedy
Plug unduly hot	Loose flex terminal	Tighten terminal screws
	Fuse incorrectly fitted	Ensure fuse makes contact over whole surface area of metal ends
	Poor quality fuse	Fit BS 1362 ASTA Cert fuse
	Fuse of incorrect rating	Fit 13amp fuse if appliance rated at 750 watts or more
	Plug makes poor contact in socket	Renew plug and, if necessary, socket
	Inferior quality plug	Fit plug of reliable make
	Sustained load of 3kW causing reduced conductivity of pins and contacts	Renew plug
Sparks at socket outlet	Effect of breaking current in AC circuit	No action – natural phenomenon
	If other than when operating switch, loose wire or faulty switch or socket	Tighten terminals, replace switch or socket
Intermittent power	Loose terminal or fuse or broken conductor	Tighten terminals and refit plug fuse; if only one appliance affected, check flex terminals in appliance
	Severed flex wire	Replace flex
Smell of burning in and around house	Old wiring or frayed flex; loose connection; insulation of wires in heater or other appliance touching hot parts of heater	Tighten terminals and replace damaged flexes and damaged exposed cables
	Lamp of too high wattage in enclosed light fitting or shade	Fit lamp of lower wattage
	Electric motor windings of powered appliance burning out, possibly due to blockage	Check and clear mechanical parts of appliance; otherwise call in electrician
Smell of burning near meter and consumer unit	Cable overheating between consumer unit and Board's service fuse unit. Circuit fuse wire in consumer unit hot and burning plastic before blowing. Loose connection. Fault in Board's terminal box, fuse holder or meter cables	Call Board's emergency service; any fault in this area will almost certainly require withdrawal of Board's service fuse which consumer must not touch
Fuse blows repeatedly without obvious cause	Cable or accessory fault; serious overloading; fuse of incorrect rating; faulty light fitting or appliance; TV suppressor faulty	Reduce load on circuit; fit fuse of correct rating; if circuit fuse, disconnect each appliance in turn to ascertain which causes fuse to blow
Intermittent switch or lamp failure; constant need for lamp replacement	Damaged or worn switch	Replace switch
	Faulty wiring or loose switch connection	Check wiring and connections
	Lamp of wrong voltage	Fit long life lamp of correct voltage
	Lamp burning in cap-down position	Replace fitting with one which has lamp burning in cap-up position – could lengthen lamp life
	Mains voltage fluctuation due to nearby substation or mains tester	Ask Board to fit recording voltmeter
Loose switch	Age and wear	If switch body affected, replace switch; if loose in box, tighten fixing screws
Interference on hi-fi, TV or radio	If recent, faulty suppressor on appliance or new appliance has no suppressor	Check each motor driven appliance; replace faulty suppressor
	Faulty thermostat	Check each thermostat; replace if necessary
	Faulty fluorescent tube	Replace starter switch
	Faulty dimmer switch	Fit new (suppressed) dimmer switch
No light or power	Mains switch accidentally turned off	Check mains switch
	Board's fuse blown; supply failure or power cut	Check power available in neighbouring houses; if so, call Board

Maintenance and repairs

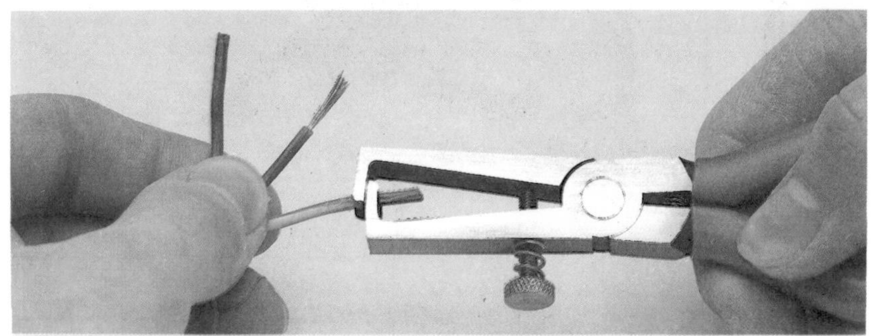

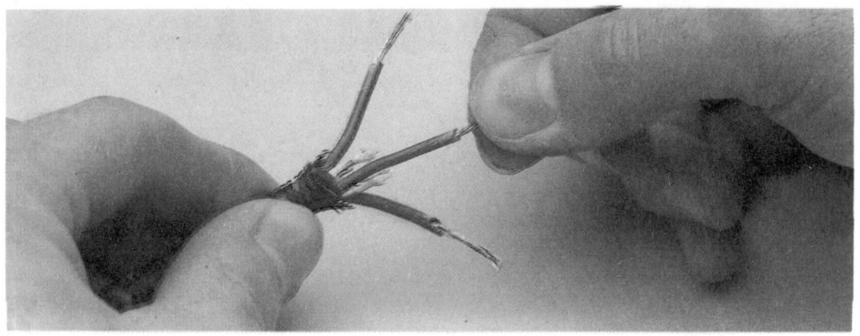

Usually your electrical circuits will function without any problems provided they have been correctly installed. Your appliances and fittings too should rarely give you trouble if they are properly treated. Most of the day- to-day faults are in the connections – the plugs, flex or cable and the fuse. Fuses can be replaced easily and quickly, but always check the circuit is not overloaded and you are using the recommended size of fuse. Make sure you are wiring plugs correctly and that they contain the correct fuse. Learn the correct way to strip cable and flex and how to connect separate lengths if you have to.

Consumer unit and fuse types

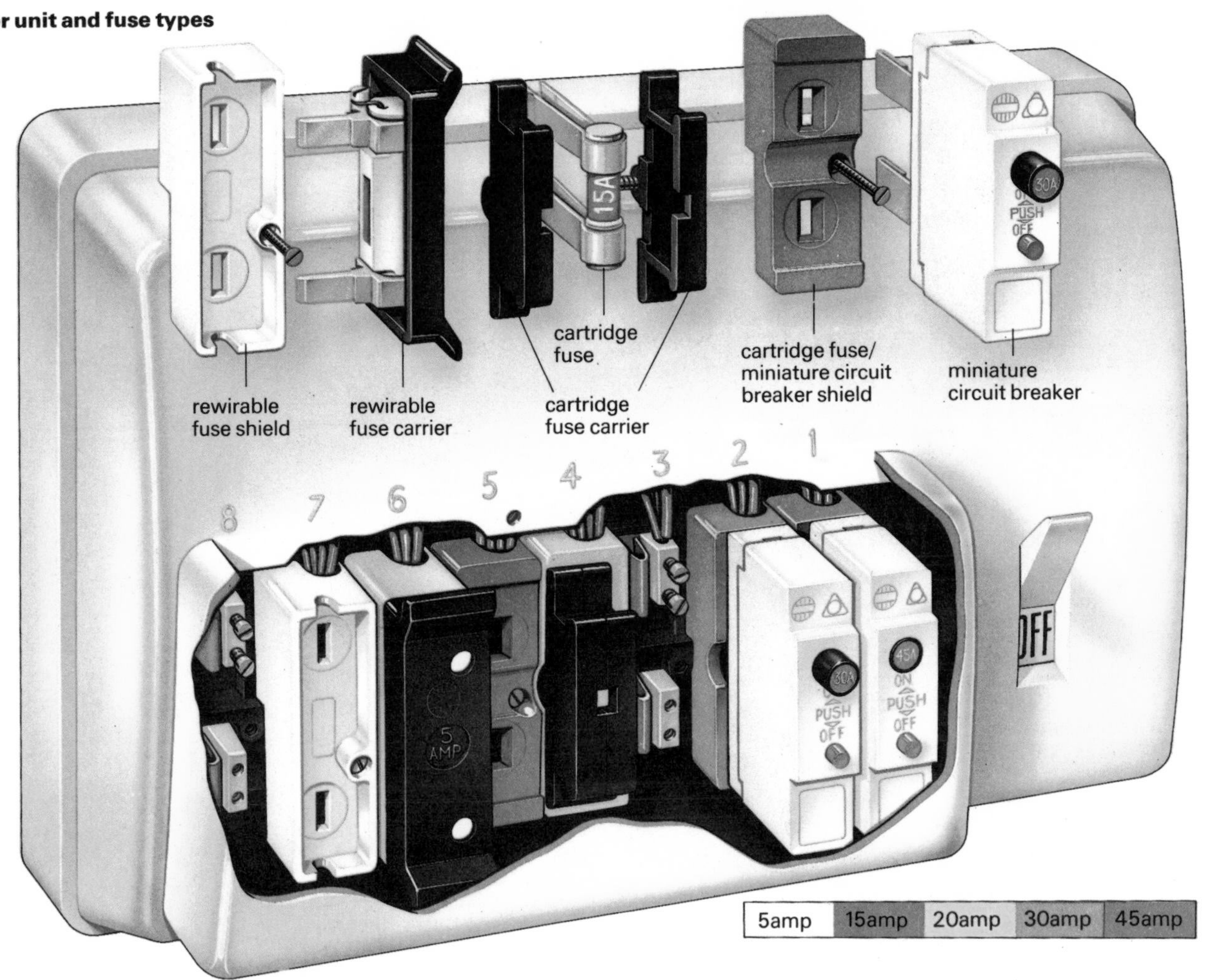

Repairing fuses

When electric current passes through a wire it causes heating: the thinner the wire the greater the heat. Even the thick wire used in domestic wiring will overheat if too much current passes through it – and may easily set the house on fire. To prevent this, a fuse is built into every circuit. This is a particularly thin piece of wire which will heat up quickly and melt if a more than safe quantity of current passes through it.

Types of fuses

All master fuses – one for each circuit – are mounted on fuse carriers in a fuse box close to the Electricity Board's supply meter. There are two main types, rewirable and cartridge, although miniature circuit breakers are sometimes fitted instead of fuses.

Rewirable This type has fuse wire stretched between two retaining screws on the porcelain or plastic fuse carrier. The wire is available in three ratings – 5, 15 and 30amp – and you can usually buy a card of wire carrying a supply of all three.

Cartridge This type cannot be rewired since the fuse is sealed inside a tube; once it blows the fuse must be replaced. The advantage of the master cartridge fuse is it is impossible to fit the wrong one because each rating has a different size cartridge (as compared to plug fuses that are uniform in size). The fuses are also colour coded so they can be easily recognized: 5amp is white, 15amp blue, 20amp yellow, 30amp red and 45amp green.

Miniature circuit breakers Used in domestic fuse boxes instead of fuses, these automatically switch themselves off if a circuit is overloaded. When the fault has been corrected the circuit can be reconnected just by resetting the on/off switch.

Why fuses blow

A master fuse will blow if the circuit is overloaded, if the fuse wire is of too low a rating or if a faulty appliance is used with an unfused plug or socket. Before repairing the fuse check you are not using too many appliances on one circuit and make sure you are using the right size fuse for the circuit. If you suspect a faulty appliance, even though it seems to be working adequately, stop using it and call an electrician or contact the manufacturer.

Sometimes a fuse blows simply because it is old; all you need to do is replace it with a new one of the correct rating. If a fuse still blows after being replaced, call an electrician.

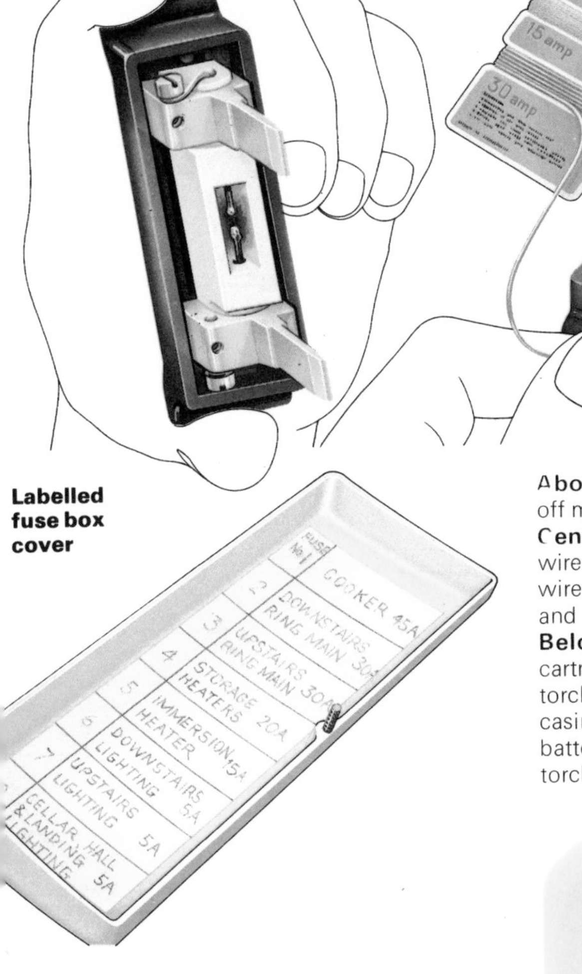

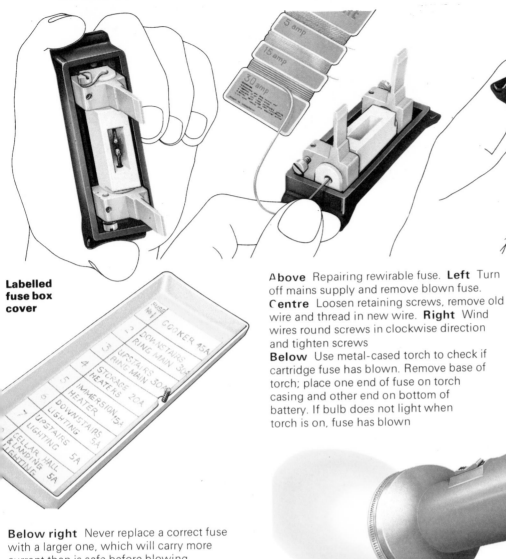

Labelled fuse box cover

Above Repairing rewirable fuse. **Left** Turn off mains supply and remove blown fuse. **Centre** Loosen retaining screws, remove old wire and thread in new wire. **Right** Wind wires round screws in clockwise direction and tighten screws

Below Use metal-cased torch to check if cartridge fuse has blown. Remove base of torch; place one end of fuse on torch casing and other end on bottom of battery. If bulb does not light when torch is on, fuse has blown

Below right Never replace a correct fuse with a larger one, which will carry more current than is safe before blowing.
For lighting circuit (up to 1kW) – 5amp
For immersion heater (3–4.8kW) – 15/20amp
For ring main circuit (up to 7.2kW) – 30amp
For cooker (up to 10.8kW) – 45amp

Warning Don't try to stop a fuse blowing by putting in a higher rated one.

Tracing faults

If one of your lights goes out see first whether those nearby are still working; if they are it is likely only the lamp bulb has blown. If all your lights are out check whether the street or your neighbours are in darkness too; if they are there is nothing wrong with your fuses – there is a general power failure and you will just have to wait for the power to be restored. If everyone else's lights are working you have an internal power failure, so turn off the relevant switch before investigating.

You will save time and trouble by keeping a small electrical screwdriver, a torch and replacement fuses or fuse wire handy by the fuse box. A supply of candles in the house is also good sense.

Rewiring fuses

Always turn off the mains supply switch before attempting any repairs. If you are really efficient you will have made a numbered plan of the carriers in your fuse box, labelling each one according to the circuit it controls (cooker, downstairs sockets, upstairs lights etc.). This plan should be taped on the inside of the fuse box door so, when investigating a blown fuse, you can pick out the relevant carrier first time.

If you have not labelled them you must pull out each carrier in turn to find the blown fuse – look for one which has a broken or melted fuse wire. Undo the screws which clamp the fuse wire in place and remove the remains of the old wire. Stretch a new wire of the correct rating loosely between the screws and wind the ends in a clockwise direction round the screws, which must be carefully tightened until the wire is firmly held. Replace the fuse holder and close the fuse box before reconnecting the supply.

Replacing cartridge fuses

The only way of telling which cartridge fuse has blown is to remove one carrier at a time. Turn off the mains switch, remove a carrier, close the fuse box cover and switch on the mains supply. If everything else continues to work you have found the failed fuse. Take out the cartridge and replace it with a new one of the correct rating, refit the fuse carrier, close the box cover and turn on the main switch.

Cartridge fuses

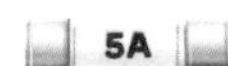

Stripping cable and flex

1

2

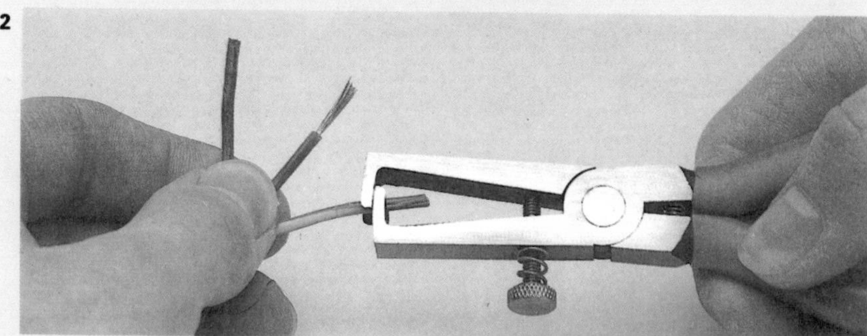

3

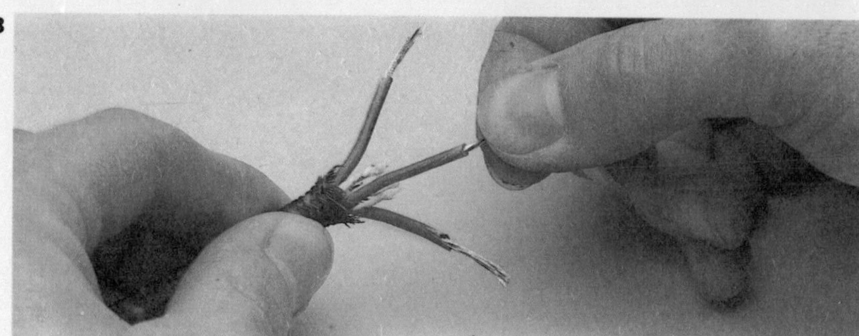

1 Cut carefully along the length of the flex with a sharp knife
2 Use wire strippers to remove the sheathing and expose the insulated cores
3 Twist the wires together with your fingers
4 After stripping the insulation from cable, slip a length of PVC sleeving over the earth wire
5 On heavy cable, twist the conductors together with pliers

4

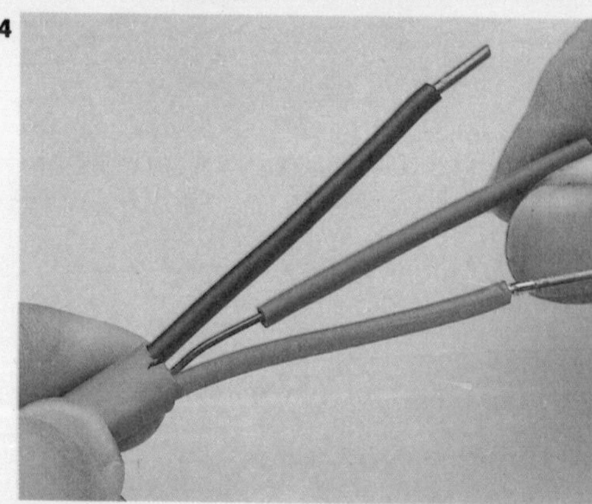

5

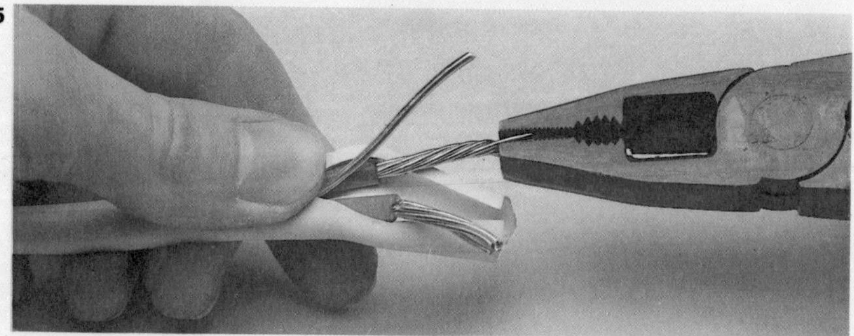

There are certain basic rules you must remember before you start to strip flex or cable for connecting to a plug or appliance or for wiring power or lighting circuits.

● Remove only sufficient insulation to enable the cores to be connected to the terminals; none of the bared wires should be exposed.

● Don't stretch the insulation when stripping or you will weaken the portion remaining on the conductor.

● Take care not to cut through the insulation of conductors, or through a conductor itself, or you will have to shorten the flex or cable and start again. If you damage a conductor the effective current capacity will be lowered and this could cause overheating. Current capacity will also be reduced if you sever any of the fine strands in a length of flex.

Stripping flex

The two most commonly used flexible cords are circular sheathed and braided circular flex. A third, now largely replaced by circular sheathed flex, is twisted twin non-sheath flex.

Circular sheathed Measure the length of sheathing to be removed and carefully run a knife round the sheath, making sure not to damage the core insulation. From this point, make a cut along the length of the flex to the end, cutting through to the inner insulation. Remove the sheathing with pliers, leaving the insulated cores exposed. Measure the length of insulation to be removed from each core and carefully take it off with wire strippers. Always twist the bared ends of each core together to ensure there will be no stray whiskers to cause a short circuit when the conductors are inserted in their terminals.

Circular braided Measure the length of braiding to be removed and cut it off with a sharp knife. Trim off the frayed edges and any textile fillers inside the braid and slip a rubber sleeve over the end to prevent further fraying. Strip the required length of insulation from each core and twist the wires together as before.

Twisted twin Since this type has no sheathing, you only need to strip insulation and twist the cores together.

Stripping cable

The method for stripping cable is basically the same as for stripping flex, but you must take extra care not to damage the conductors since cable is expensive to replace.

Sheathed Measure and strip off the required amount of sheathing using a knife and pliers as previously described. Strip off the insulation from each wire and slip a length of green (or green/yellow) PVC sleeving over the end of the earth wire. With the smallest cables (1.0 and 1.5sq mm), double the bared ends to provide greater contact area in the terminals. Cables of 4sq mm and above have stranded conductors and the ends must be twisted together with pliers.

Non-sheathed single core An example of this is the green/yellow PVC insulated earth cable; simply remove the insulation with wire strippers as described above.

Joining flex

One of the real dangers involving electricity is the joining up of flex, which can be a fire hazard. If you really have to do this job, always use a proper connector and check you have wired it up in the correct way.

Whenever possible avoid joining flex. If you have to, always use a proper connector and never try to join two pieces of flex by twisting the bare wires together and covering them with insulating tape. No matter how careful you are there is always a danger the join may work loose or come apart because it is suddenly stretched. If a join does work loose it can create sparks that may in turn lead to a fire. Among the other hazards, the earth safety lead may become detached in a three core flex join or the essential separation between the live and neutral wires break down, causing a short circuit.

Flex connectors are useful for portable appliances like irons and hairdryers, if you want to use them some distance from a socket. But never use more than one connector on a length of flex and don't trail it under carpets, up the stairs or across a passageway. Apart from the electrical dangers, there is always the risk someone might trip over it. When you require temporary lighting for a Christmas tree, for example, the flex and connector should be tucked against a skirting board and secured with adhesive tape, never by staples.

Before you decide you need to make a connection, consider whether it is easier, possibly cheaper, and certainly safer to buy a longer length of flex and fit it permanently to the lamp or appliance. Alternatively it could be preferable, though more expensive, to have a new power socket fitted, especially if it is for a semi-permanent appliance like a fridge, television or room heater.

Fitting connectors

Proper flex connectors do not only keep the cores separate but the screw terminals keep them securely fixed. Always use the same kind of flexes when making a join; although they need not be the same exterior colour, the amps and number of cores must match – three core must be matched with three core and two core with two core.

Only trim sufficient outer insulating sheath and inner insulation to leave the minimum bare wire to enter the connector terminals. Make sure there are no bare strands of wire exposed by twisting together the strands in each core before connecting. Always connect the brown core with brown, the blue with blue and the green/yellow earth with earth and check the plug at the end of the extension flex is correctly wired and fused.

Types of connectors

Three kinds of connectors are available for use in the home. But check which one is most suitable for the type of appliance involved and where it is to be used.

Connector strips Sometimes called block connectors, they are made of plastic and pairs of screws hold the flex ends. The plastic section can be cut to suit single, two or three core flex, but since the screw heads are not insulated they are only suitable where they can be protected and insulated, such as inside a table lamp or appliance, or in a plastic box with a screw-down cover.

Insulated flex connectors These consist of a screw-down plastic cover with screw terminals inside. You buy them to suit the flex and the appliance: 5amp for small lamps and 13amp for most other uses. They are generally designed to accommodate the live, neutral and earth of three core flex but can be used with two core flex.

Insulated detachable flex connectors Made of rubber or a tough plastic, these are like a self-contained plug and socket and strong enough for outdoor use. They are available in 5 and 13amp sizes. You must always fix the 'male' or plug part of the connector on the flex leading to the appliance and the 'female' or socket half should be connected with the flex end that will be joined to the plug connecting with the mains. If you join them the other way round and they become detached, the part with the pins would be live to the touch – and therefore very dangerous.

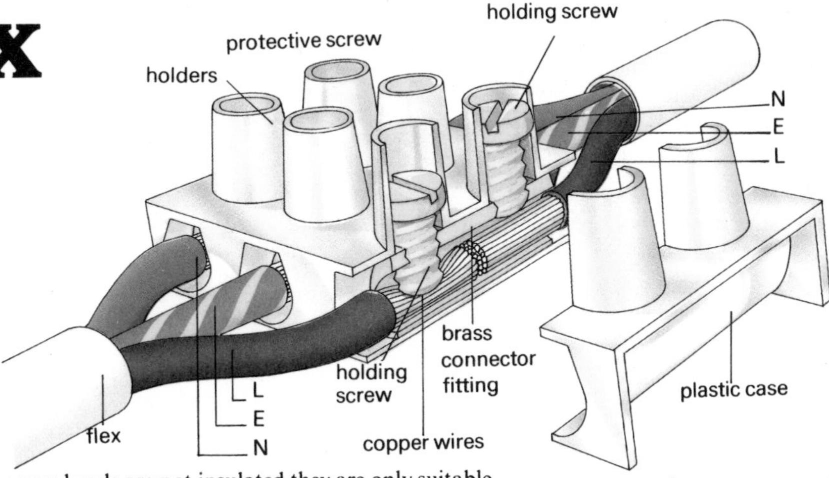

Connector strip

Above Plastic connector strip can be cut to suit single, two or three core flex
Below Insulated flex connector suitable for extending portable appliances such as hair dryers
Bottom Insulated detachable flex connector. Plug half must be connected to flex from appliance

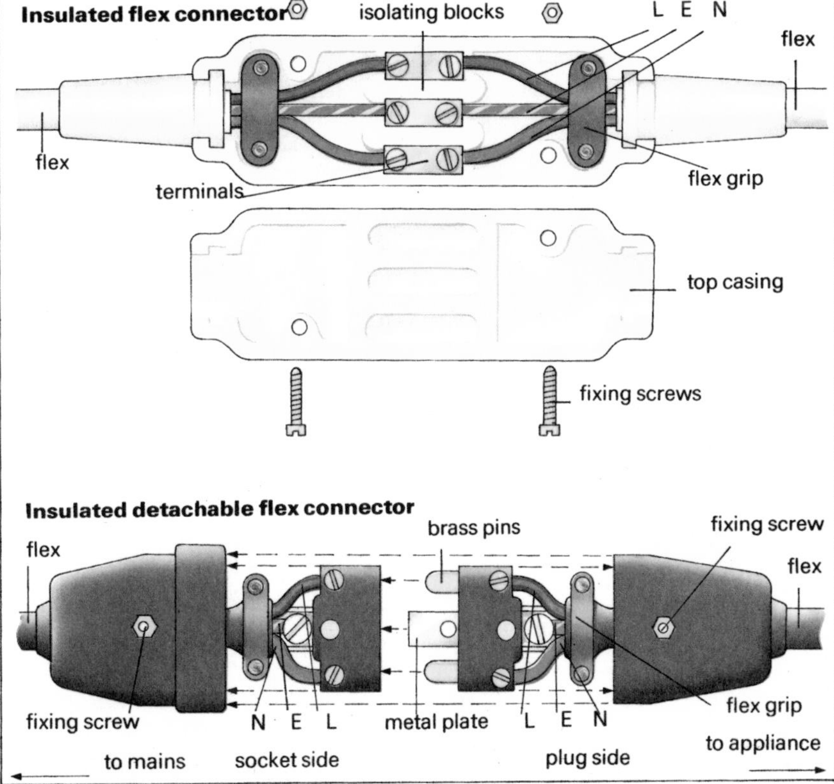

Wiring plugs

Probably the most common electrical job in the home is wiring a plug. It is crucial that the right core is fitted to the right terminal and that all connections are tight.

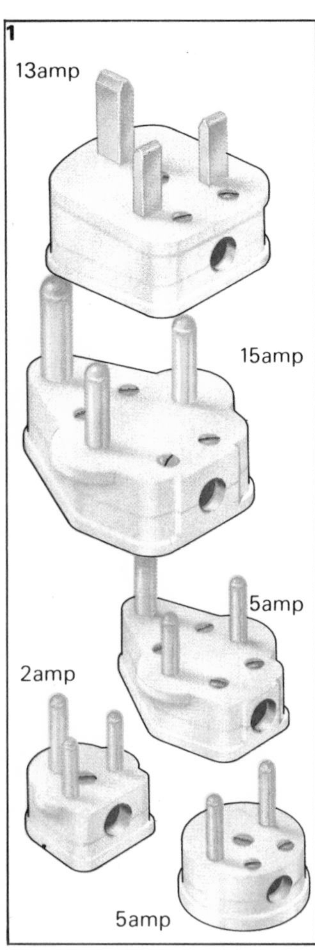

1 Types of plug: 13amp square pin; 15, 5 and 2amp round pin
2 Always check flex colour coding as right core must go to right plug terminal

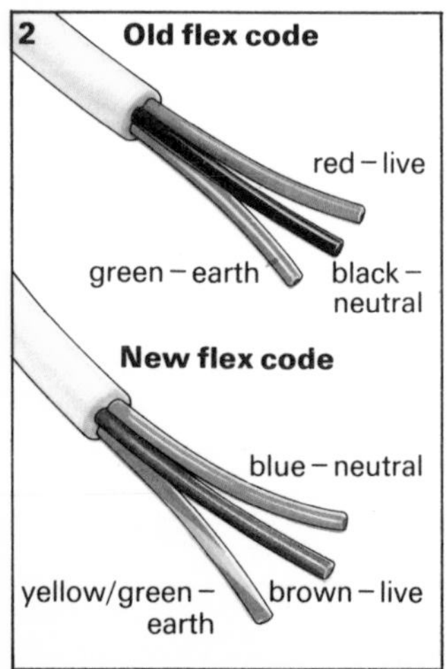

Houses that have been wired or rewired in Britain since 1947 will be fitted with ring main circuits. These are continuous loops of cable linking all wall sockets. The sockets are uniform 13amp outlets with rectangular holes to take the three flat pins of 13amp plugs.

This type of plug is supplied with a 3 or 13amp cartridge fuse (colour coded red and brown respectively). Always fit the fuse recommended by the manufacturer; as a general guide 3amp fuses are used with appliances rated up to 720 watts (for example table lamps) and 13amp fuses are used with larger appliances rated above 720 watts and up to 3000 watts (including kettles, irons and heaters). Some appliances (such as colour televisions, vacuum cleaners and spin dryers) although rated at less than 720 watts require a high starting current and should be used with 13amp fuses. In every case check first with maker's instructions.

Older houses will have radial wiring where separate cables radiate from the fuse board to each socket. These sockets are usually round pin in three sizes. The largest takes a 15amp plug used with larger appliances (such as heaters) while the other sizes take 5 and 2amp plugs used with smaller appliances (drills and table lamps respectively). The outlets may have two or three holes. The two pin sockets are not earthed and should only be used for light fixings with no exposed metal parts or for small double insulated appliances designed to operate without an earth connection and which are supplied only with two core flex.

Where possible it is safer to have radial wiring replaced (by your Electricity Board or a registered electrical contractor) with the properly earthed – and safer – ring main circuit.

Most plugs are made of tough, hard plastic but special rubberized types are available for equipment likely to be subjected to rough treatment, such as electric drills. Always buy a reputable make of plug because on poorer quality types the pins may move and cause a bad connection.

To fit a plug

First familiarize yourself with the colour code of the flex as it is most important the right core goes with the right terminal. With the new code blue is neutral, brown live and yellow/green earth. On older flex black is neutral, red live and green earth.

Remove the cover of the plug by undoing the large screw between the pins. When you look at the plug, with the largest pin (the earth) at the top and the flex outlet at the bottom, the live terminal is on the right (marked L) and the neutral terminal is on the left (marked N).

Prepare the flex by removing about 38mm ($1\frac{1}{2}$in) of the outer covering with a knife and fit the flex through the flex grip. This will be either a clamp type secured with two small screws (in which case loosen the screws, thread the flex through the grip and tighten the screws) or a V-shaped grip which

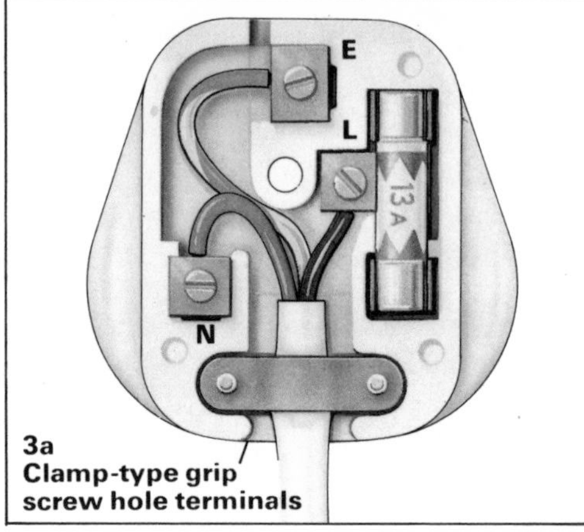

3a
Clamp-type grip screw hole terminals

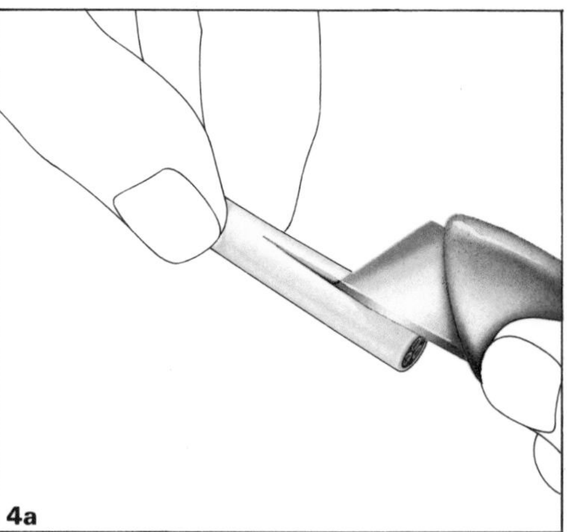

4a

5a

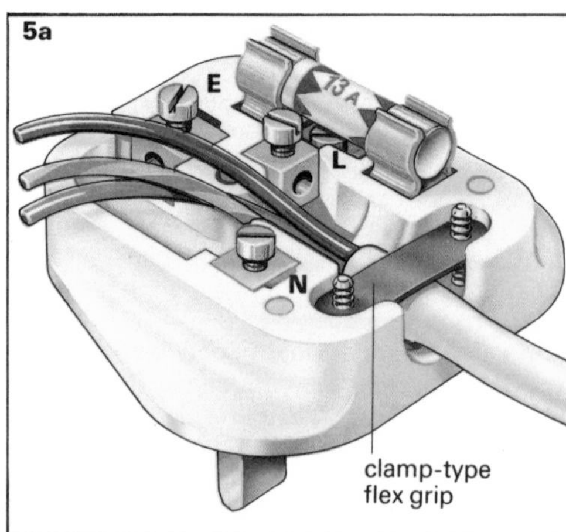

Earthing

When rewiring a plug make absolutely sure the earth wire (yellow/green or green) is properly connected. If it is not you run the risk of an electric shock should the metal casing of an appliance become accidentally live.

The only appliances which do not need earthing are double insulated ones supplied with two core flex and mains operated shavers which are intended for use with special shaver sockets.

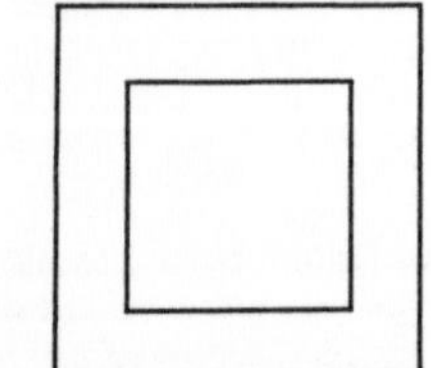

Left symbol for double insulation

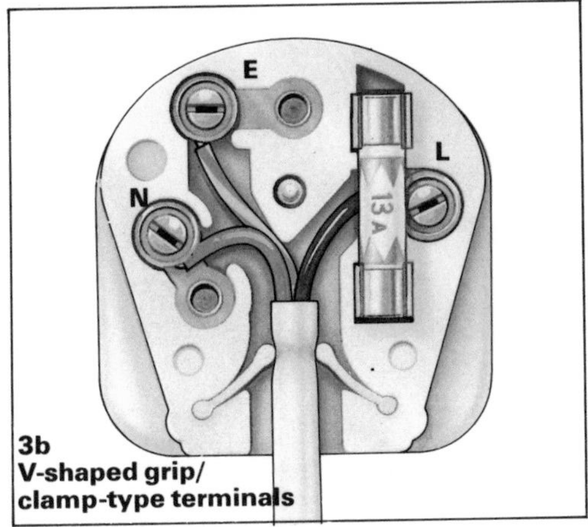

3b V-shaped grip/ clamp-type terminals

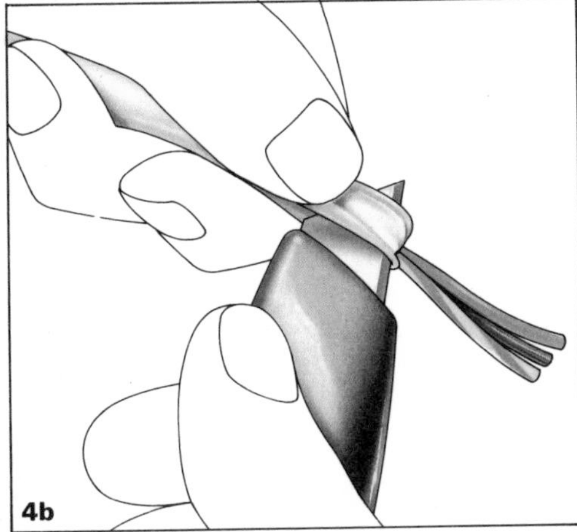
4b

holds about 6mm ($\frac{1}{4}$in) of the flex covering inside the plug. Make sure each core of the flex will reach its terminal, then cut 12mm ($\frac{1}{2}$in) beyond this for joining to the terminals. With wire strippers carefully remove about 12mm ($\frac{1}{2}$in) of the insulation at the end of each core and twist the loose strands neatly together.

Check which type of terminals the plug has. If it has screw holes double back the wires, insert them into the terminal holes and tighten the terminal screws with a small screwdriver to secure the wires. If the terminals are of the clamp type remove the screws, wrap the wires around the terminal posts in a clockwise direction, replace the screws and tighten them. On some plugs the live terminal is under the fuse housing, in which case you will have to remove the fuse before wiring that terminal. Make sure the plug is neatly wired: the insulation must go right up to the terminals and there must not be any straggling wires.

If a fuse is required simply snap the cartridge into the holding clips. Finally double check wires are connected to correct terminals before refitting cover. **Warning** If a plug gets hot the terminal screws may have worked loose and need to be tightened. Always replace a cracked plug immediately; never repair it, even temporarily, with insulating tape since there is a considerable risk the casing will come apart as the plug is put into or removed from the socket and you could get an electric shock.

It is important to check the flex regularly since the point where it joins the plug is particularly susceptible to breaking and fraying (especially on irons and vacuum cleaners). At first sign of wear cut frayed piece to make new end and rewire plug.

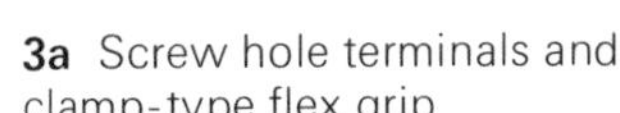

3a Screw hole terminals and clamp-type flex grip
3b Clamp-type terminals and V-shaped flex grip
4a Remove outer insulation by cutting along its length with sharp knife
4b Bend insulation away from flex and cut through fold
5a To insert flex in clamp-style grip, undo retaining screws, thread flex through grip and tighten screws
5b With V-shaped grip, simply push flex between two plastic strips
6 Check flex cores will reach terminals, allow 12mm ($\frac{1}{2}$in) extra for joining and cut off excess. Carefully remove insulation with wire strippers or sharp knife
7 Twist strands of each core neatly together

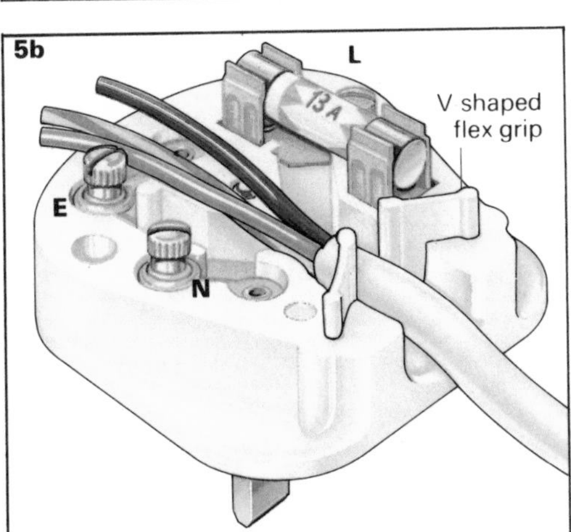

5b

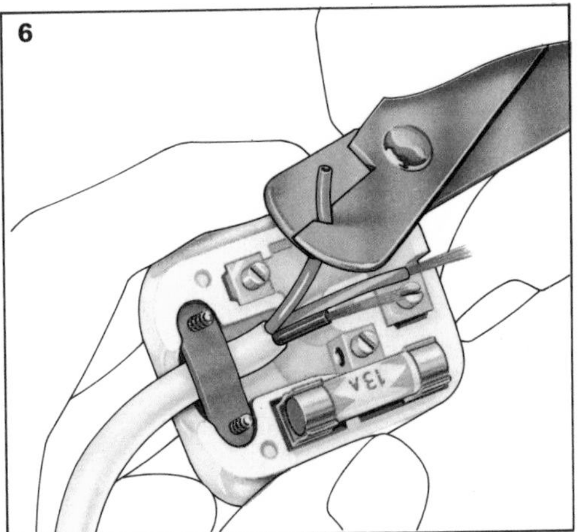

6

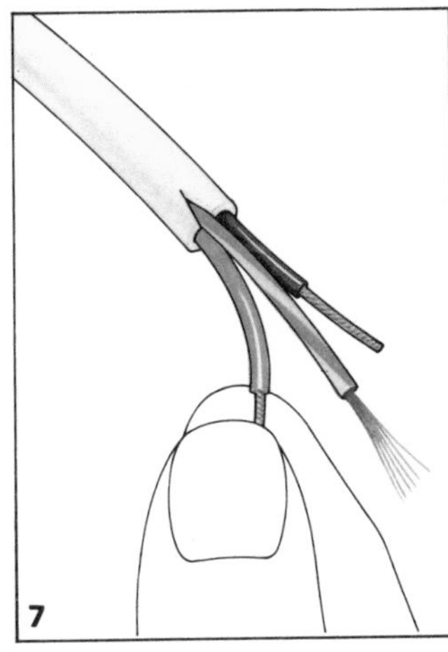
7

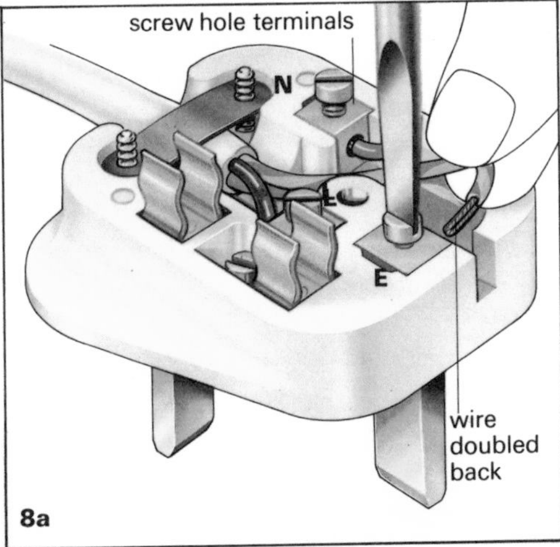

8a

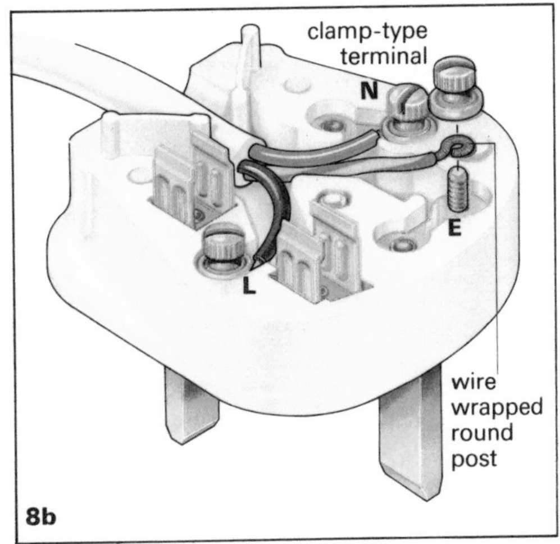

8b

8a With screw hole terminals, double back wires, loosen terminal screws and insert wires in terminals. Gently tighten screws, taking care not to sever wires
8b With clamp terminals, remove screws and wrap bare wires round terminal posts in clockwise direction. Replace screws and tighten

Wiring up the circuit

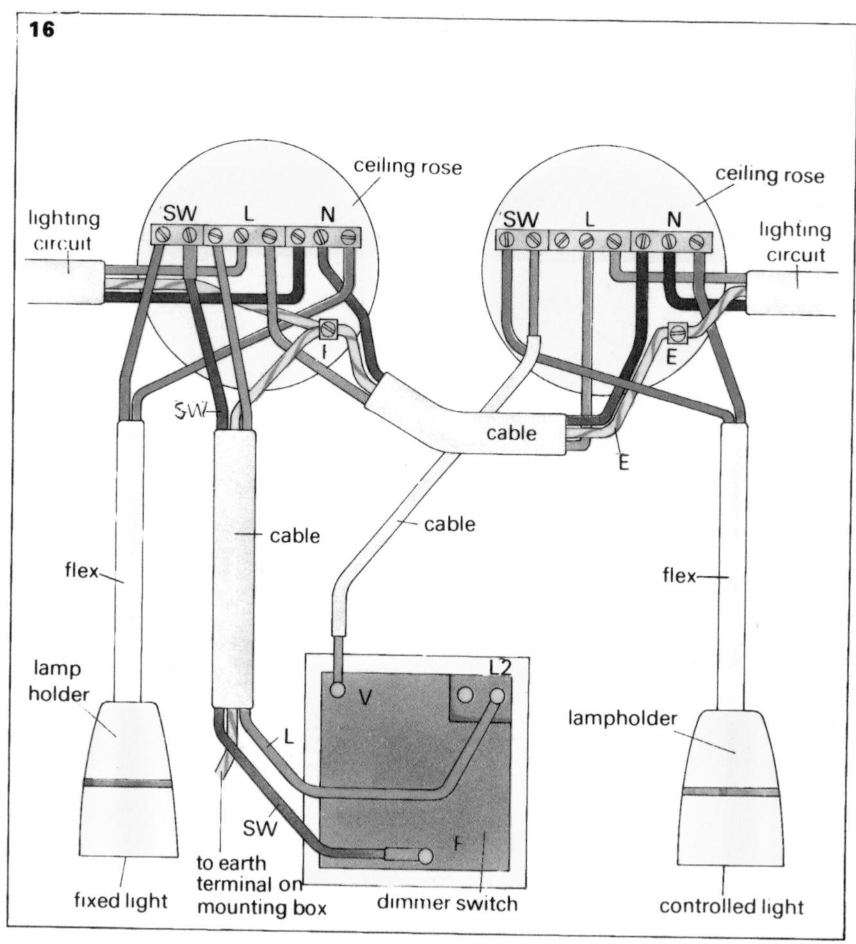

Electrical circuits run through walls, along skirting and under floorboards to all parts of your home, carrying current to feed the various fittings and appliances. All circuits run from the main fuse box or consumer unit, which in turn is fed from the mains supply from outside. Once you have learnt how these circuits are wired up, you can move and add lights, switches and sockets where you want. You may decide to run electricity to areas that previously were without – for example the loft, outbuildings or into the garden. Bear in mind that new wiring will involve a certain amount of redecorating afterwards.

Fitting a new consumer unit

There is nothing more aggravating than wanting to add new electrical equipment in the home and not being able to include a new circuit to supply it. You may find you need to install a larger consumer unit than the one already fitted in order to cope with this, which is a job you can do yourself.

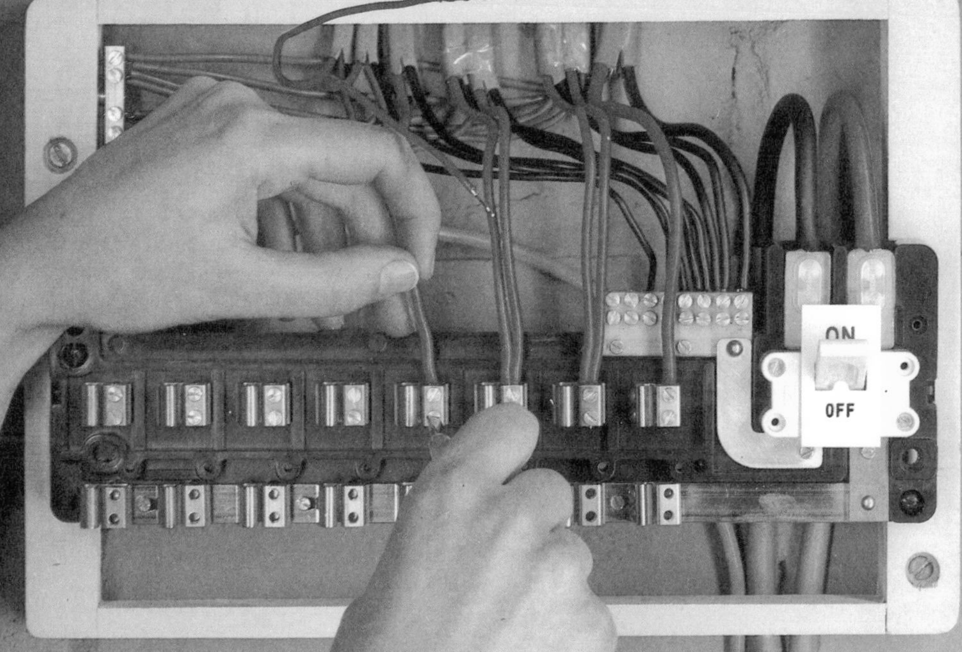

The final stage of wiring up a new consumer unit
Inset Check whether your unit has miniature circuit breakers **(left)** or fuse carriers **(right)**

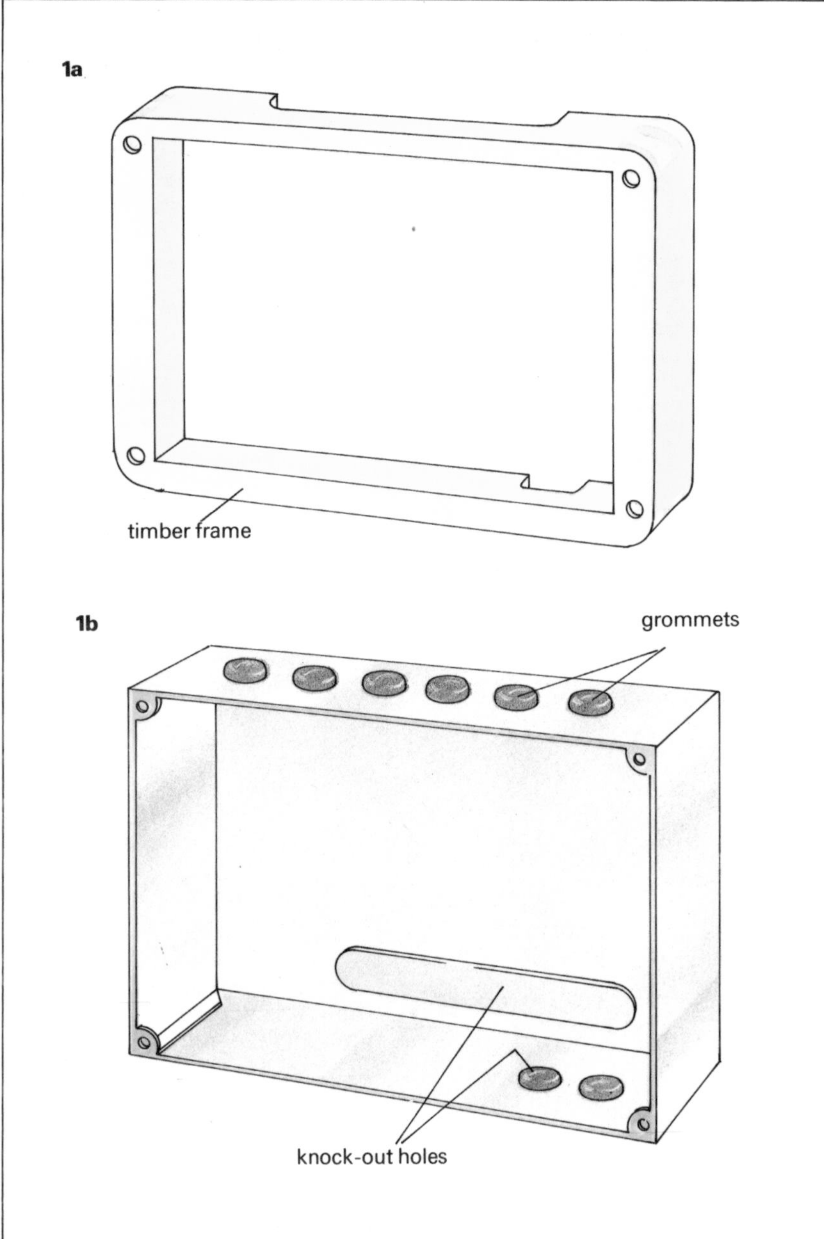

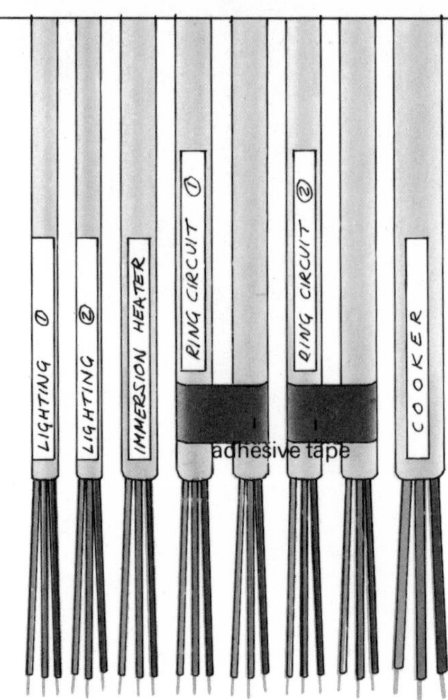

A consumer unit is a comparatively modern piece of electrical equipment which combines the necessary double pole main switch with a single pole fuseboard in one casing. It should be situated as close as possible to the Electricity Board meter, to which it is connected by the meter tails which provide the supply. The switch is double pole so both the live and the neutral supplies are cut off simultaneously when the main switch is turned off. The fuses in the consumer unit, which protect individual circuits and equipment from excess current caused by a fault or overloading, interrupt the current in the live circuit.

Deciding number of circuits

The size of consumer units varies from two-way, for an installation with only two-circuits, to 12-way; the most common unit installed in a home is eight-way. Generally the size is determined by the number of circuits involved when the house is built. So when an additional circuit is required, perhaps for a shower heater or power point in your garage, there is no spare fuseway. As the wiring regulations do not permit any fuse to supply more than one circuit, you have two alternatives: either fit a main switch and fuse unit next to the consumer unit or replace the unit with a larger one with more fuses. A separate switch and fuse unit needs a separate mains connection and since Electricity Boards will not allow more than one pair of leads connected to their meter, a special terminal box has to be fitted on the consumer's side. Another disadvantage is that this will only provide one extra circuit. It is more satisfactory to replace the consumer unit and normally it is a waste of time and money to fit one smaller than an eight-way; this will, for example, supply two lighting circuits, two ring circuits, a cooker, an immersion heater and leave two spare fuseways for future expansion.

Choosing unit

There are three principal types: one with fuses that can be rewired or fitted with cartridge fuses, another fitted with miniature circuit breakers (mcb) and a third which accepts either fuses or mcbs. The circuit breakers give the best protection, while cartridge fuses are next best; most units have wire fuses because they are cheapest. New consumer units now often incorporate mcbs and an ELCB.

The current required to blow a wire fuse is twice the rating of the fuse, which means a 10amp current is required to blow a 5amp fuse. A cartridge blows at one and a half times its rated current and an mcb operates when only one and a quarter times its rated current flows in the circuit. An mcb also operates much quicker than a fuse and reduces the risk of fire or damage to the circuit or appliance. If price is a consideration, it is worth remembering an mcb costs about three times as much as a fused unit. You do not repair an mcb; you simply press a button or turn on a switch to reactivate it – as long as you have dealt with the problem that caused it to break the circuit. Fuse wires and cartridges must be replaced and it is vital to keep spares.

Five ratings Circuit fuses and mcbs are made in five ratings, each with a different colour code, for domestic use: 5 (white), 15 (blue), 20 (yellow), 30 (red) and 45 (green). Consumer units do not usually have provision for a 45amp fuseway, which occu-

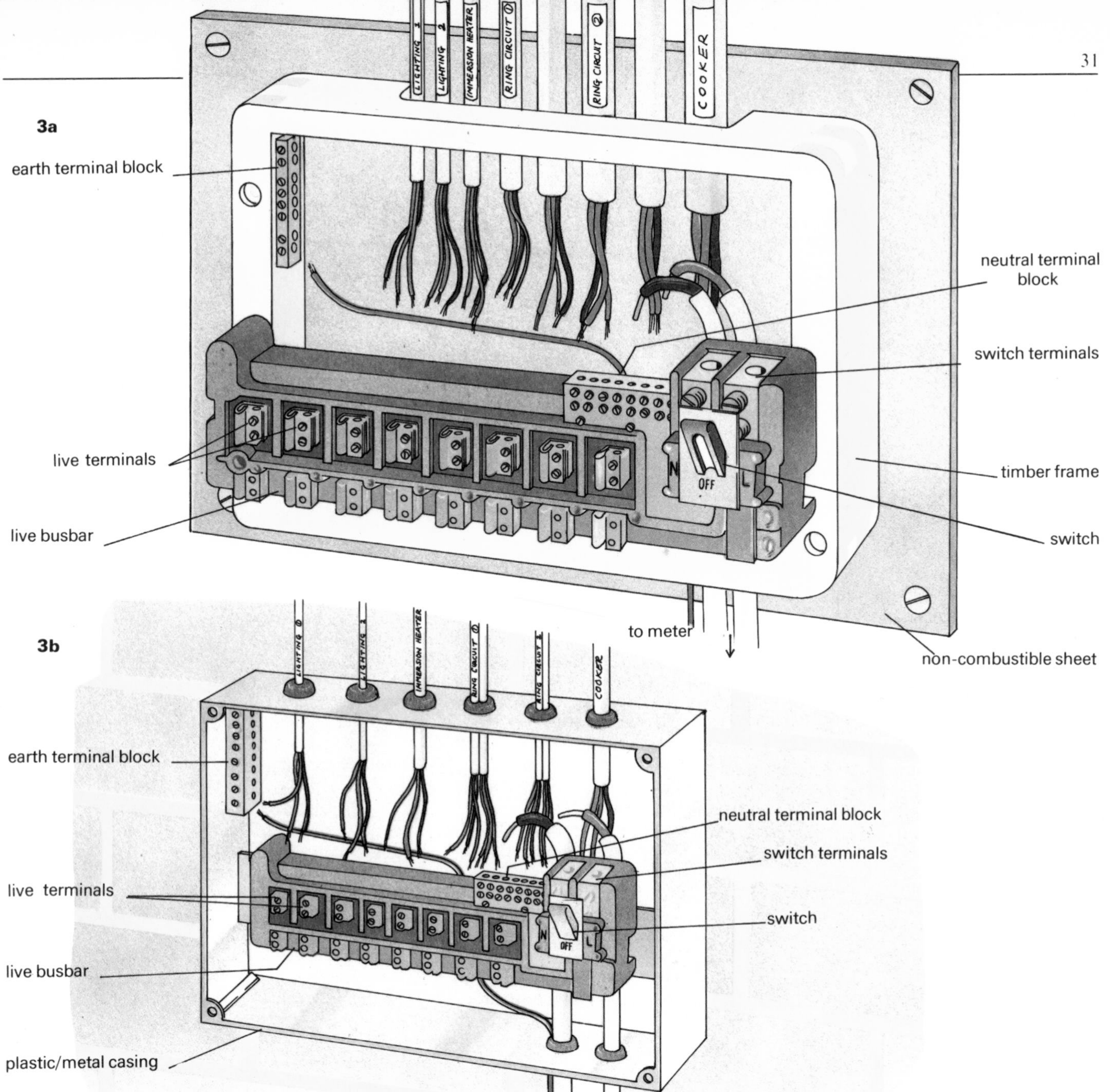

1a Recesses for meter leads in timber frame of plastic consumer unit
1b Knock-out holes for circuit cables in all-metal – or plastic – units. (Terminals are omitted in these diagrams)
2 Labelling cables and taping ring circuit cables together
3a Feeding cables into plastic/timber frame unit
3b Feeding cables into all-metal – or plastic – unit

pies the space of two standard fuseways in some units and is needed only for a circuit supplying, for example, a large cooker with a loading of 17kW or more. If you are changing your existing unit for a larger installation, you will probably find your present fuses or mcbs will be suitable for your new unit and will save you some expense.

Disconnecting mains
Before you remove your existing consumer unit or fuseboard, the power must be disconnected at the mains by the withdrawal of the service fuse and you must give your Electricity Board at least 48 hours' notice, in writing, that you require a temporary disconnection.

Electricity Boards are obliged by law to isolate a consumer's installation from the mains on request during normal working hours.

You can usually make the change in one day and if electricity is disconnected at 9am you can have the supply restored at 5pm. If by midday you realize you cannot complete the job in time, you can always ask for reconnection to be postponed.

Preparing for installation
Some preparatory work can be done a day or so before you have the electricity cut off. Check you have all the materials and equipment you require. Remove the cover from the new unit and the fuses or mcbs, if they are bought already fitted. This leaves only the main switch, terminal banks and the copper busbar to which the fuse units are screwed. Consumer units are made entirely in metal, or plastic, or a plastic casing with a timber frame. The metal and all-plastic units have knock-out holes at the top and bottom and at the back. If it is a plastic case on a timber frame, you should either drill holes or cut recesses for the cables in the timber frame (at the top or bottom or both, depending on whether your circuit cables run up from ground level or down from ceiling height); if the cables are channelled into the plaster, they can be brought into the unit through the back of the timber frame. If the unit is to be mounted on a combustible material a sheet of non-combustible material should be fixed between the unit and the wall.
Strip cable Strip about 50mm (2in) of sheathing

4

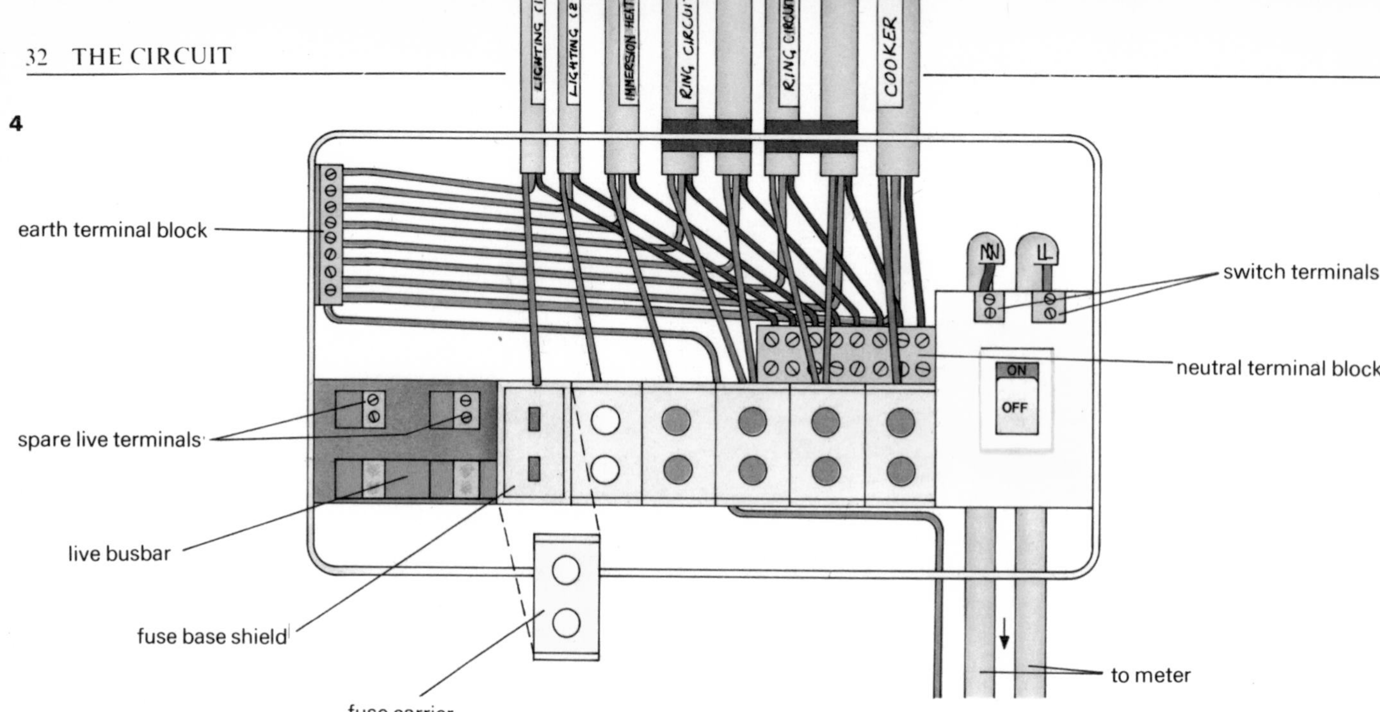

4 Circuit cables wired up correctly into new consumer unit

from the 16sq mm cable and take about 13mm (½in) of insulation off each conductor. Connect the red (live) conductor to the L terminal and the black (neutral) conductor to the N terminal. Tighten the screws and replace the insulated sleeves, where fitted. Make sure you have enough cable for the Electricity Board official to connect up. Your existing earthing lead should be connected to the earthing terminal on your new unit after the supply has been disconnected. If you are fitting a new earthing lead, you can fit it to the earthing terminal but don't connect it to earth; the Electricity Board official will do that.

Check all the circuits are labelled on the existing consumer unit. If not, by switching on all lights and appliances and then withdrawing fuses one by one, turning off the mains switch before pulling out each fuse, you can identify the circuits. Label them by attaching self-adhesive stickers on the cover of the consumer unit and then prepare a second set of labels which will go on the cables.

Changing over

When the electricity has been cut off, take off the cover from the existing consumer unit and remove the fuses. Loosen the terminal screws on each fuse holder in turn and disconnect the live circuit wires, which should all be red. As you disconnect, wrap the appropriate identification label round each circuit cable. Where two cables were connected to one fuseway in a ring circuit, use a piece of adhesive tape to bind them together until you reconnect to the new unit. Release the wires from the neutral and earthing terminals. Remove the frame or casing of the unit, replaster any holes and make good any decoration as required.

Fixing unit Take the frame, or casing, of the new unit, hold it in position on the wall and mark the fixing holes. Drill and plug the holes and screw the unit into position. Don't forget to fix a non-combustible sheet between the unit and the wall if you are mounting on a combustible material. Feed the circuit cables into the casing and connect them to the fuseways (an mcb unit may require the mcbs to be positioned first). Starting at the main switch end of the unit, connect your cooker circuit (if you have one) or the first of your ring main circuits. Connect the red conductor to the first live terminal, the black to the first terminal on the neutral bank and, after slipping green PVC insulating sleeving on if it does not have it, connect the bare earth conductor to the first earthing terminal. The end of the cable sheathing must be within the case or the frame. Continue to connect up in descending order of rating: 30, 20, 15 and 5. Any spare fuseways must be fitted with blanking plates until required. The circuits should, ideally, be rearranged where necessary when the current rating of any new circuit is known.

Fitting fuse bases

Screw the fuse bases – they are sometimes called shields – into their correct position according to their rating on the live busbar. This is important because it would be dangerous, for instance, to fit a 30amp base and fuse carrier to a 5amp circuit. The fuse bases and carriers are sold together, so when you buy your new equipment you must know exactly what your circuit ratings will be. The bases are manufactured to accept only a carrier of their own rating (or sometimes smaller) – you can never fit a 15amp fuse carrier into a 5amp base and so on. The colour coding of bases and carriers helps to eliminate mistakes and aids quick identification when you are changing a fuse wire or a cartridge if a circuit blows. When the bases are installed, replace the terminal cover if there is one and insert the fuse carriers. Finally replace the fuse cover (having taken care to identify the circuits with adhesive labels inside the cover) and wait for the electricity man to call to reconnect you. It is unlikely he will test your work unless new circuits have been added at the same time as you installed the new consumer unit: but the decision is his and you must be prepared for him to check out the work.

Earth sleeving Until recently sleeving on earth wires was always green in colour; this has now been standardized to green/yellow, although you are still likely to come across the old sleeving, particularly in older houses.

Outside wiring

Wiring to sockets or lighting points attached to the outside walls of a house can be part of the domestic circuit. Wiring to a point in the garden, greenhouse or separate garage, however, has to be treated as a different installation, with its own main switch and 20amp fuse unit close to the meter. It is now also recommended you fit an ELCB on this circuit.

Because wind and rough weather will cause wear and tear, sockets, switches and cables must be tough, weatherproof and protected from the possibility of accidental damage. Professional help with outside wiring is essential because electricity used outside is potentially more dangerous than inside.

Surface wiring

Wiring a porch light, socket or switch onto the outside wall of a house is not difficult as long as you use weatherproof equipment. Sockets are usually in galvanized steel with covers and the switches are plastic. It is best to keep wiring on an outside wall to a minimum; it should be protected in plastic tubing or conduit and the connections, where the cable joins the switch or socket or light fitting, have to be water- and weatherproof. The wiring can be taken as a spur from the ring main, although a porch or outside light can be taken from a lighting point, as described earlier in the book; in this case the cable goes through the wall as close to the light as possible. Study the wiring layout of the house to plan the shortest route from the new position to the existing wiring; this will give a neater installation.

To take a cable from the inside of a house to the outside, drill a hole through the wall using a masonry bit of up to 300mm (1ft) long if it is a cavity wall. Insert a short length of plastic tube or conduit; this must be angled so the outside end is lower than the inside (to keep out rainwater) and cemented in place. Fit an elbow to the outside end.

Overhead wiring

With the overhead method of wiring, the PVC twin core and earth cable is supported by a galvanized steel cable called a catenary wire. The power cable is relieved of any stress or strain by being clipped and taped to the catenary wire which is itself suspended from permanent supports not less than 3.5m (11ft 6in) above ground or 5.2m (17ft) if above a drive. To get the right height you may have to attach a weather-treated post to the greenhouse or garage and brace it to withstand strong winds. You must fit supporting vine eyes, one into a heavy duty plug on the house wall and the other into the side of the post near the top. The ends of the catenary wire are threaded through the eyes and twisted firmly round the main length of wire.

Since the catenary wire will be under strain for many years, it is vital to have a strong joint at each end. It is also a good idea to have an adjustable eye bolt fitting or a turnbuckle at one end of the catenary wire so it can be stretched tight. The catenary wire must be earthed using single core 6sq mm PVC-insulated earth wire connected to it by a corrosion-resistant screw-type connector and connected to the mains earth point in the house. Cable from the switch fuse should come through the wall using a tube or conduit as already described. The mains cable should be 2.5sq mm or 4sq mm and in one continuous length from the switch fuse to the new switch or socket.

A downward rainwater 'drip loop' of slack is usually left at each end and the supply cable is attached to the catenary wire by using slings or bitumen-impregnated insulating tape; this is turned two or three times between the cable and wire. Non-corrosive buckle-type cable clips are wrapped round the tape for strength.

Underground wiring

Running cable underground is the least obtrusive method and is worth the extra trouble and expense – although this is reduced if the cable is laid during landscaping. You will need special cable, armoured PVC-insulated cable being recommended. It has two cores – red and black insulated – and an extruded covering of black PVC over the galvanized wire armour; the wire armour usually serves as the

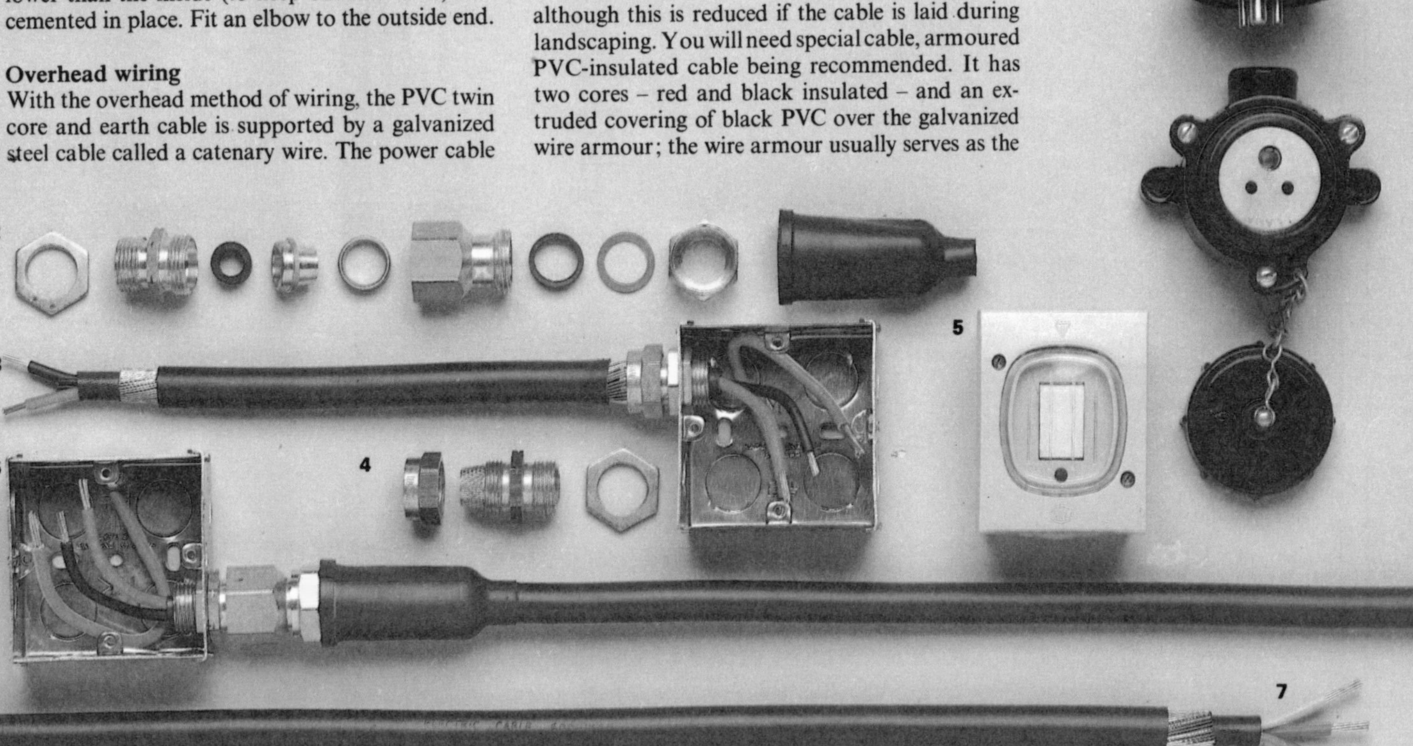

1 Outdoor plug, socket and cover
2 Components of outdoor gland used for connecting armoured cable to metal box
3 Twin core armoured cable, stripped back to show various layers, connected to metal box with indoor gland; separate earth wire connects to earth terminal on metal box
4 Exploded indoor gland
5 Weatherproofed switch
6 Twin core armoured cable connected to metal box with outdoor gland
7 Three core armoured cable stripped back to show various layers; yellow core is used as earth wire

earth conductor. It is necessary to fit a metal screwed compression gland, secured by a lock nut and bush, over the wire armour at each end of the cable; this gland fits the conduit entry hole of a flush metal box, fixed inside the building or house, which is used as a junction box if the entry point of the armoured cable is some distance from the main switch or switch fuse. A terminal block inside the box is used to connect the armoured cable to ordinary twin core and earth PVC-sheathed cable. Alternatively the cable can be run to the switch mounting box. In both cases a short length of 4.0sq mm single core green/yellow PVC-insulated cable is used to connect the switch or terminal block earth terminal to the earth terminal on the box.

Some Electricity Boards may insist on the use of three core armoured cable, the yellow core being used for the earth and enclosed in green/yellow sleeving for identification.

A more expensive cable is the mineral-insulated, copper-clad type (MICC); this has two wires inside a protective copper tube which also serves as an earth connection. With mineral-insulated cable it is necessary to fit a seal at each end; if the cable runs directly into the switch and fuse unit, choose a seal which has an earth wire termination. A screwed gland can also be fitted with each seal if required. The cable runs from the main switch and fuse unit in the house to the control panel in the building outside, taking as direct a route as possible but avoiding all places likely to be disturbed in the future. The trench must be dug about 500mm (20in) deep and care taken not to damage any water or drainpipes and other cables you encounter. If there is a space below the ground floor of your house, it is easy to have a hole knocked through the wall; but be careful not to interfere with the damp proof course. The cable needs to be protected at points where it is exposed and securely fixed to the wall using special clips designed for the purpose. Additional protection can be given by galvanized steel channelling screwed to the brick or woodwork.

Below Layout showing wiring from house to outbuildings – over or underground – with details of connections to consumer unit inside house (**inset A**), taking cable through wall inside conduit pipe and connecting to catenary wire (**inset B**), fixing catenary wire to post (**inset C**) and outbuilding control panel (**inset D**); when wiring up use cable for lights and flex for other appliances

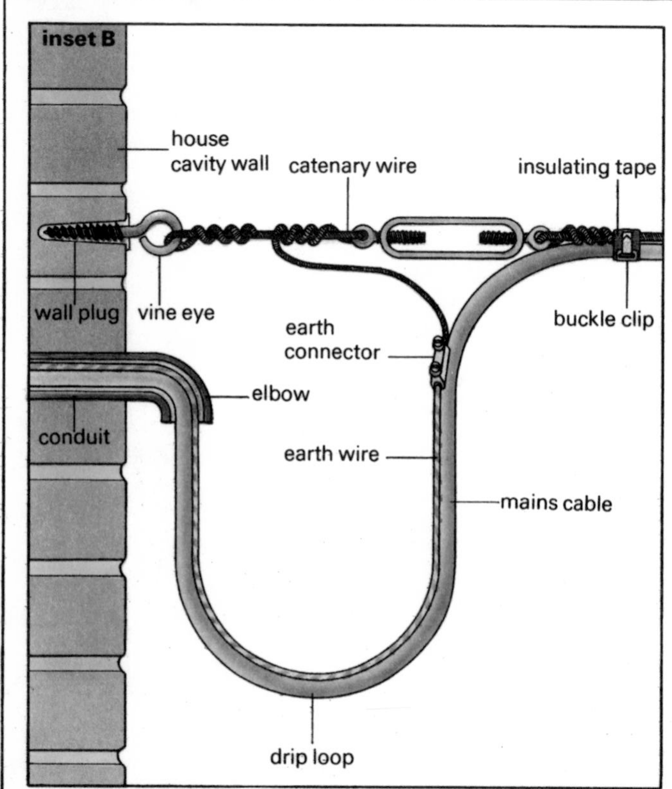

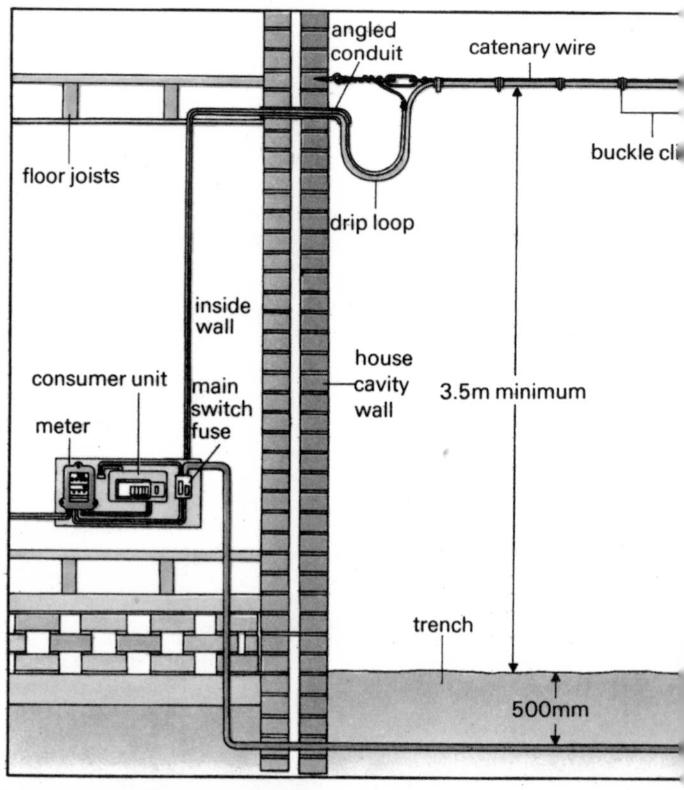

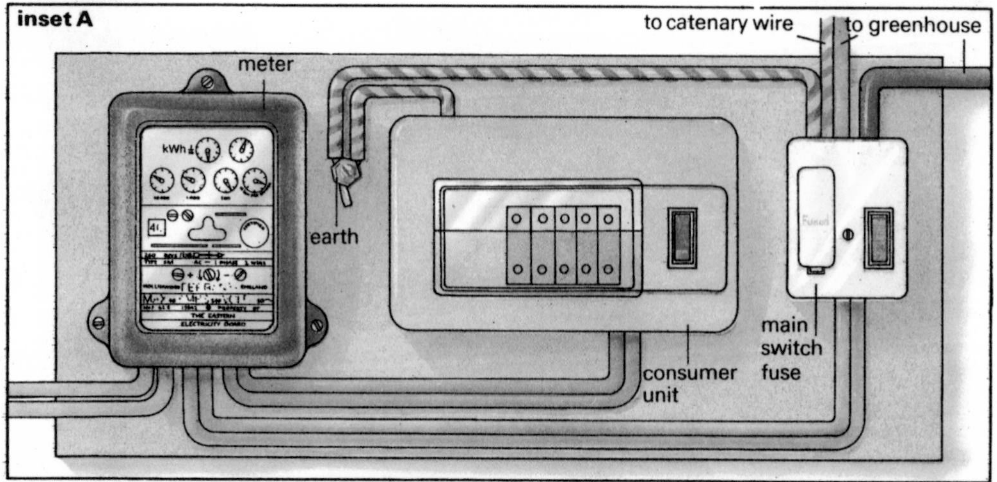

Control panels

In an integral or attached garage the cable can run direct to sockets and light fittings; but ideally the cable should terminate in a control panel with a main switch. In the damper atmosphere of a greenhouse or garden shed, a control panel is strongly advisable for safety; switched points and socket outlets can then be connected to the switch. Permanent switches and fused connection units with red neon indicators are preferable, since most of the equipment will be permanently connected. With a plug and socket there is always a risk of damp working its way between the face of the plug and the socket surface, resulting in a current leakage. Provide at least one socket for connecting portable aids used in the garden and two for use in a garage.

Fused connection units, switches and sockets should be installed 1200mm (4ft) from the floor and wired with twin core and earth PVC-sheathed 2.5sq mm cable. The cable is taken from each in turn back to the outlet on the main switch. Fused connection units and sockets should be mounted on metal mounting boxes inset into a timber board, or on moulded plastic surface-mounted boxes, with cable holes drilled through the board.

In a greenhouse fit a strong frame to the back of the board to protect the cable and leave access for the mains cable. Once the wiring is complete, fit a back cover of weatherproof plywood and mount the board at chest level on a strong support. The wiring to the electrical equipment and heaters can be by PVC-sheathed three core flex secured at intervals to the greenhouse; there should be no trailing or loose cable or flex. With aluminium greenhouses you may have to drill small holes in the appropriate positions to allow buckle clips to be fixed with screws and nuts. In this case the PVC-sheathed cable will be in contact with metal and the greenhouse must be earthed by bolting an earth clamp to the frame and connecting a 6sq mm green/yellow PVC-insulated earth cable to this and to the earthing terminal of the main switch.

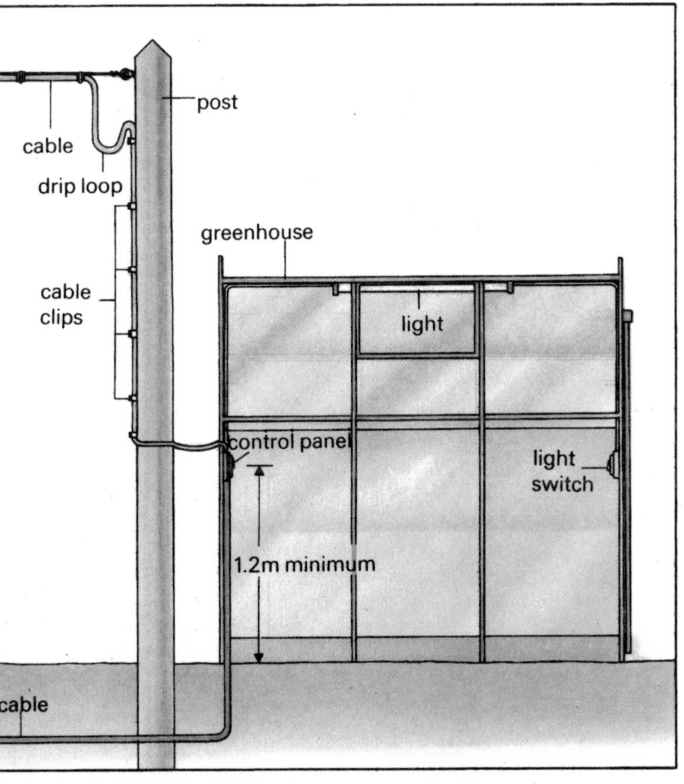

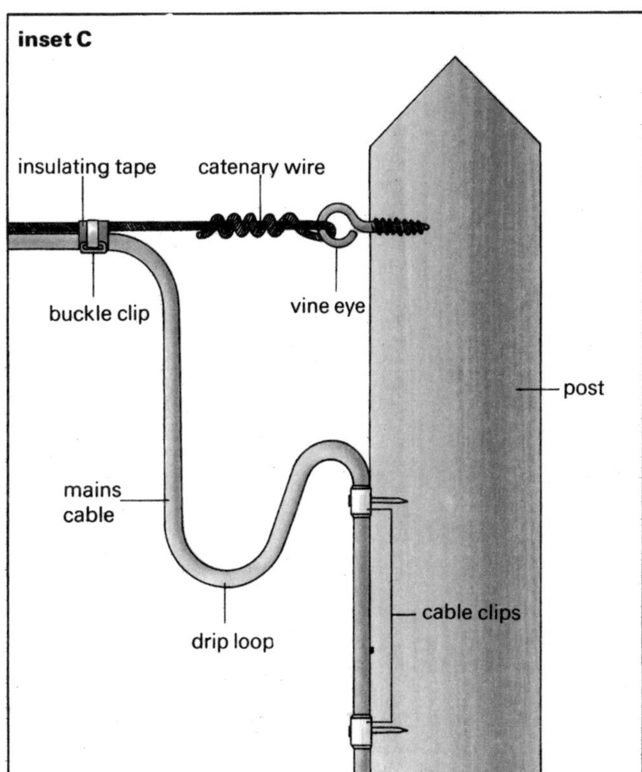

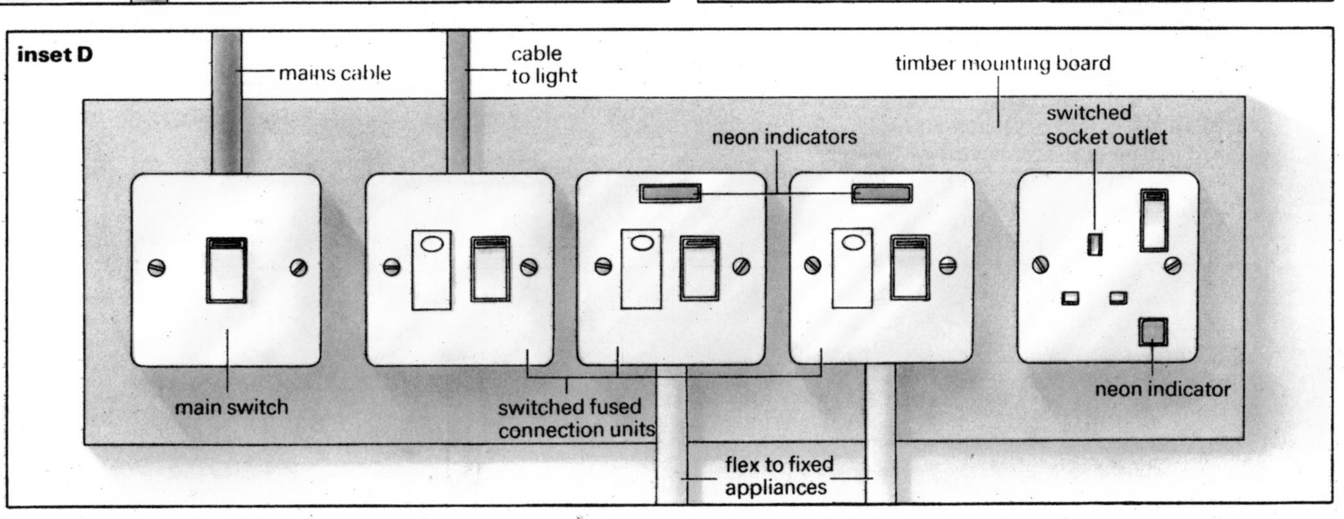

Garden lighting

Garden lighting is practical, attractive and not expensive to run; two units of electricity will light the average garden from dusk to midnight. The lighting of walls, patios and possible danger points such as steps helps prevent accidents and discourages intruders. Effective outside lighting also lengthens the time you can enjoy the garden and can reveal an unexpected attraction in familiar surroundings. This can be achieved by using fittings attached to the outside of the house or with the more mobile low-voltage lighting set. But whichever you use, it must be safe.

Mains voltage lighting

There are complications in using mains electricity outdoors. Many lighting fittings can be fixed to the wall of the house and connected through the bricks to the house wiring; but garden spotlights, pool lights and lights in herbaceous borders will need an outdoor connection. Weatherproof 13amp sockets mounted on the outside wall of the house are an inexpensive way of providing temporary lighting for the patio, but will not have the same atmospheric effect as lighting sited away from the house.

Types of light Spotlights are the most effective way of lighting a garden. Mains voltage 100 and 150 watt spotlamps screw into waterproof holders and are tough enough to withstand most outdoor conditions; the holders can be supplied with an earth spike or a mounting bracket. Spotlights can also be mounted on trees or walls to light a path or section of the garden. When lighting trees, the spotlights should be placed at ground level or low down on the trunk and directed so their light goes up into the branches.

Tungsten-halogen miniature floodlamps give 300–500 watts of brilliant light from a small finger-size glass phial mounted on a fitting about 150 × 75mm (6 × 3in). They are powerful for their size and have a life of about 2000 hours. To light the garden, they should be placed high on a wall and must be fixed in a horizontal position.

The simplest method of lighting paths, patios and porches is to use the 'light brick' or 'bulkhead' fitting; this is a square or oval of opal or moulded glass which clips over a weatherproof holder. The fitting is commonly available in sizes from 200 × 125 × 114mm (8 × 5 × 4½in) and is suitable for a 60 or 100 watt lamp.

Post lanterns wired with buried armoured cable can be mounted on a low wall or on anti-tamper bollards and used to light entrances and drives.

Low voltage lighting

There are several low voltage lighting sets available; these can be safely installed even at ground level, where children are likely to touch them. They operate at 12 volts through a portable mains transformer (the output of the transformer is described in volt-amps rather than watts); you simply plug the transformer into any convenient socket outlet and trail the cable down the garden, connecting in spotlamps at any point in the length of the cable. The lamps are easily attached and can be pushed into the earth on spikes or fixed to trees.

Types of lighting set The 'ropelight' is a recent innovation and operates from a 12 volt DC supply, which can either be a special mains transformer/rectifier or a car battery. It consists of a line of coloured lights within a hose-like flexible plastic tube. The lights come in 10m (or 33ft) lengths which can be draped around the garden. Fixed flashing lights are available or you could use chaser lights, which appear to move along the rope.

There are also specially mounted lighting units which can be used under water or floating on the surface. If these lights are used with a 12 volt submersible pump, special water jet rings can be clipped around the lights to give illuminated fountains. Both fountains and lights can be controlled on one cable from an indoor switch or a waterproof junction box and transformer can be concealed close to the water in a simple rockery stone or brick housing to protect it from the weather.

A waterfall can look particularly effective when lit. Small lights can be concealed among the plants and stones on the edge of the stream and low

Equipment for garden lighting (Elsworthy Electronics):
1 Transformer
2 Pool lights, available with different colour lenses, which can be used under water or floating on the surface
3 Spotlights, also available with different colour lenses, which can be bracket-mounted or fixed to spikes and driven into the ground

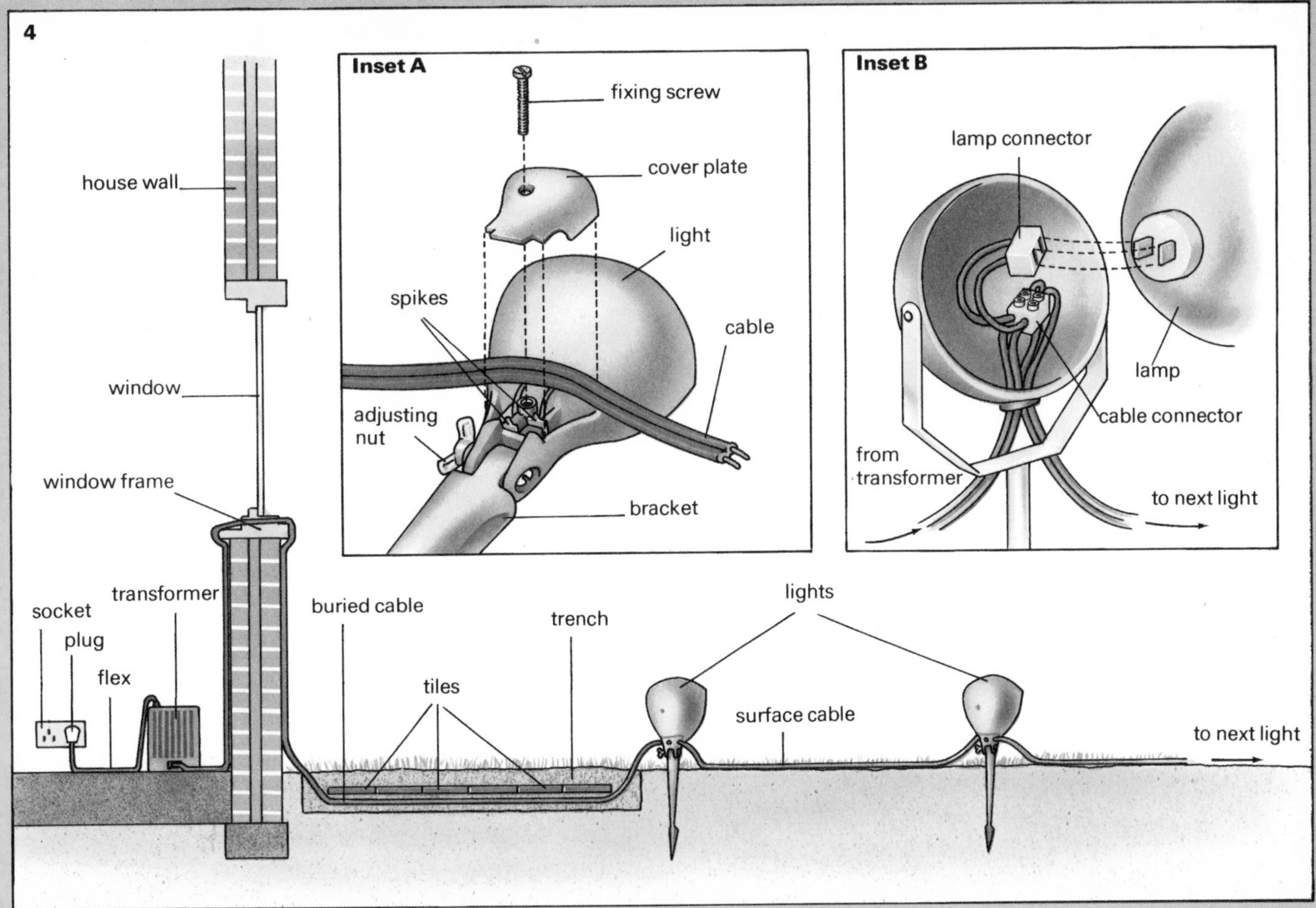

voltage lamps are purpose-made to be concealed in simulated rocky stones.

Connecting up lighting sets Position the transformer under cover in the house, garage or shed close to a 240 volt mains socket outlet. The rating of the transformer will limit the number of lamps you can have. A transformer with a 36 volt-amps output can serve up to two lamps; a 72 volt-amps rating is suitable for up to four lamps and 108 volt-amps rating is for a maximum of six lamps.

Connect special low voltage, twin core cable to the transformer output connector block. One end of the cable is sealed for weatherproofing, so be sure to connect the unsealed end to the transformer. Run the cable to where the lights are required; it can be taken outside through a small hole drilled in the fixed part of a window frame. It is safe to allow the cable to trail on the surface of the ground so the positions of the lights can be easily changed; or you can bury it in a trench, which you should then cover with tiles to prevent accidental damage from garden tools.

When the lights are roughly positioned, connect them to the low voltage cable. With one low voltage system you should take the back cover plate off each light, drape the cable in its channel and press the cable down with your thumb so the projecting metal spikes make an electrical connection. Replace the cover and adjust the light to the desired angle. Fit the transformer mains lead with a plug to suit the socket outlet; the plug should be fitted with a 3amp fuse. You can now plug the transformer in and switch it on. To ensure a satisfactory electrical connection after each season's use, you should move each light along the cable by about 25mm (1in) and then reconnect it; wrap insulating tape round the previous connection area.

Another system uses conventional connector strips and a car-type lamp connector; in this case you must bare the cable and connect it in the screw connectors at each fitting.

Planning lighting

Colour is important when lighting outdoors and most spotlamps are sold with colour filters. The thing to remember when lighting a garden is to concentrate on what is being lit and not on the lights themselves. White is most effective since it brings out colour; red turns foliage brown, while yellow turns it grey. Green highlights grass and foliage, while blue has a mysterious quality especially on birch trees; it also attracts insects, so place it away from a terrace or patio. Lights should be hidden from view or placed behind large plants; where concealment is difficult, you should mount them above the normal lines of vision.

Concentrate on trees and larger shrubs. Trees such as elm, which have a high canopy, should be lit from below so the spotlight shines upwards into the leaves. Silver birches should be lit so the beam just touches the main limbs and conifers should catch the light along the edges of their branches. One or two spotlights placed in herbaceous borders can give a dramatic effect, casting a warm glow over the flowers.

When experimenting, choose a dry night and use an ordinary 150 watt lamp in a simple bowl reflector. Seen from a distance, this will give you an idea of the effect you will get when you eventually install the proper equipment.

4 With a low voltage wiring system the transformer is connected to a socket outlet inside the house; the cable to the lights is taken through the wall or window frame and over or underground (protected by tiles) to the outside lights and looped in from light to light. The cable is fixed to each light by removing the cable cover and pressing the cable onto the projecting prongs; the cover is screwed back on to make the electrical connection (**inset A**). A car-type lamp showing the lamp connector and the cable looped into the terminal strips (**inset B**)

Moving and adding sockets

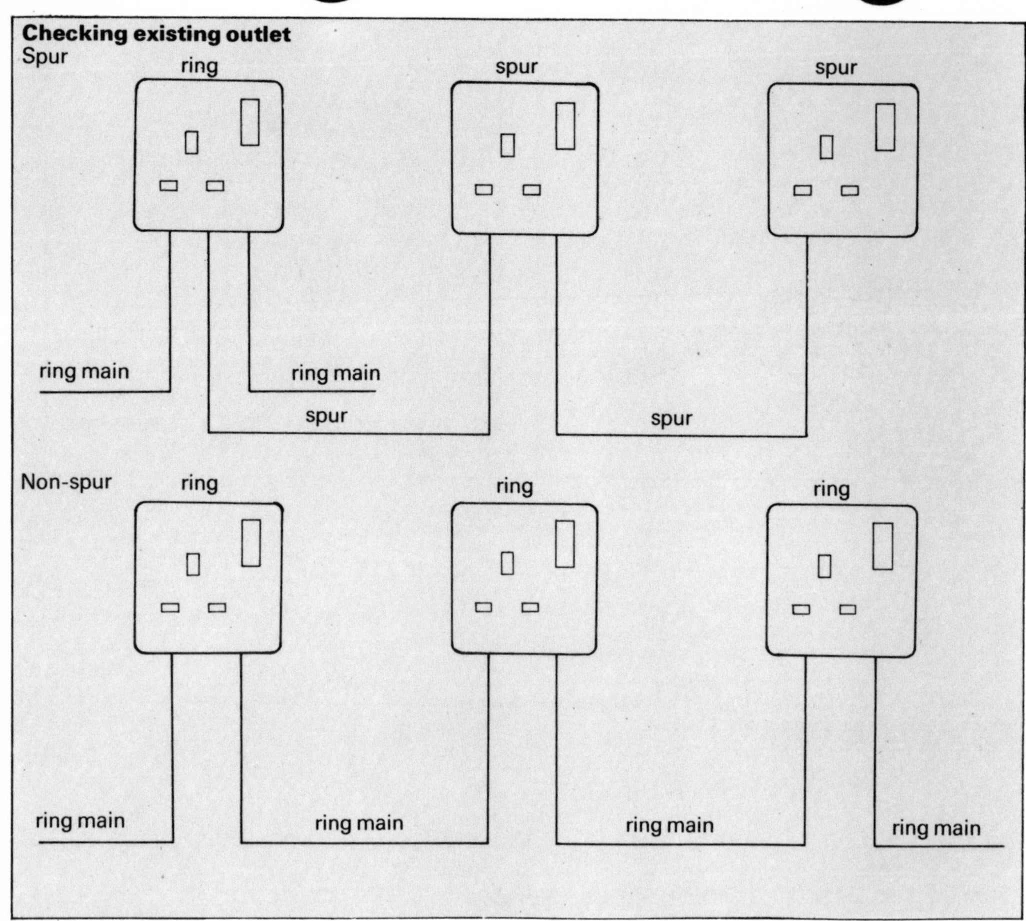

Before you start work check the wiring to make sure your existing outlet is not already a spur. If the sockets nearest to it have only one set of conductors, your chosen outlet is a spur; if nearby sockets have two sets of conductors, you can safely run a spur from your chosen outlet

Electricity is one energy source you can switch on where and when you want it. There is no reason to run a power tool off an extension from the kitchen when you need to work in the garage – or to unplug the bedside lamp when you want to use a portable television in the bedroom. The answer is to provide more socket outlets, a job you can do yourself safely if you follow the correct procedure.

Unless you were lucky enough to have supervised the installation of power points when your house was being built, you may find you have too few sockets and some that are in the wrong place. Moving sockets, adding extra ones or converting a single to a double (or twin) socket are jobs well within the capabilities of the amateur if you follow instructions carefully and make it a golden rule to switch off at the mains whenever you tackle any electrical work. A great part of the work is non-electrical: lifting floorboards to trace cables, drilling holes between joists for new cables or cutting back plastered walls and replastering them after you have buried the new cable and connected the new outlets.

Most homes take their power supply from ring circuits – but it is possible that your home's 13amp socket outlets may be on a radial circuit. This circuit consists of a number of outlets and fixed appliances supplied by one cable, from the consumer unit, which ends at the last outlet. This is quite different from the old radial system of 15amp plugs (with round pins) in which numerous 15amp circuits radiated from a multi-way fuseboard. These old installations are being phased out; if you still have this system, it could be in a dangerous condition and you should ask your Electricity Board to check the wiring – something the Electricity Council recommends people should have done every five years.

Connecting methods

There are three ways of connecting extra sockets or fixed appliances to the domestic ring circuit, all of which can be handled by the consumer.

Loops By taking a direct loop from the terminals of an existing socket outlet.

Junction box By inserting a junction box in the ring cable – generally under the floor – and taking one or two sockets from that.

Consumer unit By running a separate cable from the consumer unit.

Sockets connected by way of loops or junction boxes are called spurs; and you can take two sockets on a spur from any existing socket or from a newly installed junction box. Spurs not only supply extra socket outlets but can also be used to supply a fixed appliance, such as a wall heater.

Flush-fitted box

Surface mounted box

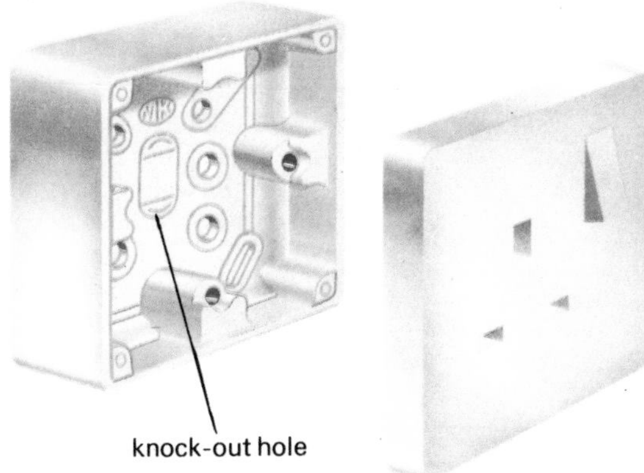

Here a fused switch connection – placed close to the appliance – replaces a socket outlet. Some fixed connections incorporate a pilot light to show when the appliance is on. Each spur may feed one or two single socket outlets, one double (or twin) socket or one fixed appliance.

Generally there is one ring circuit for each floor in a house. You should run your loop or junction box from the nearest existing socket outlet or nearest accessible part of the ring circuit to the new outlet. If you want to run the spur from a socket, make sure the outlet is not itself a spur. Undo the screws on the front plate and gently pull the outlet from the wall box and examine the wiring. If there are two red, two black and two earth (possibly green-sleeved or bare) conductors in the box, the outlet is probably not a spur. To make quite sure examine the nearest socket outlets each side of it. If there is only one set of conductors on these, your original choice is already a spur and should not be used. If neither outlet is a spur, then you know you can loop out of the first one you examined. Replace the frontplates and switch the mains back on until you are ready to begin work.

Planning outlets

While you are planning for extra outlets, you must decide what type of fitting you want. The choice is between flush-fitted sockets or sockets on wall-mounted boxes. More work is involved in installing the flush type, but the wall-mounted socket can be an obstruction to furniture and vacuum cleaners at ground level and can rob you of space when fitted above a work surface.

If you are in the habit of using an adaptor plug on some of your existing outlets, it may be worth investing in a double (or twin) socket and changing that for the single while you are working on the terminals behind it.

Socket height Socket outlets should not be less than 150mm (6in) above the floor or above a working surface in the kitchen or elsewhere. In rooms being used by elderly people or active invalids, outlets should be 1m (or 3ft) from the floor to eliminate bending.

Cable The cable used in a ring circuit is 2.5sq mm and the usual type for domestic installations is polyvinyl chloride (pvc) sheathed twin and earth, or may be tough rubber sheathed (trs) cable. Older ring circuits are wired in the Imperial-sized cable (called 7/029), which has seven strands. But it is quite all right to use the metric-size cable when adding to a ring circuit wired with 7/029 cable.

Decide carefully where your new cable will run. There will be problems, for example, if you have a modern house or flat in which underfloor wiring on the ground floor was installed before a solid floor was laid. The costly solution to this, in terms of cable, may be that you will have to run cable from the consumer unit up to the first floor, under the floorboards and then trail it down the cavity of the wall to the position of your intended outlet. Alternatively you could bury the cable in the plasterwork (the cable does not need any additional insulation) or run it on the surface of the wall – in which case you must clad it in a plastic conduit. Surface cables look unsightly in living rooms and create a further problem when decorating.

Another method is to remove your existing skirting and replace it with ducting, in metal or plastic, designed to house cables. Never consider cutting sockets into existing skirting boards. It is dangerous, illegal and may invalidate any insurance claim in the event of a fire.

If you do have a solid floor and need only one or two extra socket outlets, you will find it simpler to loop out of an existing outlet and bury the new cable in the wall.

Cutting plaster

There are two methods of making a channel in plaster. You can do it with a club hammer and brick bolster after first scoring with a sharp knife two straight lines in the plaster along the intended cable route, chipping out the depth you require. Or you can use a specially designed router, which works off an electric drill at a slow speed. Before you start routing you must drill a series of guide holes along the intended cable route. It is unlikely your plaster will not be deep enough to take a cable, but if you are unlucky you will just have to get to work again with the chisel.

Before you start laying cable, prepare the recesses or mountings for new sockets or position the junction boxes – preferably out of sight beneath floorboards. Where you run cables across joists you should run them through holes drilled at least 50mm (2in) below the top of the joists. Never lay cable in the grooves cut in the tops of joists because of the danger from nails that may be driven through and penetrate the cables.

When replacing floorboards, use screws instead of nails, which will enable you to identify the cable

Wiring new outlet in solid floor room

Cable in cavity wall

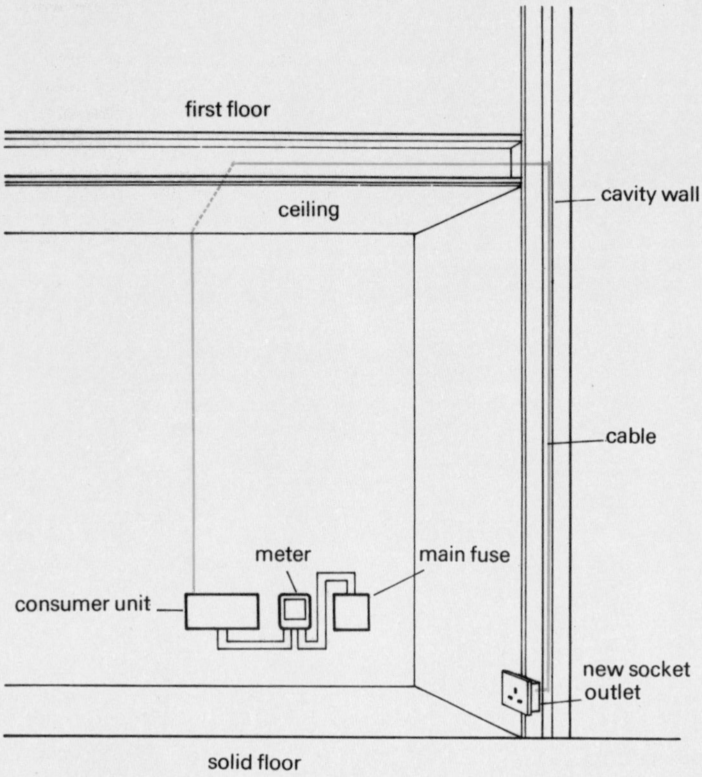

first floor
ceiling
cavity wall
cable
meter
main fuse
consumer unit
new socket outlet
solid floor

Cable in metal/plastic conduit

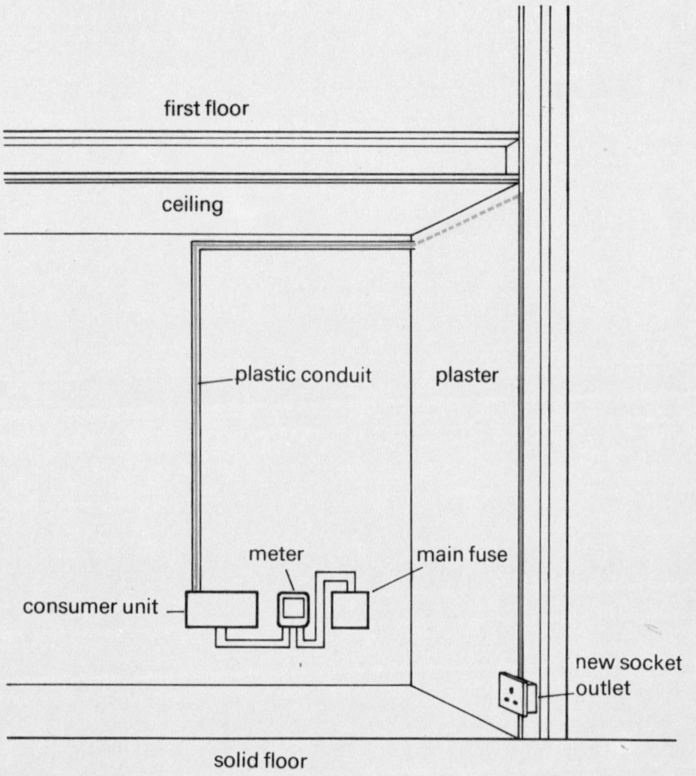

first floor
ceiling
plastic conduit
plaster
meter
main fuse
consumer unit
new socket outlet
solid floor

run and to reach it more quickly on future occasions. Before replacing the boards you should cut out a small section of the board at the skirting board end to protect cable running up or down the wall, behind skirting and then under the boards.

Warning Care must be taken not to damage any existing cables or pipes. Make sure current is turned off at the main; gas and water should also be turned off.

Wall sockets

Cutting out the recess for a flush socket box is quite simple. Mark on the wall in pencil an outline of the knock-out box, score the lines with a sharp knife and, using a brick bolster and club hammer, chip away until you reach the brickwork. Drill a series of close-spaced holes all round and then chip away another layer until you reach the required depth. Test the knock-out box fits, knock out the required access holes in it (sharp taps with a cold chisel are usually enough) and fix a grommet in each hole. This is a rubber or plastic ring, with an exterior slot which fits neatly in the hole, to protect the cable. Drill the mounting holes, plug them and screw the knock-out box into the recess, making good the edges with plaster.

Fixing a wall-mounted box is much easier. You only need to channel out enough plaster to accommodate the cable run from the floorboards and behind the skirting (unless it is being channelled into a wall from another socket) and into the box, which is plugged and screwed to the wall.

Moving existing sockets

If you intend to line your rooms with plasterboard or panel boards fixed to battens, you must plan how you are going to reposition your existing outlets. If you already have wall-mounted sockets, you can cut a snug opening into your lining where each socket is situated, turning the outlets into flush fittings. If your existing outlets are flush fitting, with a knock-out box recessed into the original wall, you have several alternatives.

You can check, by easing the knock-out box from the wall, whether there is enough slack cable on the ring to allow you to move the entire outlet forward to the new surface. If there is plenty of slack, you can fit a new wall-mounted box and reconnect to the socket terminals. If there is not enough cable, check whether the cable is fed from above or below. In each instance you will probably be able to find enough cable to enable you to reposition the outlet either higher or lower than it was on the old wall. But remember, the socket

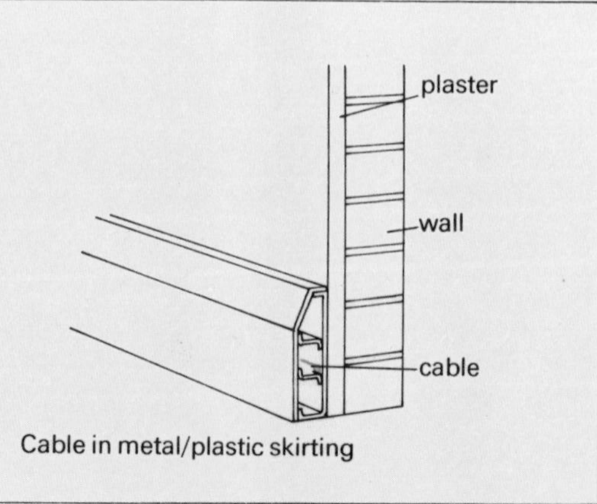

Cable in metal/plastic skirting

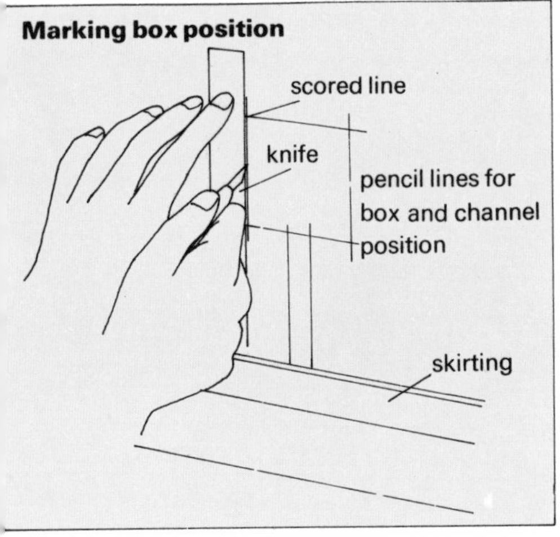

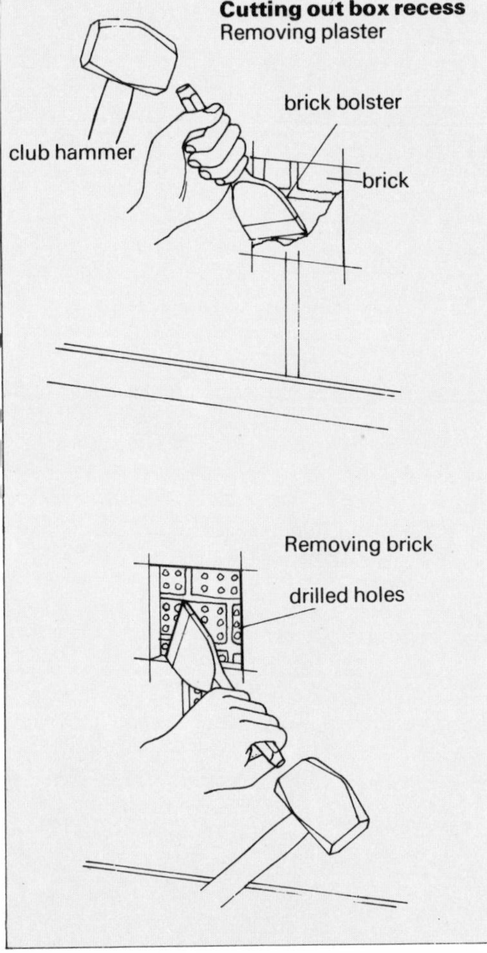

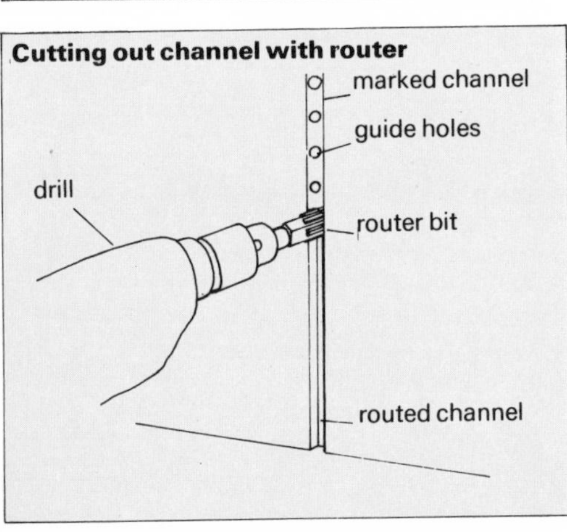

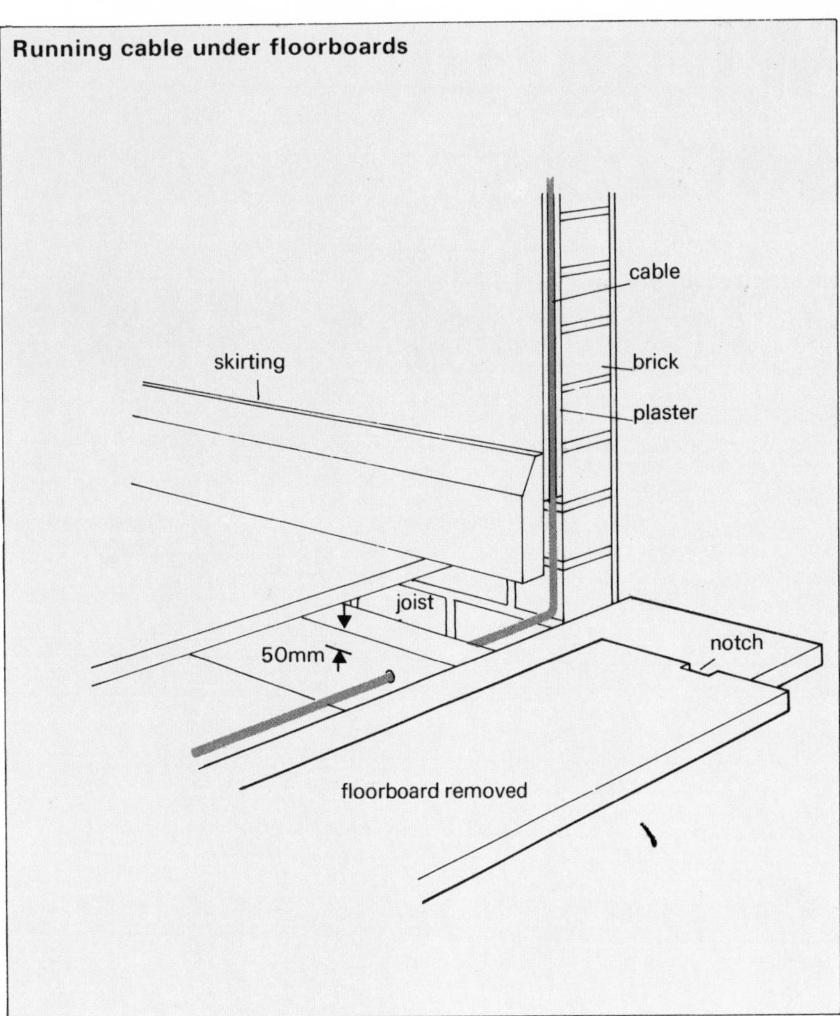

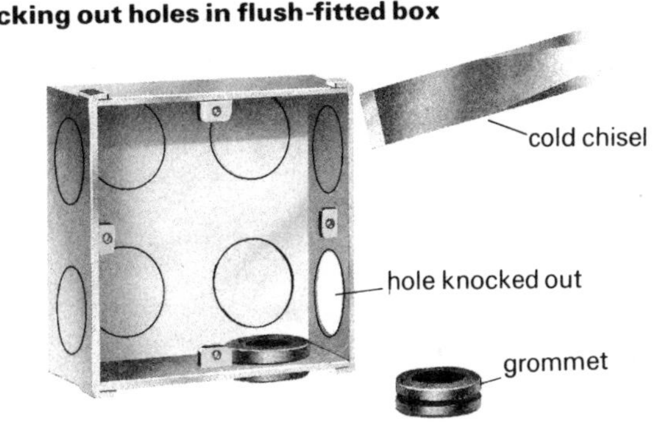

should be at least 150mm (6in) above the floor and never be installed in a skirting board.

If this is also impossible, you will have to fit a three-way terminal block into the existing knock-out box, which converts it into a junction box. You must run cable from a knock-out hole (not forgetting to use a grommet) at the top or bottom of the box and use this to feed either one double or two single wall-mounted socket outlets nearby on your new wall. You must also cover the modified knock-out box with a blank plate.

Wiring up sockets

Electricity can be supplied where you want it, as long as you have enough outlets. You can install new power points or move existing ones yourself.

Having done all the non-electrical work such as lifting boards, chanelling plaster to take cables, or cutting recesses for the new knock-out boxes and installing them, it is time to start wiring with 2.5sq mm twin core and earth PVC sheathed cable. This is quite simple and safe if you turn off the mains before you start work – and follow the instructions carefully.

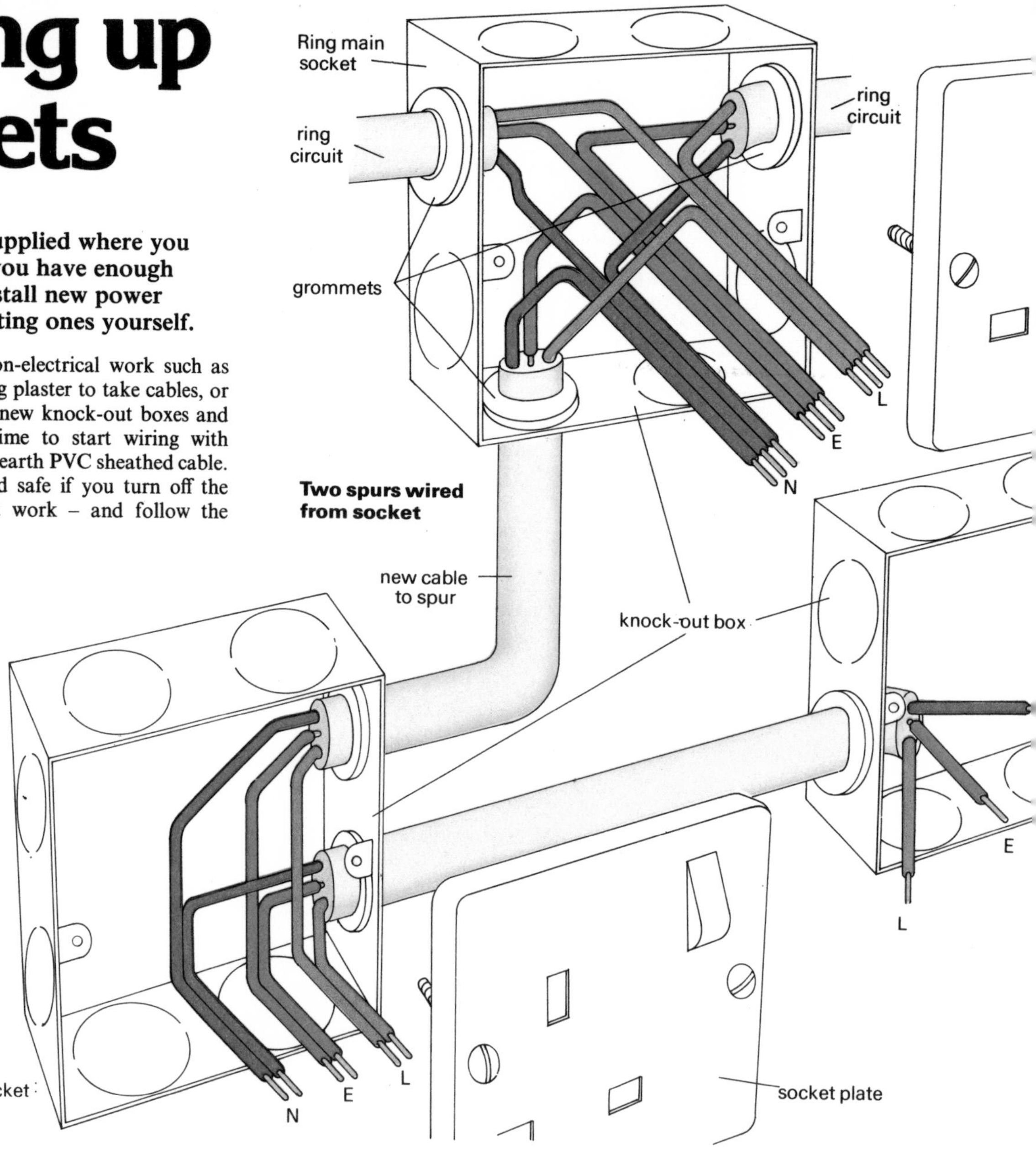

Two spurs wired from socket

Loops

If you are running a loop from the back of an existing socket to connect to one or two spur socket outlets or a fixed appliance, you must start by cutting your cable lengths. Since you will need to feed about 125mm (5in) of cable into the recessed knock-out boxes, wall-mounted socket outlets, junction boxes or spur socket outlets, you should remove about 100mm (4in) from the outer sheath and then strip about 15mm ($\frac{5}{8}$in) of the insulation material from the red and black conductors. The earth conductor will be bare and you should slip on a short length of green insulation sleeving (generally available where you buy twin core and earth cable), leaving just 15mm ($\frac{5}{8}$in) bare at the end.

You are now ready to run the cable into its chanelling or under the floor, depending on the route you have chosen. Cable under floors should be run in holes drilled at least 50mm (2in) below the top of joists and secured only by cable fixing clips. If you are running cable in plaster, you should wedge it in position while you are connecting up. The cable sometimes wriggles free and if this happens you should secure it with a couple of dabs of contact adhesive – but make sure the cable is in the right place.

Socket to socket

Thread the 125mm (5in) of unsheathed conductors into the knock-out hole you have prepared (into which you must always place a rubber or plastic grommet as protection for the cable) and loosen the wires on the terminals on the back of the socket plate. Arrange the new conductors alongside the entwined pairs already there; red with reds, black with blacks and earth (or green) with earths. Put each set of three wires in their respective terminals. Reds go to the live terminal, blacks to the neutral terminal and greens to the earth terminal. All terminals are clearly marked on the back of the socket plate. Tighten the terminal screws, check the conductors are secure and replace the front of the socket outlet.

If you are wiring up only one spur socket, you simply enter the spur knock-out box in the way described and connect each of the three conductors

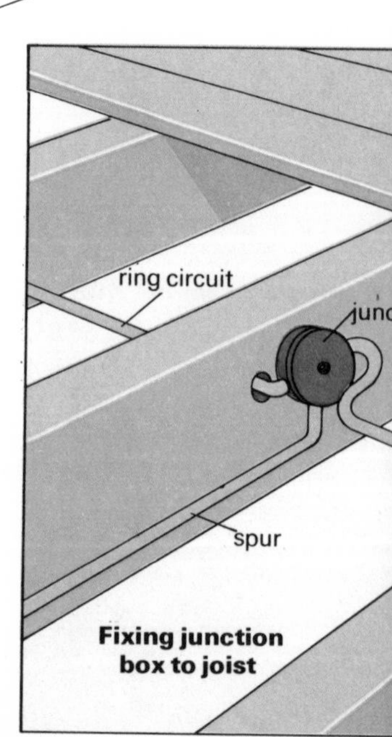

Fixing junction box to joist

Socket wired to fused connection unit

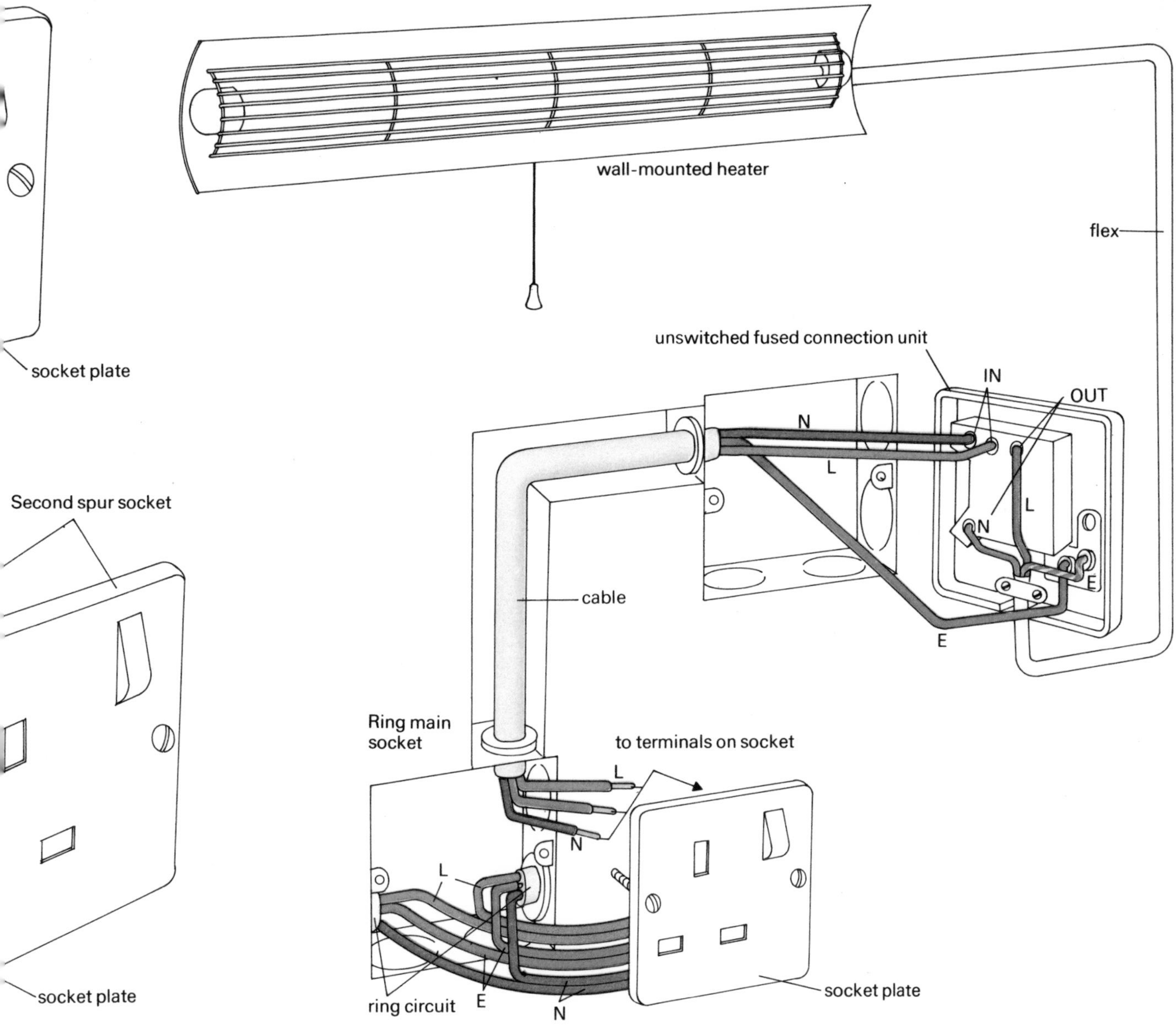

wall-mounted heater
flex
unswitched fused connection unit
IN
OUT
N
L
N
L
E
E
cable
Ring main socket
to terminals on socket
L
N
L
ring circuit
E
N
socket plate
Second spur socket
socket plate
socket plate

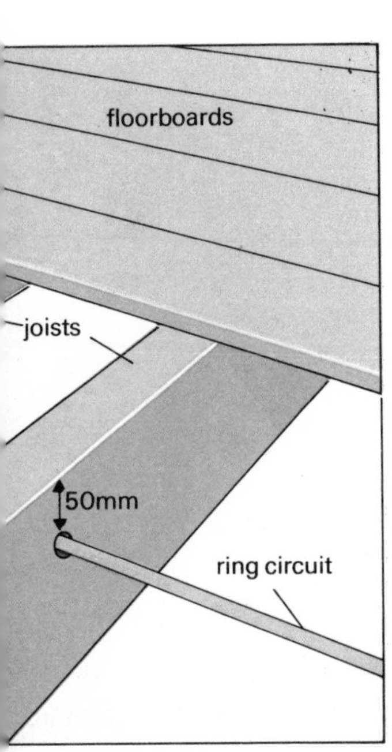

to its relevant terminal. Screw the socket plate on, plug in an appliance that you know is working, turn on the mains and switch on at the new outlet. If the appliance works, your wiring is correct. Only then – and again with the mains switched off – should you plaster the cable into the wall or replace the floorboards.

Second spur outlet

If you are running on to a second spur outlet, follow the same wiring procedure as already described, remembering you will have two sets of wires to connect to the terminals in the first new socket – the feed conductors and earth from the original socket and the feed conductors and earth leading to the second spur outlet. When the wiring is complete, test as already described.

Fused connection unit

Follow the same wiring procedure if you are running a loop from a socket outlet (or a junction box) to a fused (switched or unswitched) connection unit for connecting with a fixed appliance, such as a wall-mounted heater. At the connection unit there are six terminals – two live, two neutral and two earth. The live and neutral conductors from the loop cable must be connected to the terminals marked IN. The other terminals are marked OUT and to these you connect the live and neutral leads in the appliance's flex, feeding the flex in through a knock-out hole at the bottom of the unit. The earth leads can connect to either of the two earth terminals. When this is done, check the wiring.

Warning Check there is a 3 or 13amp cartridge fuse in the pull-out holder at the front of the unit (manufacturers sometimes forget to include one) and do not be too violent in clearing the knock-out hole or you may shatter the plastic casing. Never connect to an appliance rated at more than 13amp (or 3kW), because it will need a separate circuit from the consumer unit.

Junction boxes

If you are supplying your extra sockets or fused connection unit through a junction box, you will already have sited this within reach of the ring circuit cable and secured it to a joist, a short length of timber between joists or another suitable timber fixture. Knock out three holes: for the ring cable to enter and leave the junction box and a third for the spur cable, which should be prepared as already explained. There are three terminals in the box: live, neutral and earth. It does not matter which you use as long as you are consistent – but it is bad practice not to connect to the properly designated terminals. Try to avoid cutting the ring cable. You should be able to strip away the outer sheath and cut away enough insulation at a suitable point so there is sufficient bare wire to lay in the terminal (with the corresponding conductors from the spur cable) under the terminal screws. Connect the other end of the new cable as already described, either to a new socket outlet or to a fixed connection unit.

Terminal block conversion

If you are turning an existing outlet into a junction box by using a three-way terminal block inside an existing recessed knock-out box or surface-mounted backplate, you must first remove a knock-out hole

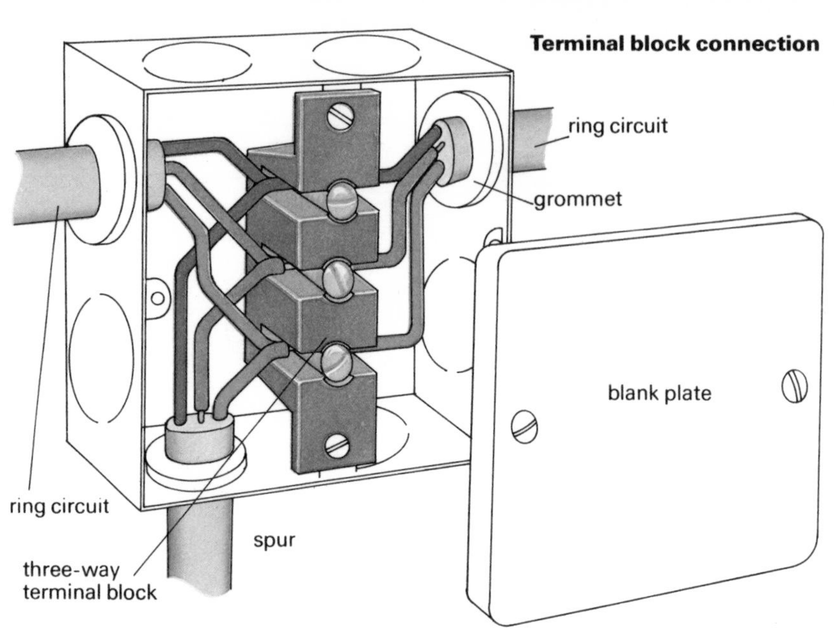

New socket to consumer unit

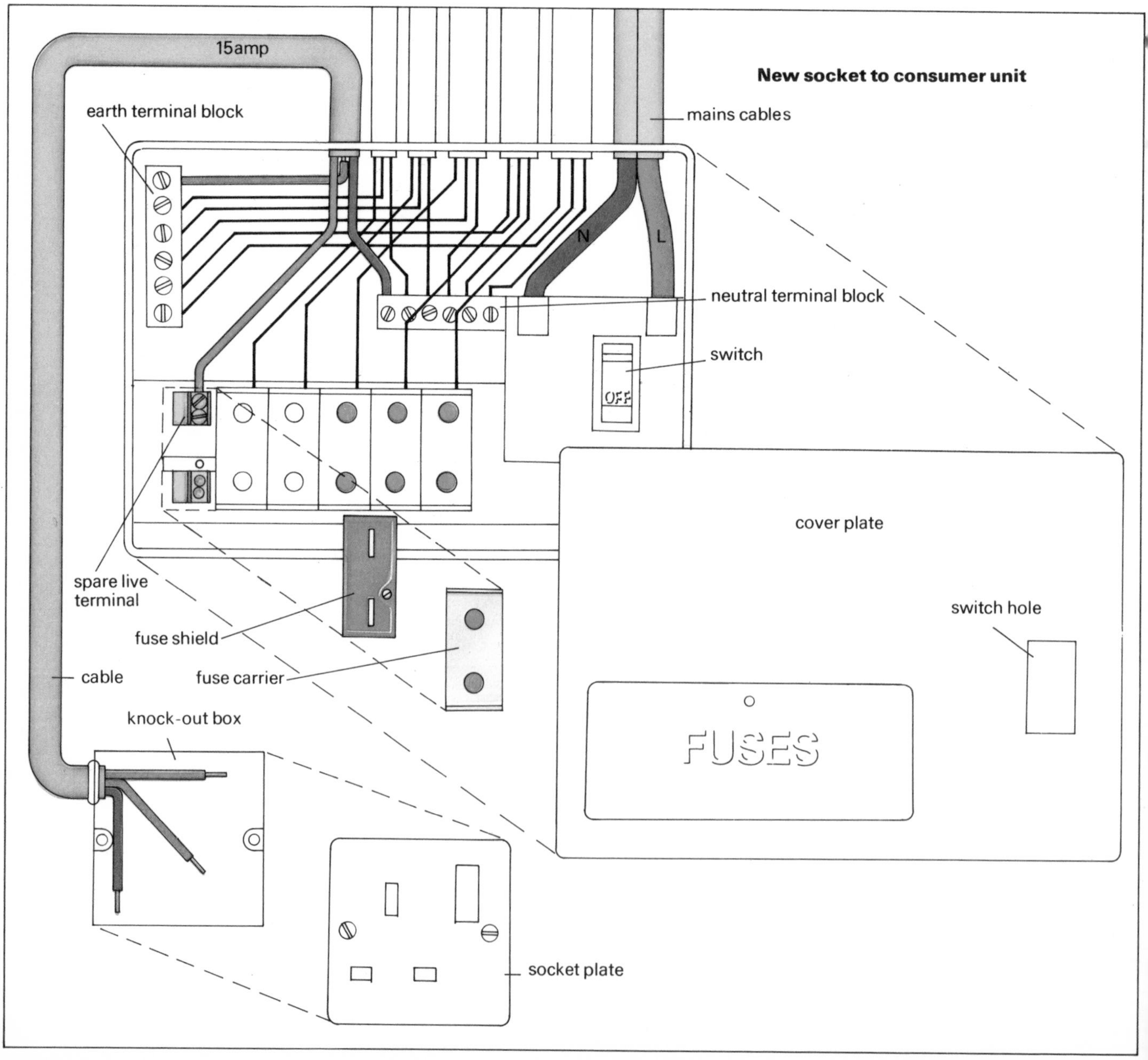

15amp
earth terminal block
mains cables
N
L
neutral terminal block
switch
OFF
cover plate
spare live
terminal
switch hole
fuse shield
cable
fuse carrier
knock-out box
FUSES
socket plate

to get the new spur cable into the box. Connect the three sets of conductors and earths: the cable going into the existing socket and the cable leaving the socket to continue the ring circuit, and the new spur cable, which can be used to connect either one or two spur outlets or one fused connection unit. Before connecting the spur, cover the knock-out box or backplate with a blank plate.

Consumer unit connection

If you are running an extra single socket outlet or a fused connection unit (up to 13amps) direct from the consumer unit, you wire the socket or unit in the normal way – but with only one set of conductors. The other end of the cable is fed directly into the consumer unit and great care must be taken here because a wrong connection could cause a lot of expensive damage.

The consumer unit is clearly marked inside: the red (live) wire from your cable must be connected to a spare live terminal block, the black conductor must be connected to a spare terminal on the neutral terminal block and the earth must be connected to its corresponding place on the earth terminal block. A 15amp fuse should be inserted in the consumer unit to protect the new circuit.

Double socket

When you are replastering a single socket outlet or removing it to run off a spur, you should consider whether it is worthwhile replacing the outlet with a double (or twin) socket outlet. The terminal connections on double sockets match those on single outlets; all you have to do is exchange them.

The easiest method is to place a slim surface-mounted box over the recessed knock-out box (if you have one and provided you have enough cable). Smooth the edges of the entry hole with a file to ensure the stripped insulation does not chafe. You will probably have to secure the box to the wall with plugs each side of the old box, so take care not to drill into the ring circuit cable. If you have an existing surface-mounted box, you must remove this and replace both the backplate box and the socket outlet.

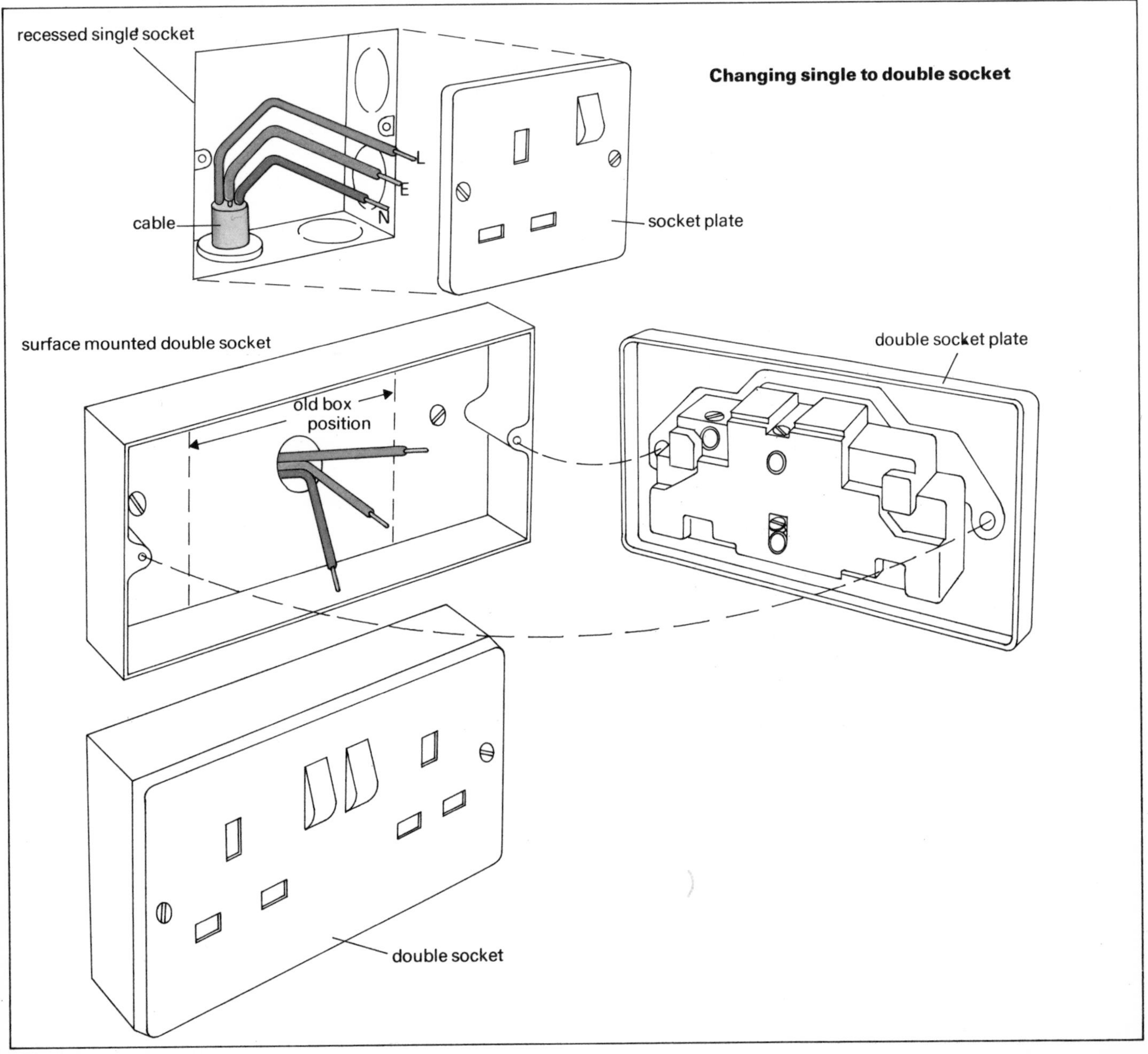

Changing single to double socket

Adding lights and switches

It is a simple operation to add an extra ceiling light, controlled by its own switch, to an existing lighting circuit. If as in most modern homes the wiring is flat twin PVC-sheathed cable, it is likely the loop-in system is used, which means an extension can be taken direct from an existing ceiling rose.

In recently wired installations the circuit cable also contains an earth continuity conductor (ecc), which is looped in and out of an earth terminal in the ceiling rose. If your lighting circuits are wired on the junction box system – common until the mid-1960s – there should normally be one junction box for every light and its switch.

Loop-in extension

Drill a 13mm (½in) diameter hole in the ceiling at the new light position and another hole in the ceiling immediately above the new switch position. Any floorboards above will have to be raised, as will some along the new cable route to gain access above the ceiling. Switch off at the mains and remove the ceiling rose and pendant flex at the connecting light. Take care not to separate joined wires; if necessary use insulation tape to keep them together temporarily.

Take your coil of 1sq mm two core and earth PVC-sheathed cable and mark 'mains' on the end of the sheath; push the end through the hole in the ceiling at the connecting light, leaving the existing wires protruding from the ceiling. Then pull through sufficient cable from the floor above (or in the roof space) to reach the position above the new light. Thread the cable through holes drilled in the joists, at least 50mm (2in) below the top of the joists, and pass the end of the cable through the hole in the ceiling, leaving about 300mm (12in) for connections at the new rose. Cut the cable at the old ceiling rose position, leaving about the same amount for connections.

Take the cable coil to the switch position and push the end through the hole in the ceiling. From above, run it to the new light and pass the end down alongside the first cable marked 'mains'.

Wiring new rose and switch
Existing ceiling rose

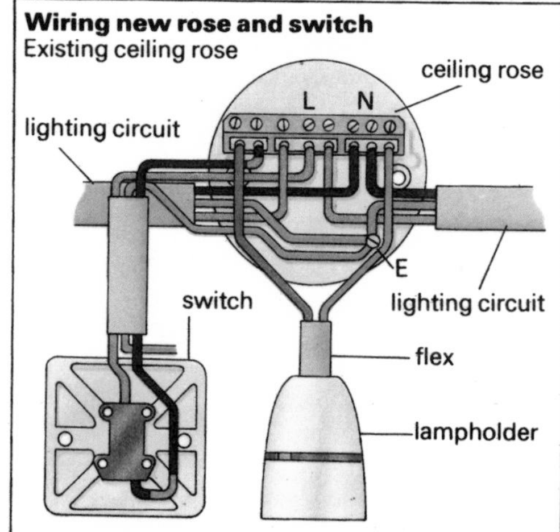

Adding new ceiling rose

new ceiling rose
old ceiling rose
cable
lighting circuit
N
L
L
N
E
E
cable
lighting circuit
cable
flex
flex
lampholder
lampholder
switch
switch

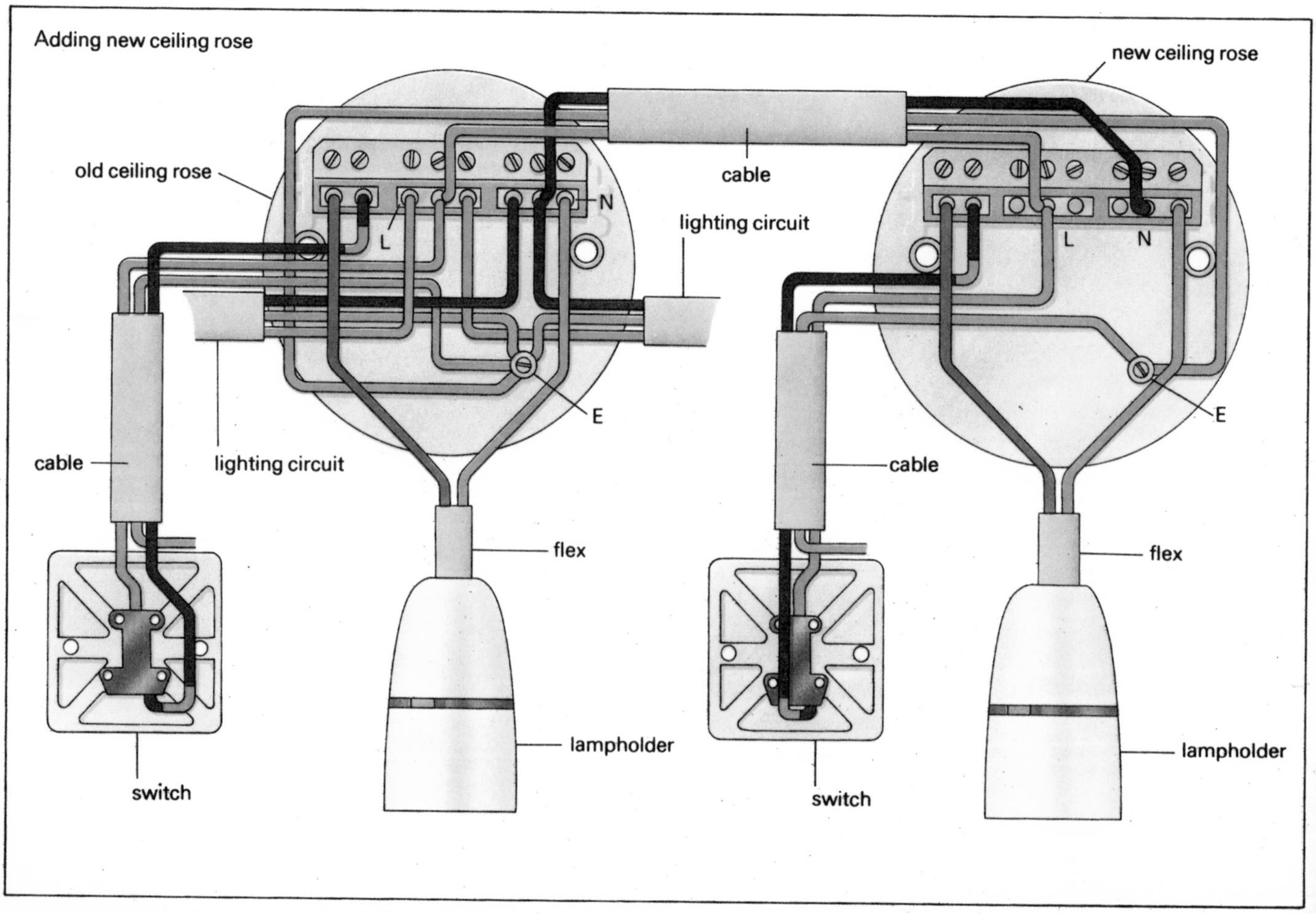

lounting a new ceiling rose

f there is no suitable mounting for the new light, x a piece of 100 × 25mm (4 × 1in) timber between he joists just above the ceiling, having first drilled a ole in the timber to take the two sheathed cables. ut the cable at the switch position about 1.37m 4ft 6in) above floor level, leaving about 300mm 12in) for connections.

Knock out the thin plastic in the base of the eiling rose, thread in the two cables and fix the ose to the ceiling with screws 25mm (1in) long. trip about 50mm (2in) of sheathing from the end f the cable marked 'mains' and about 6mm (¼in) of nsulation from the end of the red and the black vire. Insert the bared end of the red conductor into ne of the terminal holes in the live (centre) erminal and tighten the screw. Connect the black ire to the neutral terminal, using the middle hole. ush the cable slack back into the ceiling, making ure the end of the sheath will be within the rose.

Prepare the end of the other cable in the same way nd connect the red wire into one of the other two oles in the live terminal. Slip a short piece of red VC sleeving or insulation tape over the end of the lack wire and insert this into the inner terminal ole of the two-hole (switch wire) terminal bank. lip green PVC sleeving over the bare earth wires nd connect to the earth terminal.

Now connect the pendant flex. Strip about 75mm 3in) of sheath from the end of a length of two core ex. Bare the ends and connect the brown to the uter hole of the switch wire terminal and the blue the outer hole of the neutral terminal. Tighten all erminal screws and hook the flex wires over the nchor pieces: thread on the rose cover and screw to its base. Connect the lampholder to the other end of the flex, using the same method as for the ceiling rose; if the unsheathed wires protrude from the cap, the flex wires must be shortened.

Connecting a switch

If the switch is to be surface-mounted, take the plastic surface box and knock out a thin section for the cable. Hold the box in position against the wall and mark the fixing holes. Drill and plug them to take No 8 screws. If the switch is to be flush-mounted you must use a metal knock-out box. The cable from the ceiling to the box can be fixed to the surface, using plastic cable clips spaced no more than 400mm (16in) apart or buried in the plaster.

The end of the cable is stripped and the conductors prepared as for a ceiling rose. The red wire, which is the live feed, is connected to the common terminal. The black wire, the switch wire, is enclosed in a short piece of red PVC sleeving or PVC insulation tape and connected to the L2 terminal. The earth should be enclosed in a length of green PVC sleeving and connected to the earth terminal in the mounting box. The switch is secured to its box by two screws supplied.

Replacing the existing rose

Replace the existing wires as before; if you had an old type ceiling rose, replace with a modern one with in-line shrouded terminals. Strip and prepare the end of the new cable as for the first ceiling rose. Connect the red wire to the centre terminal (alongside another red wire if there is no spare terminal hole), the black wire to the neutral terminal and the earth wire, with its green sleeving, to the earth terminal. Any existing unsleeved earth wires in the rose should be sleeved before reconnecting.

Wiring new light from junction box

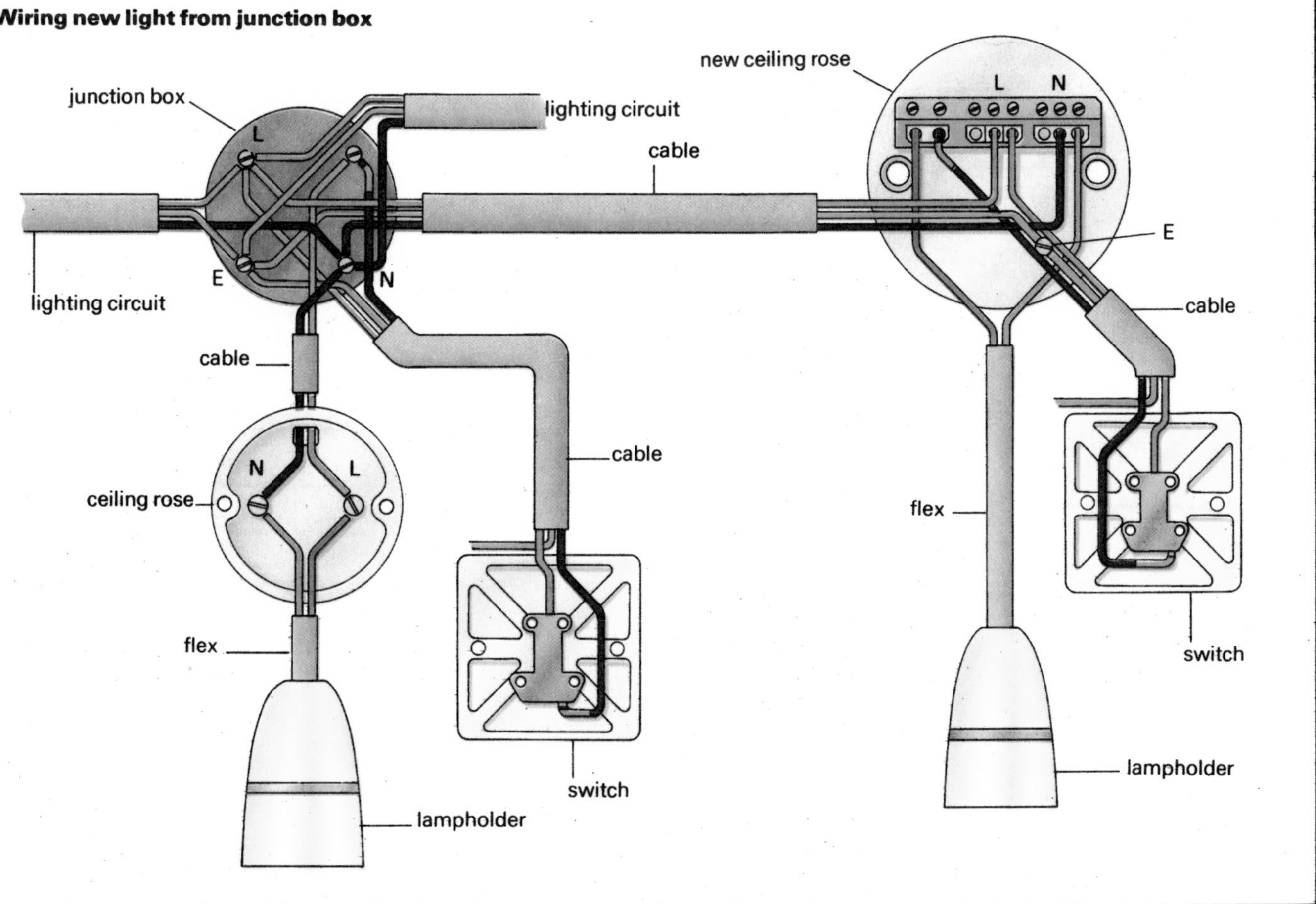

Junction box extension

After switching off the power, locate an existing, suitably placed junction box by lifting boards or checking in the roof space, unscrew the cover and examine the wires and terminals. The red live wire of the new cable is connected to the terminal having two or more red wires, the black neutral wire is connected to the terminal containing two or more black wires and the earth wire with its green sleeving, goes to the terminal containing earth wires. The remainder of the work is the same as when looping out of a ceiling rose to another rose.

Moving a light

When a ceiling light is to be moved, take down the existing pendant (having, of course, switched off the power) and pull back the cables into the ceiling space – taking care not to separate wires connected to any one terminal. Mark which of the two wires or sets of jointed wires were connected to the flex terminals, for it is from these the extension is made. Nail a piece of 100 × 25mm (4 × 1in) timber between the joists, about halfway down, and fix a four-terminal 5amp junction box to it. Drill a hole in the ceiling at the new position and lift boards and drill holes in the joists as necessary for the route of the new cable from the junction box to the light. Run a length of cable from the junction box to the light and pass the end through the hole in the ceiling. Connect the live wire to the switched live rose terminal, and the neutral and earth wires as before.

At the junction box, connect the existing wires to the box terminals. If the existing light was a loop-in ceiling rose, all four terminals in the box will be used. Otherwise only two, plus earth, will be needed. Prepare the end of the cable as already described and connect the red to the single wire which was connected to flex. If this is a black wire, enclose the end in red sleeving or PVC-insulated tape before connecting it to the junction box terminal. Connect the black wire to the terminal now containing one, two or more black wires and connect the earth, with its green sleeve to the terminal containing the earth wires; if the circuit has no earth, connect it to a spare terminal. Replace the box cover.

Fitting an extra light

When you need an extra light that is to be controlled by an existing switch, follow the instructions given for moving a light, except that instead of using a junction box you leave the original light in position, install a new ceiling rose and connect the new cable to the existing ceiling rose terminals carrying the flex wires.

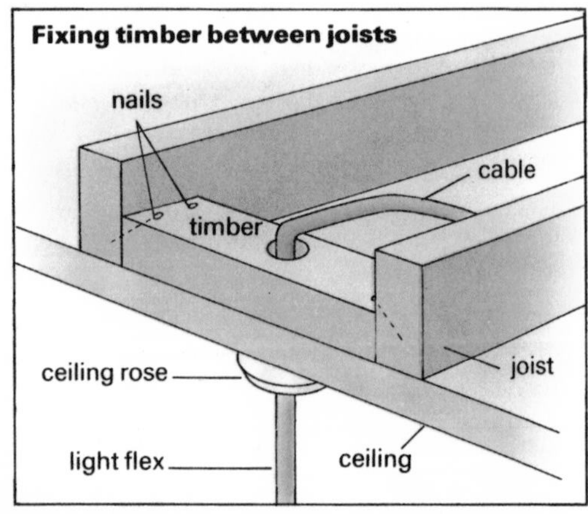

Fixing timber between joists

Moving ceiling rose

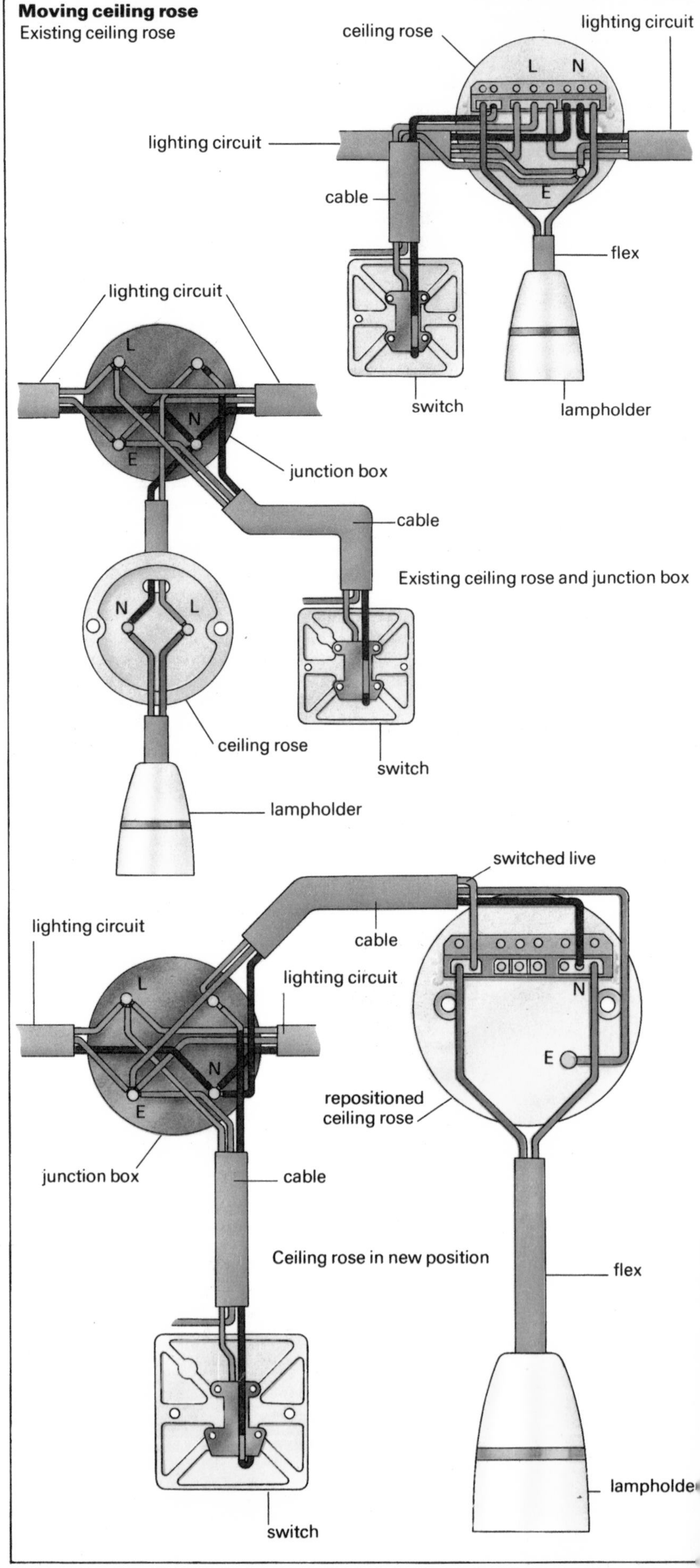

Existing ceiling rose

ceiling rose
lighting circuit
L N
lighting circuit
cable
E
flex
switch
lampholder

lighting circuit
L
N
E
junction box
cable
N L
ceiling rose
switch
lampholder

Existing ceiling rose and junction box

switched live
lighting circuit
cable
lighting circuit
L
N
E
N
repositioned ceiling rose
junction box
cable
flex
switch
lampholder

Ceiling rose in new position

Adding light using same switch

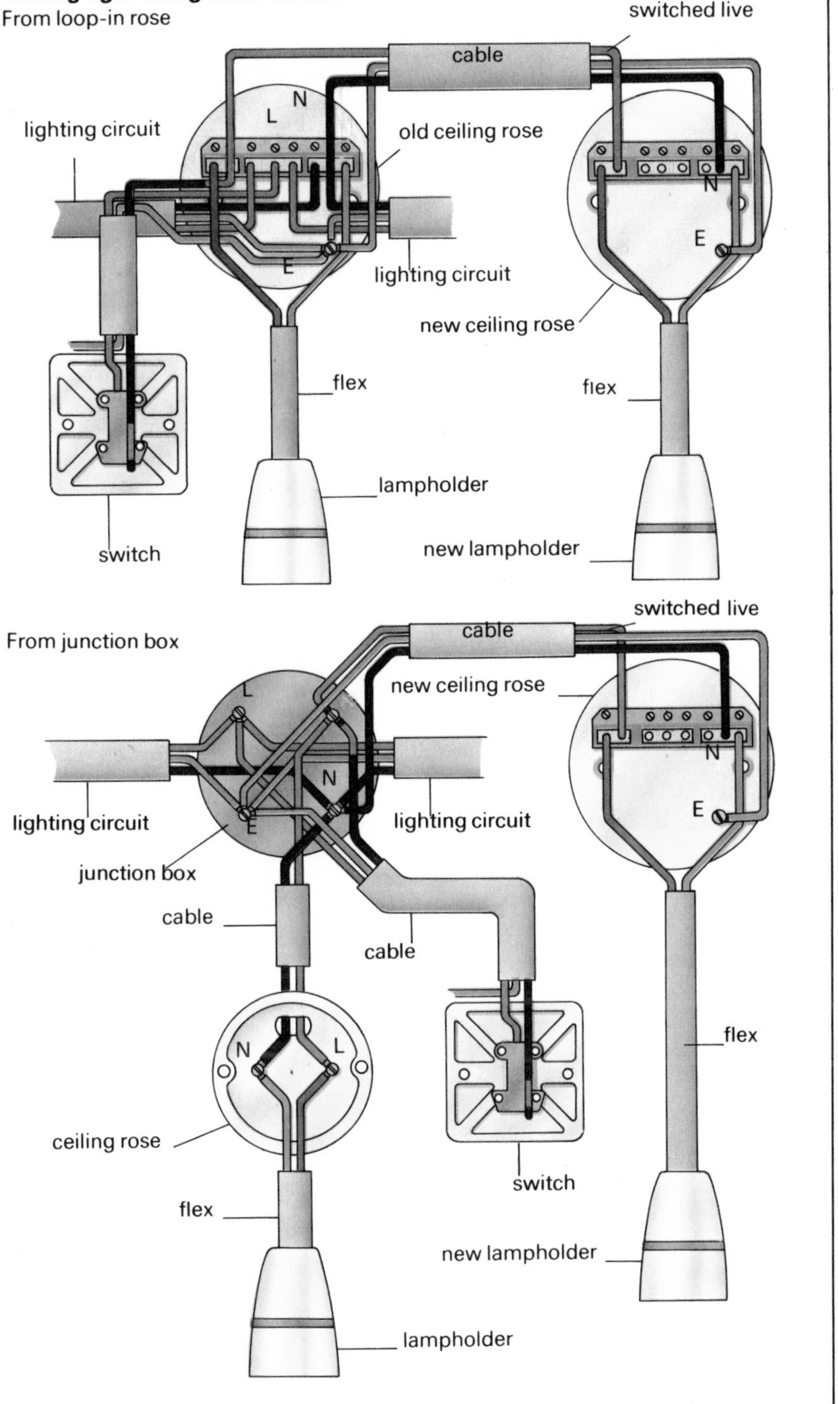

From loop-in rose

switched live
cable
lighting circuit
old ceiling rose
L
N
E
lighting circuit
new ceiling rose
flex
flex
lampholder
new lampholder
switch

From junction box

switched live
cable
new ceiling rose
L
N
E
lighting circuit
lighting circuit
junction box
cable
cable
N
L
ceiling rose
switch
flex
flex
new lampholder
lampholder

Fitting an extra switch

Adding a second switch to a lighting point, such as at the end of a hall or at the back door to provide another switch in a kitchen, not only adds to your convenience but probably helps you to save electricity. Replace the existing one-way switch with a two-way switch, install a two-way switch in the second position and link the two switches together by fitting a 1sq mm three core and earth PVC-sheathed cable.

If the existing switch is the modern square plate mounted on either a plastic surface box or a metal flush-mounted box, remove the existing switch, push the end of the new cable into the box through the existing grommet, run the cable up the wall through the ceiling, under the floorboards (or roof space) and down through the ceiling to the second switch position, where you fit either a surface or flush-mounted recess box.

Three terminals A two-way switch has three terminals – Common, L1 and L2. The two existing wires disconnected from the one-way switch are connected to terminals L1 and L2, although it does not matter which goes to which terminal. The three core and earth sheathed cable has three insulated wires: red, yellow and blue. The red wire goes to the Common terminal, the yellow wire to terminal L1 and the blue to L2. The earth wire in its green sleeving is connected to the earth terminal of the box. At the second switch there are only three new wires plus the earth. The red wire is connected to the Common terminal, the yellow to L1 and the blue to L2, and the green sleeved earth wire to the box's earth terminal. Arrange the wires neatly in each box and secure the switches with the screws provided with the fitting.

Fitting a cord switch

Cord-operated ceiling switches are made in one and two-way versions; so in a bedroom, for example, you can fit a switch on the ceiling above the bed-head as well as the normal switch by the door. The three core cable is passed down through a hole in the ceiling instead of down the wall and the switch fixed to the ceiling. If necessary mount the switch on a piece of timber fixed between the joists, as already described. The connections are the same as for a wall switch.

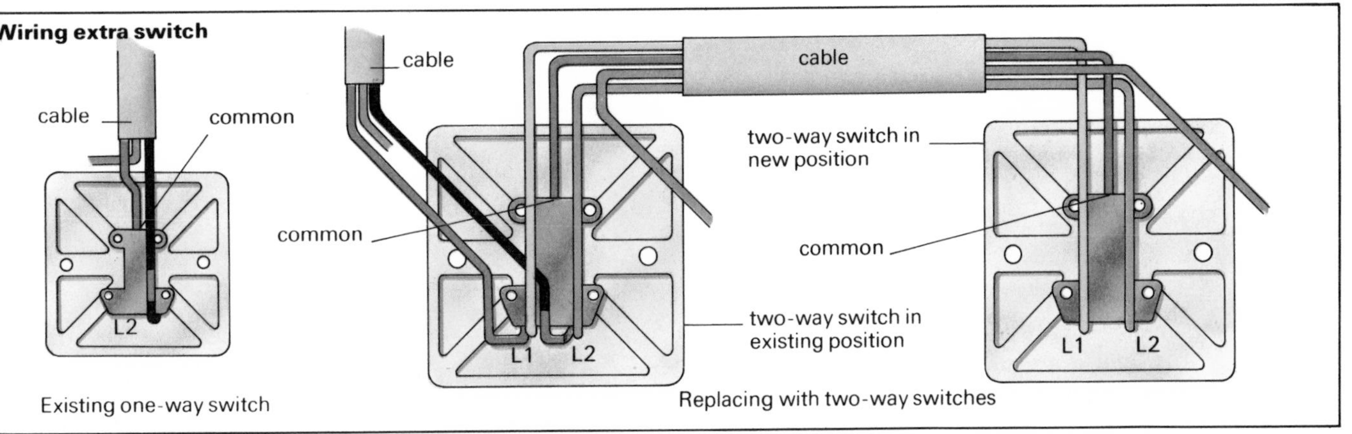

Existing one-way switch

Replacing with two-way switches

Dimmers and time switches

The dimmer is an electronic device which contains a semi-conductor, associated components and a TV suppressor. But unlike the old resistor dimmer, which consumed unwanted wattage and became very hot, the modern version does not use a significant amount of electricity and can be regarded as an energy saver.

These switches have been designed to replace any one-way lighting switch of the square-plate pattern, simply by removing the existing switch and fitting the dimmer in its place; this is connected to the same wiring and does not require any modification to the circuit.

If you are replacing the old round (tumbler) switch mounted on a wood block or plastic plate (pattress), it is necessary to replace the block or pattress with a standard flush-mounting box.

Warning In all cases follow the manufacturer's instructions for fitting and always turn off the electricity at the mains before you start work.

Types of dimmer

The low-priced dimmer consists of a rotary action knob which reduces lighting from full brilliance down to off. This is adequate for most purposes, its one disadvantage being that the control has to be set each time the dimmer is switched on, since it has to be rotated through the full dimming operation to switch off the light.

There are many situations where it is more convenient to switch a dimmed light off and on without having to adjust the control; this can be achieved by fitting a combined dimmer and on-off switch. One type has a slide control for dimming; another has a milled-edge dial and a third a single push-on/pull-off control for switching.

Two-way switch A dimmer can be inserted in a two-way switching circuit to allow, for example, a landing light operated from both landing and hall to be dimmed as required. The dimmer switch can be fixed in any position, but for ease of wiring it is best installed near one of the two-way switches and preferably mounted on the same box, which would replace the existing one gang box (which takes a single switch).

To do this, remove the two-way switch and its box and fit a dual box, which in the case of a flush-mounted fitting will mean enlarging the recess in the plaster. A dual box is slightly larger than the ordinary two gang box (which takes two switches) used for double socket outlets and has two fixing lugs in the centre to take a fixing screw for each switch.

If the existing switch, in which a dimmer is to be incorporated, is a two gang unit controlling the hall and landing light, the two gang unit is retained. The dimmer, which is a one gang unit, must only be wired to control one of the lights.

Dimming two lights Dimmer switches with a single knob incorporating push-on/pull-off action are made in two gang versions to control two different lights.

Dimming part lighting A special combined dimmer/

1 Wiring for dimmer switch and for ordinary switch
2 Wiring two-way dimmer with ordinary two-way switch
3 Portable plug-in dimmer incorporating on/off switch
4 One or two-way dimmer with separate on/off switch
5 One or two-way dimmer with separate on/off switch
6 One or two-way combined dimmer and on/off switch
7 Light sensitive dimmer (on at dusk, off at dawn)
8 One or two-way combined dimmer and on/off switch with chrome finish
9 Master/slave touch dimmer
10 One or two-way sliding dimmer and separate on/off switch
11 Milled-edge drum dimmer and separate on/off switch
12 Combined dimmer and on off switch which has facility to provide both dimmed and fixed lighting
13 One or two-way combined dimmer and on/off switch
14 Combined dimmer and on off switch with chrome finish
15 Time lag dimmer

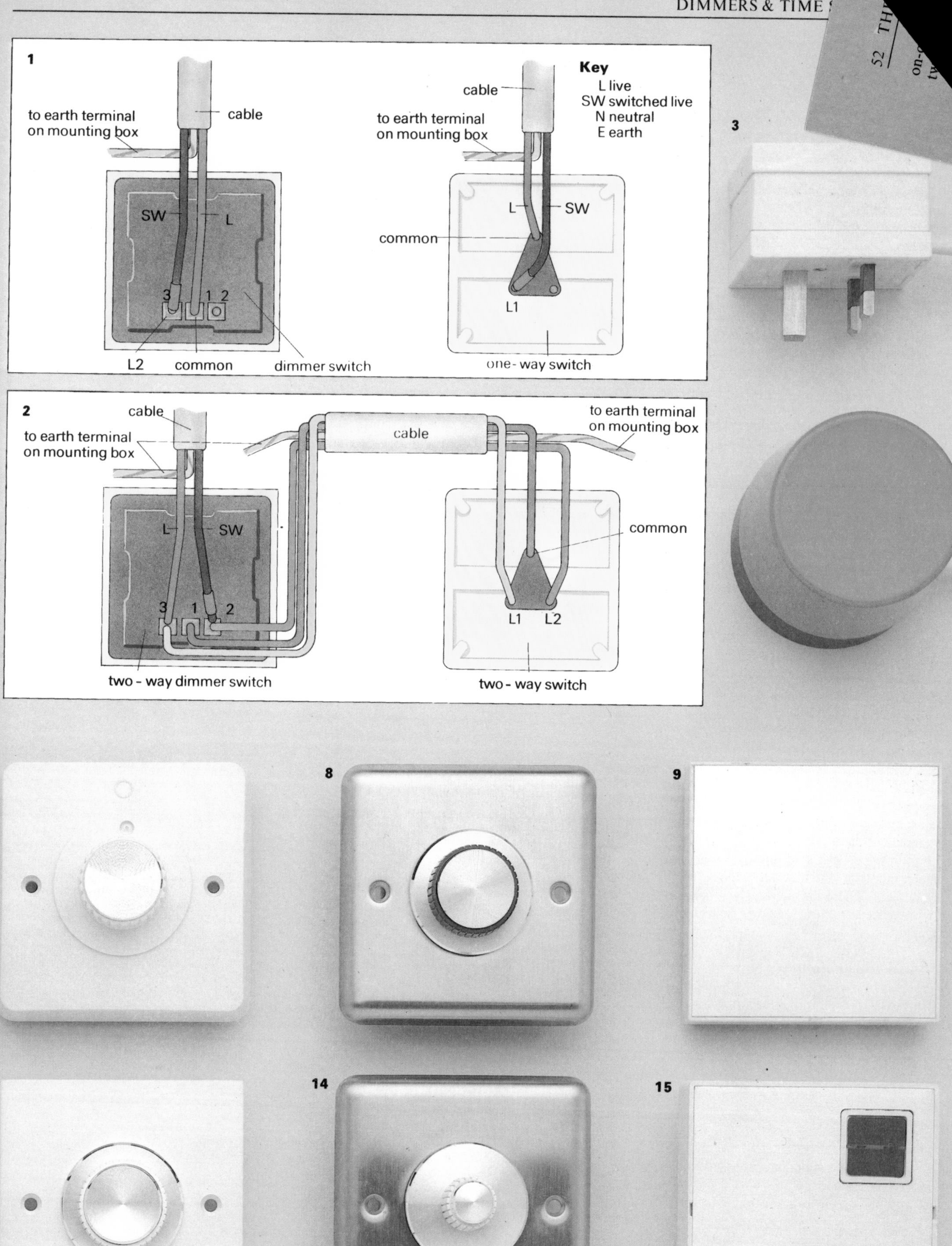
1
Key
L live
SW switched live
N neutral
E earth
cable
to earth terminal
on mounting box
SW
L
3
1 2
L2
common
dimmer switch
common
L1
one-way switch
2
two-way dimmer switch
two-way switch
L1
L2
3
8
9
14
15

…ff switch can be used to replace any existing …o-gang switch unit to provide the facility for dimming some lighting in a room, while using the rest of the lighting at a fixed intensity. In a dining/living room, for example, you can have a rise-and-fall pendant over the dining table under dimmer control, while the centre light, wall lights or spotlights may be at fixed intensity, or vice versa.

There is a more expensive unit available which provides dimming facilities on two different sets of lighting and, like all the other dimmers, requires no alteration to the wiring when replacing a conventional switch, in this case a two gang switch.

Table lamp dimmer
Table or standard lamps may be put under dimmer control by fitting a lampholder adaptor. You simply remove the lamp, fit the dimmer in its place and insert the lamp in the dimmer lampholder. Intensity is controlled by a knob on the side of the dimmer.

Another version is available in the form of a plug adaptor. This is either connected to the flex of the portable lamp or has its own pins to connect with a socket outlet and has a socket of its own into which the lamp is connected.

Armchair or bedside dimming is possible with a portable dimmer switch, which is sold in either white or orange and has a black weighted base. The dimmer is controlled by rotating the top and slight downward pressure switches the light on or off. The control unit is connected by a flexible cord to a socket adaptor, into which the portable lamp is plugged.

Touch dimmer
The most recent type available is the touch dimmer, which is operated when a gentle touch on a small touch pad, fitted flush into the switch plate, operates the dimming and/or switching. These dimmers all fit standard square flush-mounted metal boxes.

One touch on the pad dims the light; repeated tapping varies the dimming until the desired level is reached. There are separate touch pads for changing the light level up and down and the unit has a memory which restores the light level after a power cut. These dimmers, which contain a fuse to protect the circuitry, must not be fitted into a two-way circuit.

Master touch dimmer
Another version of the touch dimmer enables dimming to be controlled from more than one switching position. For two-way switching, a master touch dimmer is fitted in place of a switch at one position and a slave dimmer at the second point or each point on an intermediate switching circuit. The master has a neon indicator.

Dimmer switch failure
Dimmers should be chosen and treated carefully because they contain delicate components. Never exceed the watts rating. Low-priced equipment with ratings of only 200 watts are satisfactory for simple light fittings; but if you are likely to install a multi-light fitting at a later date, it is better to fit a dimmer in the 400–500 watts range. This also applies to wall lights when there is a chance that more powerful replacement bulbs will be fitted later on.

If a dimmer is overloaded it will almost certainly fail. Dimmer failure is sometimes caused by failure

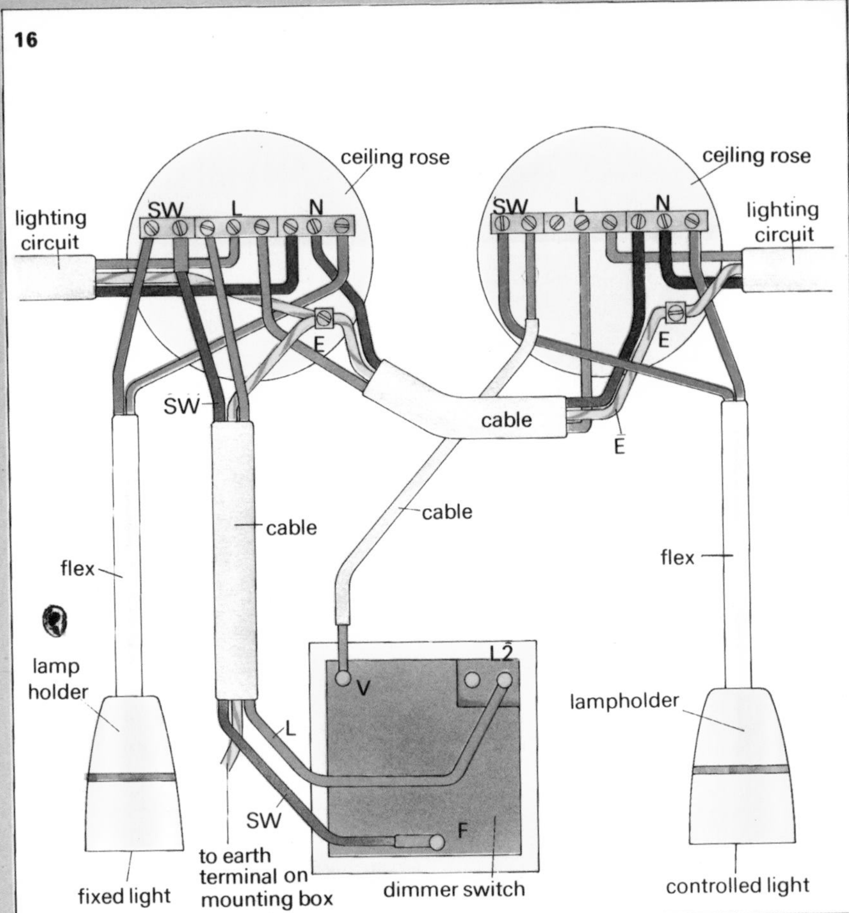

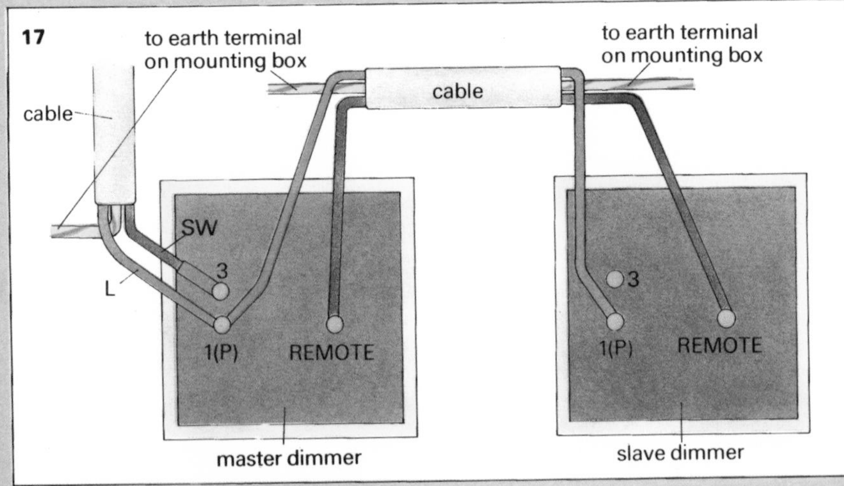

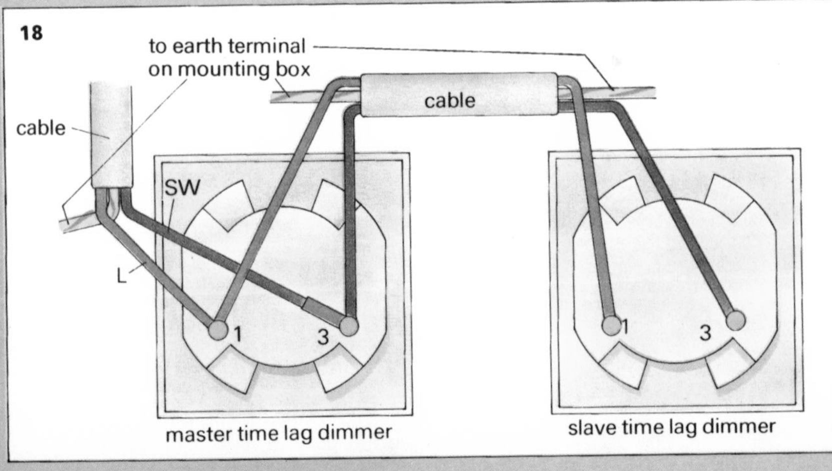

of a light bulb when a surge of heavy current flows in the circuit and through the dimmer: this short circuit can exist long enough to destroy the semiconductor. To eliminate these risks, manufacturers are beginning to introduce small sand-filled cartridge fuses – similar to, but smaller than, a 13amp plug fuse – into their dimmer switches.

Types of time switch

The conventional vacuum-operated time lag switch – used with stair and corridor lighting to save electricity – will operate for up to five minutes, but can be dangerous to stair users because it gives no warning before cutting out. The control, which can also be fitted in place of any square-plate switch, comes in a touch pad version.

However the most up-to-date version is a device which incorporates a time lag control with the touch pad facility but maintains a degree of light; the light does not cut out, but fades and then holds indefinitely at a safety level. A slight touch will then turn off the light electronically. This is also a standard square-plate switch and can replace any one-way switch without wiring modifications.

Also available is a master time lag dimmer of the touch pad type which can be used in a two-way or intermediate switching circuit. It is fitted in place of one of the two-way switches (or intermediate switches in a multi-switching circuit) and the other remains as an ordinary switch; but it also operates the light or lights and begins the time lag sequence.

Burglar deterrent switches

Leaving lights on in a house may deter a casual would-be intruder, but it is unlikely to fool a professional house-breaker. Deterrent lighting should be switched on and off at the proper time and solar-operated devices, which go on at sundown and off at sunrise, are available.

One of the most useful for the home is a dimmer switch fitted with a photo cell which enables the light to be left on at a low level and therefore is not expensive to run. This can be used to replace any modern square-plate one-way or two-way switch without modification to the wiring.

Another type of burglar deterrent is the combined on-off time switch which operates as an ordinary switch and can be set to turn lights on or off automatically at frequent intervals to give the impression the house is being used. Bear in mind, house-breakers know which rooms are used when.

16 Wiring dimmer switch to provide both fixed and controlled light in same room
17 Wiring master dimmer to slave
18 Wiring master time lag dimmer to slave
19 Slimline time switch with socket outlet, override switch and facility for two on/off switchings in 24 hours
20 Time switch with socket outlet, override switch and facility for one or two on/off switchings in 24 hours
21 Time switch with socket outlet, override switch and facility for hourly on/off switching

19

21

Wiring a converted loft

Extending existing electrical wiring into the roof space to allow extra lighting points and socket outlets is generally similar to wiring extensions in other parts of the house. Adding lights to an existing lighting circuit and sockets to an existing ring circuit have been covered earlier in the book.

Switches, ceiling roses, socket outlets and other wiring accessories can be similar to those used in other parts of the house. They will usually be made of moulded plastic and you can locate them in positions of your own choice. There are no special regulations for loft conversion schemes in IEE Wiring Regulations, but the whole conversion must conform to them as in other parts of the house. Where the scheme includes a bathroom, special electrical precautions must be taken; these are the same as for a conventionally situated bathroom.

Lighting wiring restrictions

It is usually a simple job to connect new wiring to the lighting circuit supplying the upper floor of a two-storey house, but you must consider the restrictions in terms of the electrical load. Before running new cables, check how many lights are already supplied from the circuit. The normal 5amp lighting circuit has a maximum load of 1200 watts; this figure is obtained by multiplying the current rating (5amps) by its voltage (240 volts). The figure does not mean 1200 watts of lighting is actually connected to the circuit at any one time; in practice it is somewhat less.

Assessing load The regulations stipulate you treat each lampholder, containing a lamp of 100 watts or smaller, as 100 watts for the assessment. Lampholders containing lamps larger than 100 watts are assessed at their actual wattage; most lamps used on a domestic lighting circuit are 100 watts or less, including common fluorescent tubes (fluorescent tubes are rated above the stated wattage, so check on this when buying them). A 150 watt lamp is equivalent to one-and-a-half lampholders and a 200 watt lamp is equivalent to two. Count the number of lampholders on the circuit, add the number you wish to include in the loft conversion and adjust your figures for any 150 or 200 watt lamps. If the final figure is no more than 1200, you can add the chosen number of new lights as described earlier in the book.

If there are two lighting circuits, use the most convenient; in a bungalow for example, the cables will already be in the roof space, running across and between the joists.

Socket wiring restrictions

You can normally add extra sockets to a ring circuit, but you will again have to assess the number already in existence. The cables forming the ring circuit on the floor below the loft conversion will normally be under the floorboards. It is rare to find a ring circuit cable which has already been run into the roof space, except possibly to supply a heat/light unit mounted on a bathroom ceiling. Such a cable is most likely to be a spur; as such, you should not use it to supply any other

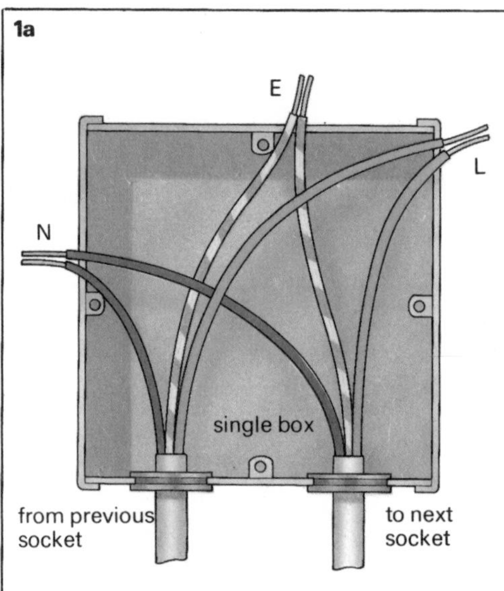

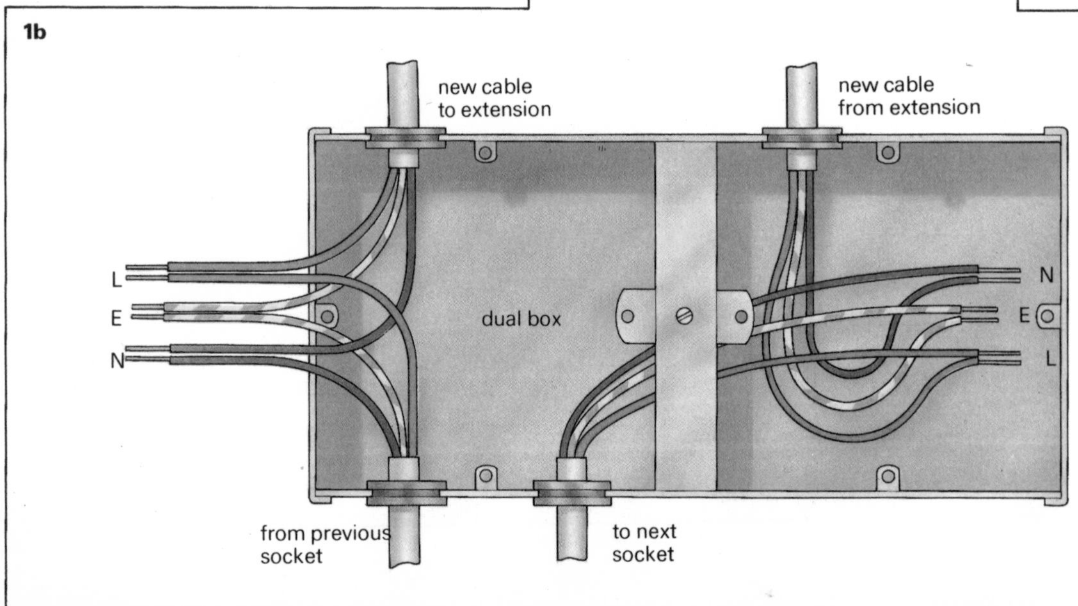

Extending ring main from socket outlet:
1a Existing socket wiring
1b Extended wiring with single box replaced by dual box; if extending from double socket outlet, replace double box by dual box and connect two single socket plates in place of original double plate
2a Circuit at original ring socket outlet
2b Extended ring circuit. Fused connection unit, protected by 3amp fuse, can be installed to supply lighting in converted loft area; cable for lighting circuit should be connected to load terminals on fused connection unit (**inset**)

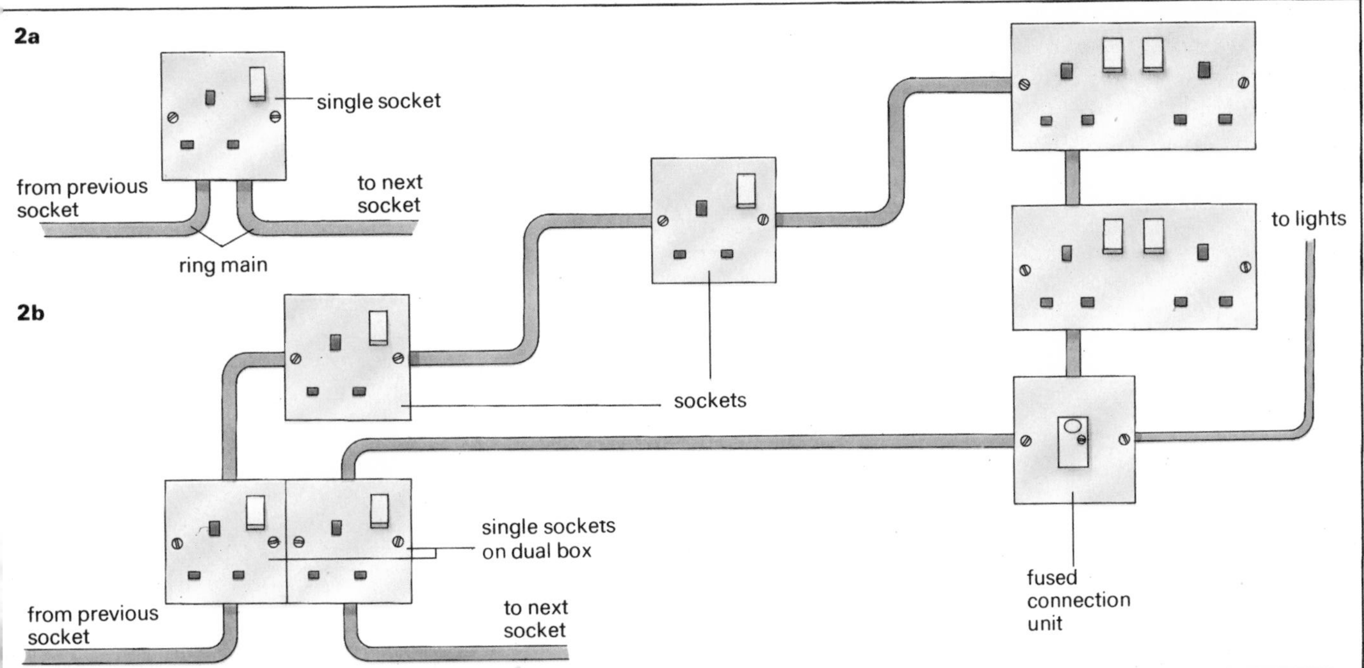

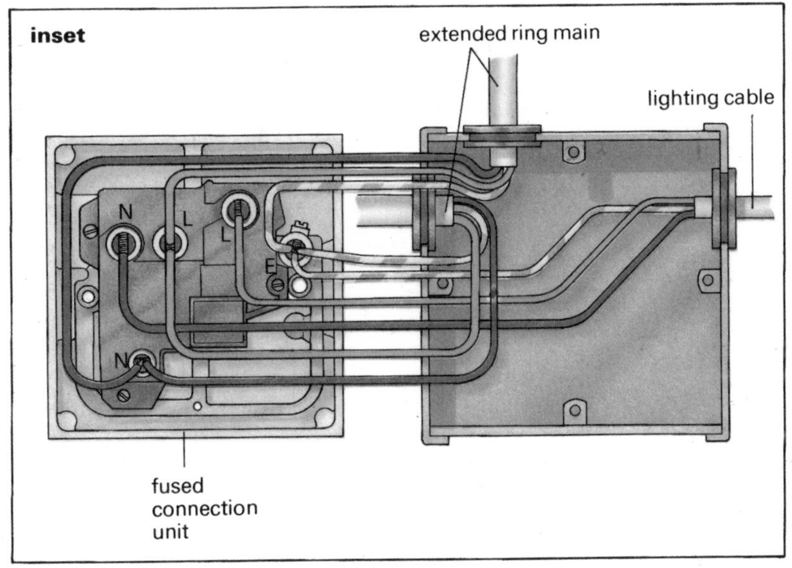

outlets apart from the one appliance it serves.

Assessing load Before you run new cables from an existing ring circuit you will have to check on the location of existing socket outlets to ascertain the floor area already served. A domestic ring circuit can supply an unlimited number of 13amp socket outlets and fixed appliances supplied from fused connection units; the latter should have an individual rating of not more than 3000 watts, but an immersion heater or water heater should preferably be wired on a separate radial circuit. Any one ring circuit, however, is limited to supply an area of not more than 100sq m (or 1000sq ft). Before you extend the ring circuit, measure the area of the rooms which have socket outlets run from the circuit and add the area of the proposed loft conversion; if the total is below 100sq m, you can extend this circuit into the loft conversion.

Most three or four-bedroomed houses have two ring circuits; one supplies outlets on the ground floor and the other supplies those on the upper floor. In this case it is a simple matter to measure the area of each; in most cases it will be no more than about 50sq m (or 500sq ft) so you can add the loft space and still not exceed 100sq m (or 1000sq ft). If there is only one ring circuit, you will almost certainly need a new circuit for the loft conversion; this has been covered earlier in the book.

Check which sockets are on which circuit; if you have two ring circuits, remove each of the relevant 30amp circuit fuses in turn and test each socket by plugging in a table lamp. Any fixed appliances, supplied from fused connection units, have to be checked individually as the circuit fuses are removed.

Extending a ring circuit

Use 2.5sq mm twin core and earth flat PVC-sheathed house wiring cable when extending a circuit. The type of extension will depend upon how many outlets you require. If you only need two single socket outlets or one double socket outlet, with no lighting or fixed appliances included in the power circuit, you only need a single length of cable forming a spur. This is connected to the ring circuit at an existing ring socket outlet or at a junction box inserted into the ring cable; this technique has been described earlier in the book.

Extending cable If the loft space is being converted into a living and/or sleeping area, you will need more than two single socket outlets; you may also need one or more fixed lights as recommended and possibly one or more fixed appliances.

When extending the ring circuit for a full-scale conversion such as this, you will need to extend the ring cable itself. This is done either by opening it up at a socket outlet on the floor below or by cutting cable under the floorboards and running two cables from the break; choose the most convenient method. The two cables resulting from this operation will be the outward and return legs of your ring cable extension. One cable goes to the first new outlet and the other to the last; the remaining outlets are linked together by cable in the form of a ring between these two cables, which are connected into your existing ring circuit at the break in the cable on the floor below. Use two single sockets mounted on a dual box to restore the final ring if connecting in at a socket outlet or two 30amp junction boxes if cutting into the cable.

Running cable The two cables of a ring circuit extension (or the single spur cable if you are using this method) have to be run up the wall from the floor to the loft space via the ceiling. You could run the cables up through a cupboard, but not against a hot water cylinder since the cable will only withstand a maximum temperature of 65°C (150°F). Since structural work will be necessary during the conversion, you should be able to cut a chase into the wall to bury the cables. Make sure you fit all your circuits before decorating.

Different methods

If the existing ring circuit cannot be extended into the loft space because of the area calculation, there are three other possible methods of providing a power circuit for the conversion; you can provide a new ring circuit, a 30amp radial power circuit or install a new one or two-way consumer unit in the loft space. The last method is particularly suitable if the conversion is to be a self-contained flat.

New ring circuit You can fit any number of socket outlets and fixed appliances on a ring circuit. To install it, run two 2.5sq mm twin core and earth PVC-sheathed cables up into the roof space and connect them to a spare 30amp fuseway in the consumer unit. If there is no spare fuseway then you will have to fit a one-way consumer unit or switched fuse unit beside the main consumer unit; this should be connected to the meter by the Electricity Board. Run the ring cables from this unit, using 2.5sq mm twin core and earth PVC-sheathed cable, and protect the circuit with a 30amp fuse. You should provide two lengths of 16sq mm single core PVC-sheathed cable to connect the switched fuse unit to the meter.

Radial power circuit This will only permit six outlets, made up of socket outlets and fixed appliances. One outlet could comprise a fused connection unit supplying the lighting for the loft conversion. This method will also require its own 30amp fuseway in the consumer unit, but in this case the cable size depends on the type of fuse used. With a miniature circuit breaker (MCB) or a cartridge fuse, 4.0sq mm twin core and earth PVC-sheathed cable is used; but with a rewirable fuse, 6.0sq mm cable must be used. The latter is extremely difficult to work with and this method is best avoided. The same size cable is used to link all the outlets on the circuit.

If there is no spare fuseway in the consumer unit, you will have to fit a switched fuse unit as before; buy an MCB or cartridge fuse type and use 4.0sq mm cable as previously described.

Separate consumer unit Install a two-way consumer unit in the loft space and connect it with 4.0sq mm twin core and earth PVC-sheathed cable to an MCB or cartridge type switched fuse unit next to

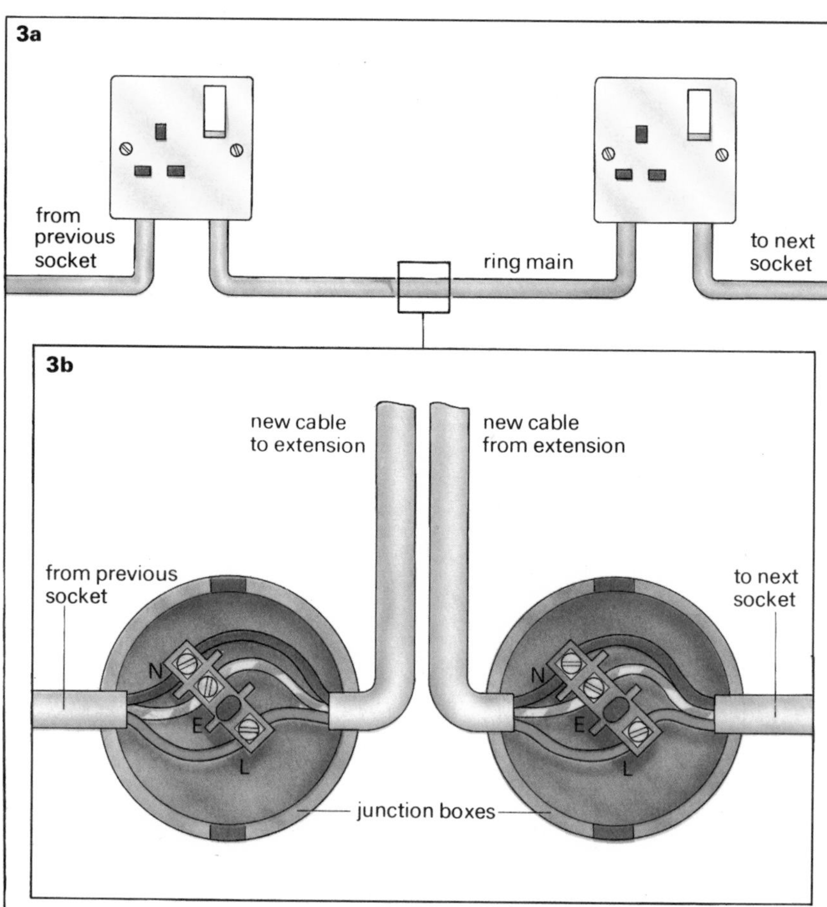

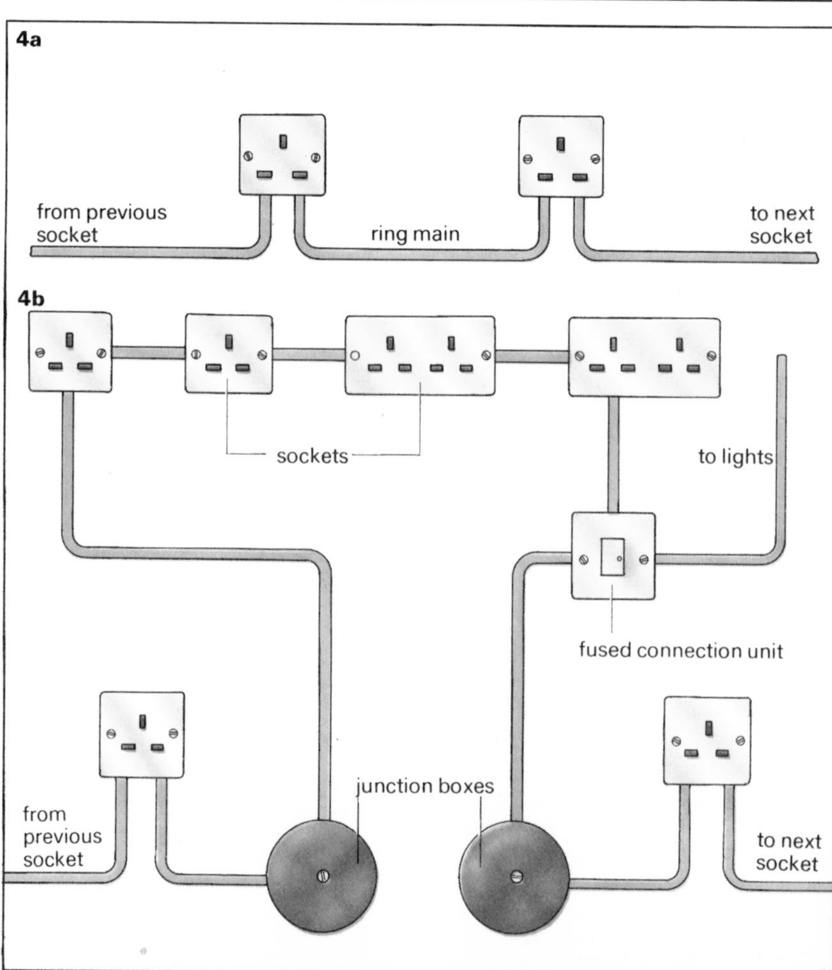

Extending ring main between socket outlets: **3a** Existing ring cable. **3b** Ring main extended using two 30amp junction boxes. **4a** Original ring circuit. **4b** Extended ring circuit
Installing new ring main: **5a** Ring cables run from spare 30amp fuseway in consumer unit; detail of consumer unit wiring (**inset**).
5b Ring cables run from switch fuse; detail of switch fuse wiring (**inset**)

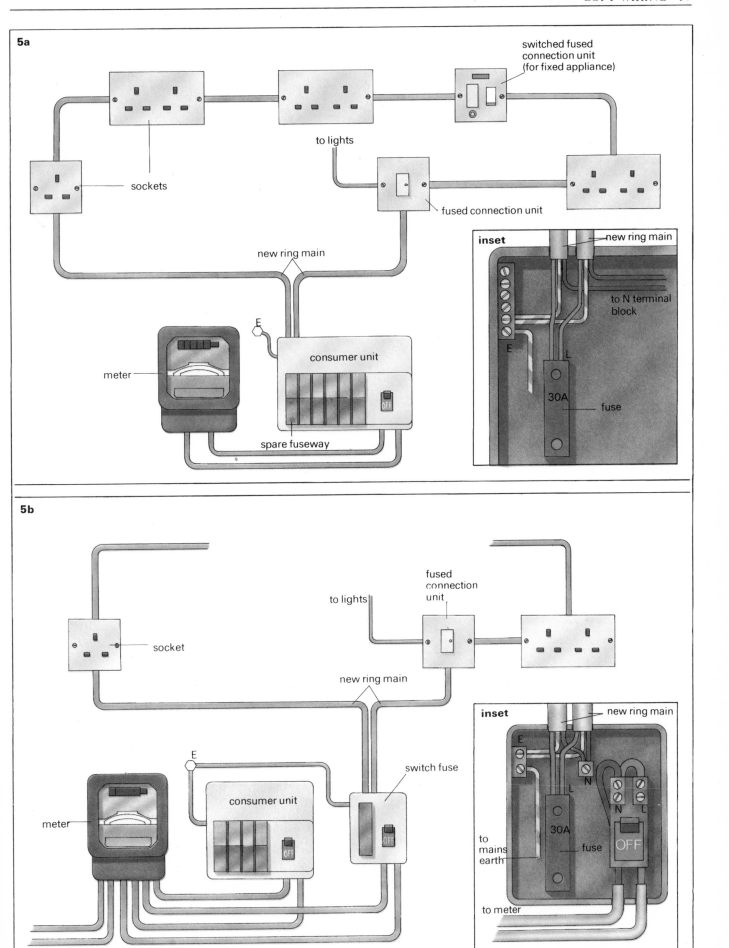

5a

switched fused
connection unit
(for fixed appliance)

sockets

to lights

fused connection unit

inset

new ring main

to N terminal
block

E

L

30A

fuse

new ring main

E

meter

consumer unit

OFF

spare fuseway

5b

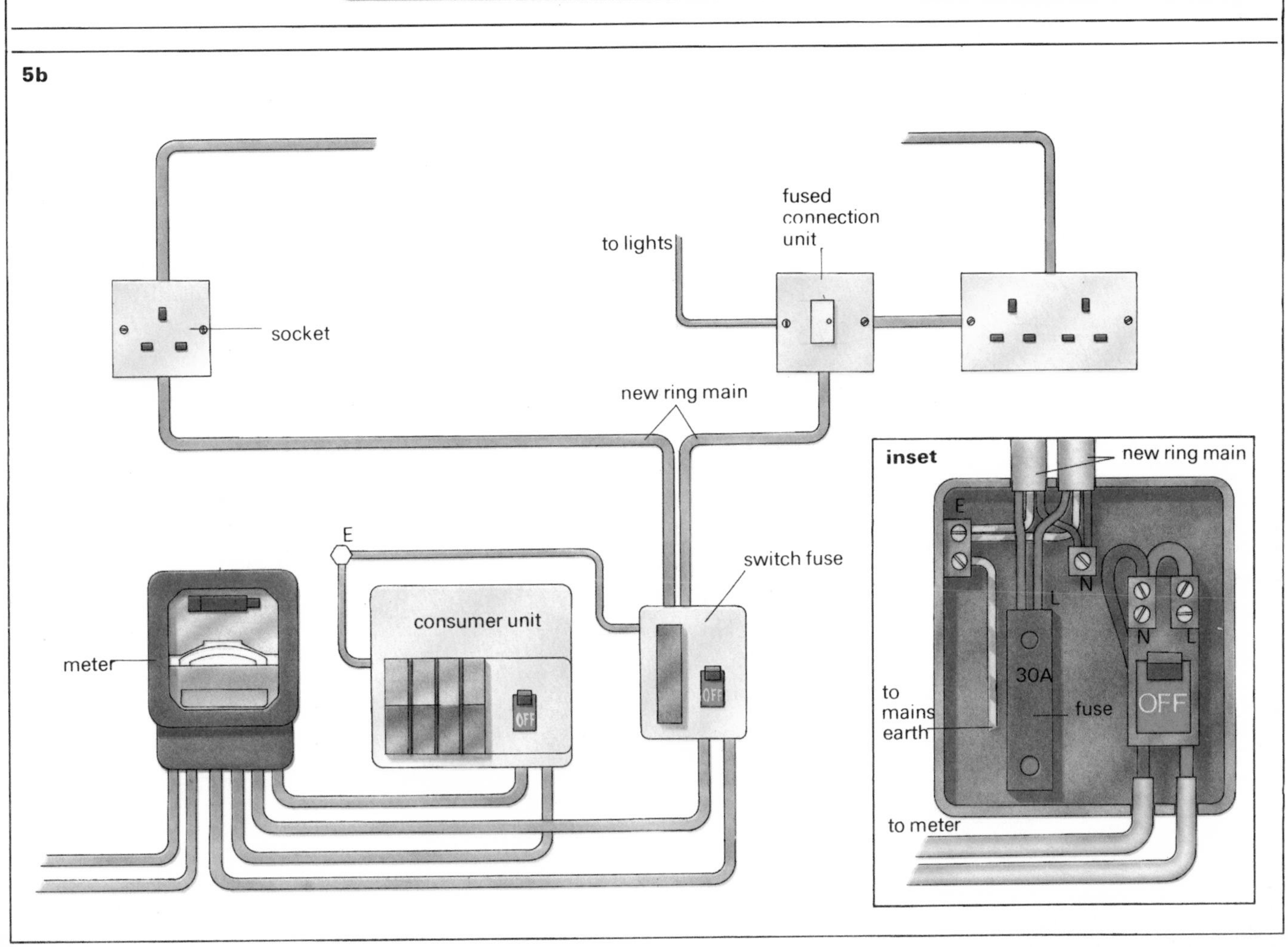

6a

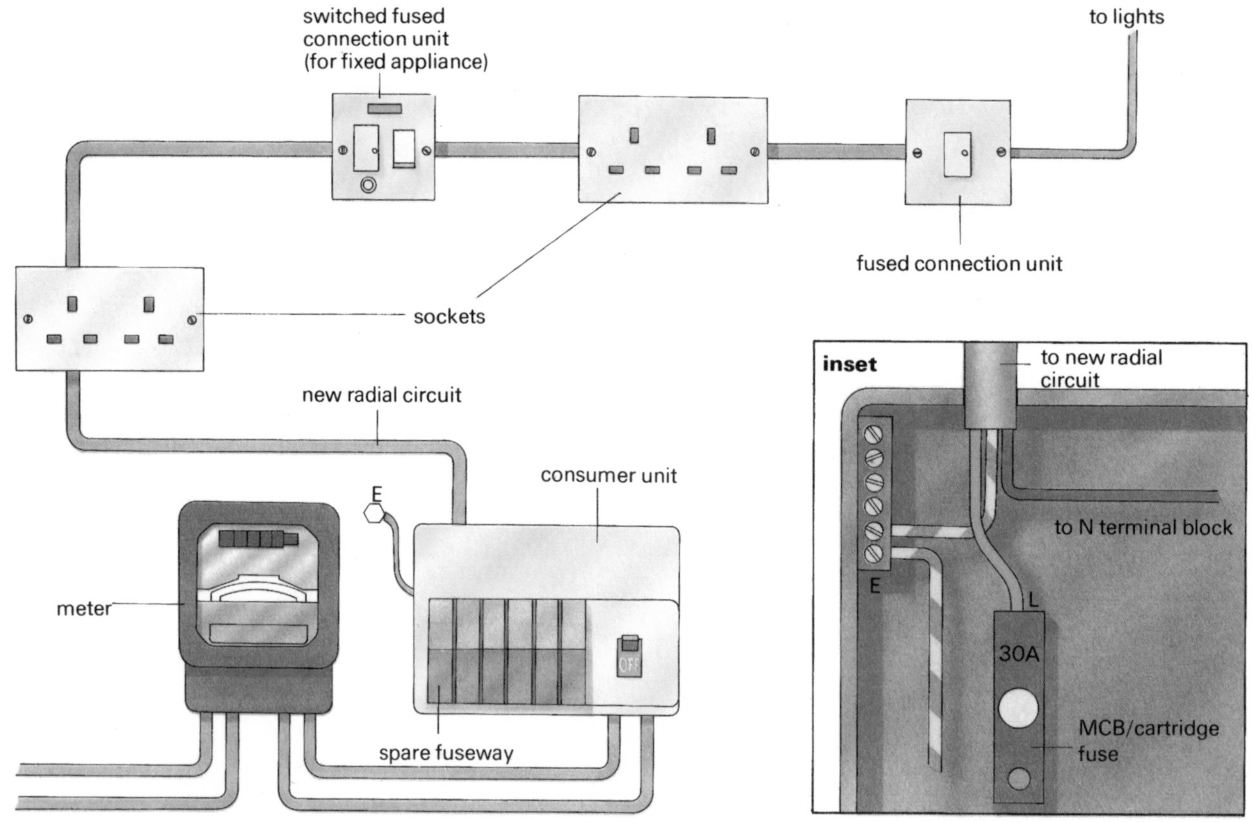

switched fused
connection unit
(for fixed appliance)
to lights
fused connection unit
sockets
new radial circuit
consumer unit
E
meter
spare fuseway
inset
to new radial
circuit
to N terminal block
E
L
30A
MCB/cartridge
fuse

6b

switched fused
connection unit
socket
new radial circuit
E
meter
consumer unit
switch fuse
inset
to new radial circuit
E
N
L
MCB/
cartridge
fuse
30A
N
L
OFF
to mains
earth
to meter

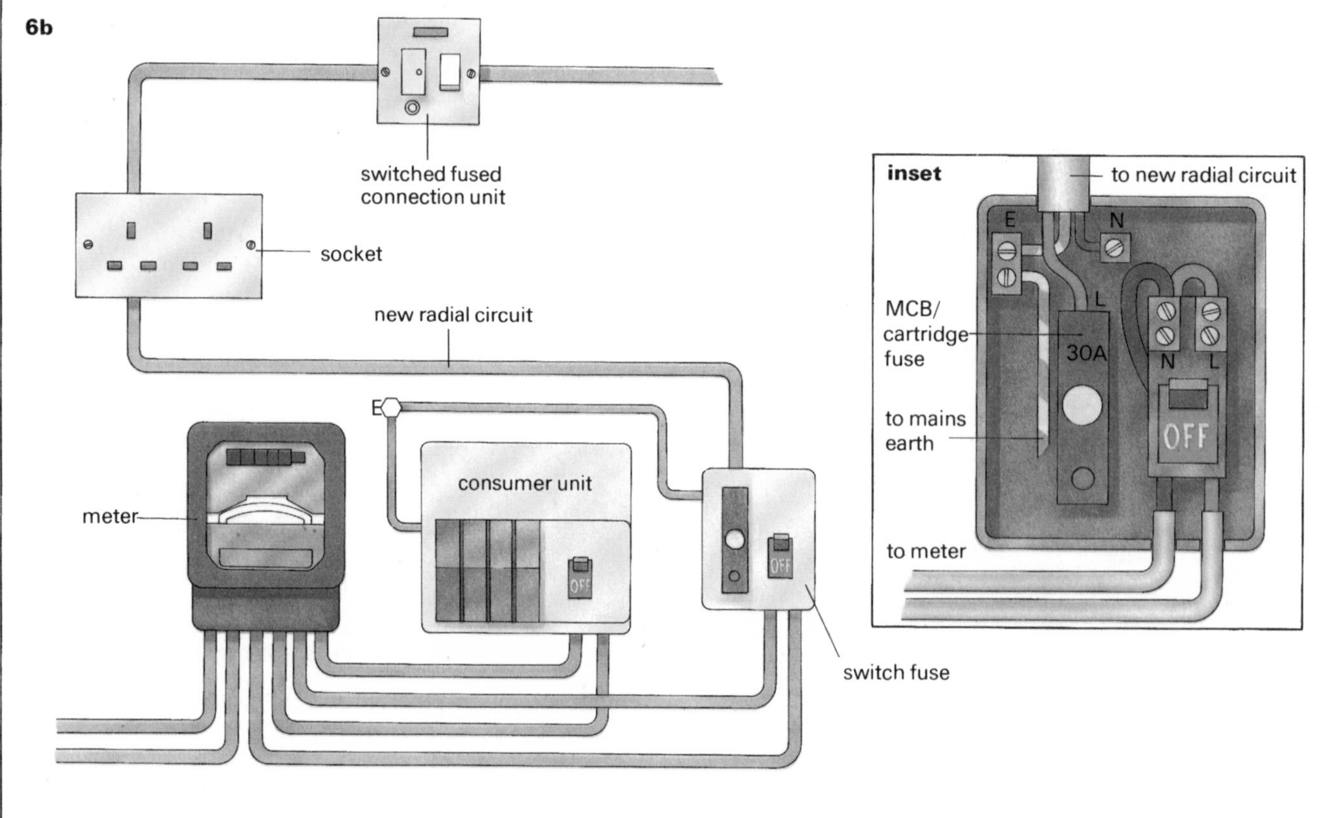

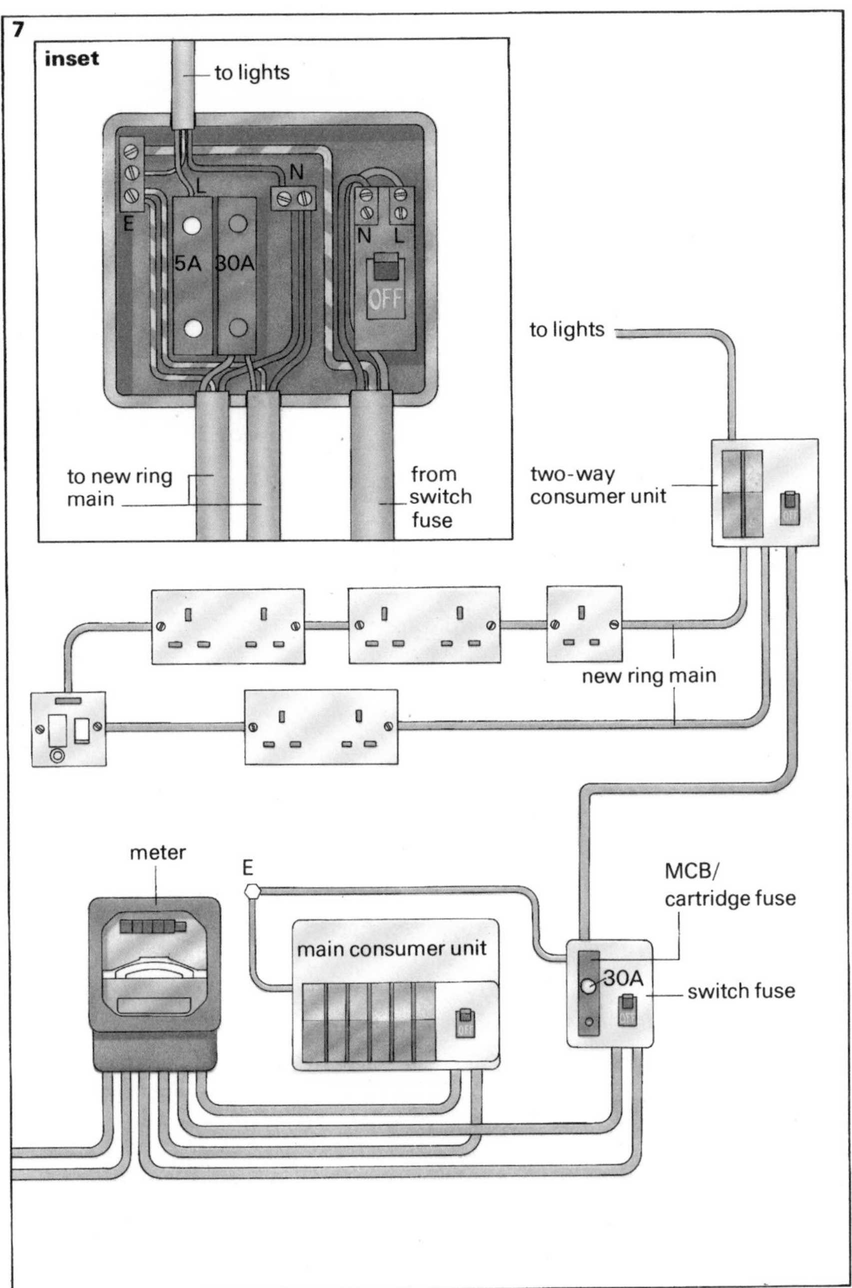

Installing new radial circuit:
6a Circuit run from consumer unit; MCB or cartridge fuse must be used at consumer unit (**inset**)
6b Circuit run from switch fuse; again MCB or cartridge fuse must be used at switch fuse (**inset**)
Installing new two-way consumer unit in loft area:
7 Circuit fed from 30amp switch fuse at meter; detail of new consumer unit wiring (**inset**)

the main consumer unit. The switched fuse unit should be fitted with a 30amp fuse; the two-way unit should have a 5amp fuseway for the lighting circuit and a 30amp fuseway for the ring main in the loft. Use 1.0sq mm twin core and earth PVC-sheathed cable for the lighting circuit and 2.5sq mm cable of the same type for the ring main.

Extending a lighting circuit

Use 1.0sq mm twin core and earth PVC-sheathed cable. It is normally only necessary to insert a junction box into the cable running between the joists in the roof space. Alternatively you could connect the new cable to a loop-in ceiling rose mounted on the ceiling immediately below the roof space; pass the cable through the existing hole in the ceiling after you have moved the ceiling rose.

However, since the construction of the loft conversion will probably require re-routing of existing lighting cables and possible partial rewiring (as described below), make provision to connect the roof space lighting wiring at the appropriate stage.

Using power circuit Although technically correct, it is not always the best installation practice to have all the new lights on the same lighting circuit. If the lights immediately below, including those serving the landing or hall, are on the same circuit and the fuse blows, the exit route and the loft conversion itself will be in darkness. Check whether the hall and landing lights are on the same circuit as the bedroom lights by withdrawing the bedroom lighting circuit fuse and trying the landing and hall lights. If these are on a different circuit to the bedrooms, connect into the bedroom circuit; if they are on the same circuit, it is a good idea to supply one or more of the fixed lighting points from the power circuit in the loft conversion.

Connect these lights to the power circuit via a fused connection unit containing a 3amp fuse. If you supply only one light in this way, its location will depend upon the nature and layout of your loft conversion scheme; the light should be near the entrance. You could fit another light on the stairway outside the entrance to the loft area. This should be controlled by two-way switching, with one of the two switches fitted at the bottom of the stairs. If your conversion warrants only one light of this kind, the fused connection unit can be a switched version so you can use it to control the light. If you require two-way switching in this case, fit a special switched fused connection unit which has a two-way switch instead of the usual one-way switch.

The above considerations are obviously unnecessary if you are installing a separate two-way consumer unit in the loft since the lighting circuit will be independent of those below.

Wiring alterations

Existing wiring in the loft space will usually be lighting circuit wiring; although it is unlikely to be associated with your new wiring, it is almost sure to be disturbed as the structural alterations are made. This will probably mean all cables are re-routed; where they cross joists they should be threaded through holes drilled in the joists at the regulation (minimum) depth of 50mm (2in) below the tops of the joists.

If all the existing wiring is in metal conduit, it can be difficult and often impossible to move the conduit; in some cases you may be able to let the conduit into notches cut into the tops of the joists. Such conduit installations in the home are generally old and will require rewiring and the fitting of outlet boxes at lighting points. The better and less costly alternative is to replace the conduit with a new PVC-sheathed cable installation. This is still more desirable since earthing is often ineffective or non-existent in an old conduit installation. If conduit drops to switches are buried in plaster, you can leave them and run the new cables down the conduits to the switches.

If your wiring is old, the sheathing will be tough rubber or lead; in either case the insulation is likely to have perished and you should renew the installation. It is therefore important to have the present wiring surveyed before you start the conversion, even if rewiring or re-routing is not required. Make sure you make any wiring additions or changes needed in the bedrooms below your conversion before the conversion is finished; once it is completed, the changes will become difficult and costly.

Earth leakage circuit breakers

An earth leakage circuit breaker (ELCB) is a double pole mains switch which automatically trips (switches off) when there is sufficient leakage of current from a live wire or earth terminal to earth. It does not normally operate, however, when a circuit is overloaded or if it develops a short circuit (when the live and neutral wires are in contact with each other). Some models do also serve as excess current devices, but these are not normally used in the home.

The ELCB is used as an alternative or back-up device for earthing; in other words it is used where earthing is likely to be poor or ineffective. It is fitted with a tripping coil which is energized by current leaking to earth through it or in some part of the installation, producing an out-of-balance current in the circuit breaker. When the tripping coil is energized, an electro-magnet lifts a latch and releases the switch mechanism which is operated by a powerful spring. On release, the switch contacts open and the circuits and/or faulty apparatus are isolated from the mains electricity.

The current required to energize the trip coil is a tiny portion of the current flowing through the circuit breakers under normal conditions. By cutting off the current to a circuit when there is an earth leakage, the ELCB does the work of a fuse – but with much less current and with greater speed. For example, a 30amp rewireable fuse (the largest in most homes) requires 60amps to blow it; a 30amp cartridge fuse requires 45amps and a 30amp miniature circuit breaker (MCB) requires 37amps. The large currents required to cut off the supply when there is an earth leakage put great strain on the circuit wiring and a very good earthing system is needed if the fuse is to blow or the MCB is to operate. But the ELCB needs only 1amp (and often less) to operate, so the fuses and any MCBs remain intact since the ELCB does the work for them.

How it works

An earth leakage current returns to the electricity supply system, usually at the substation which might be some distance from the house. But instead of returning through the neutral conductor, as current does in its normal state, it has to follow an alternative path. Originally the faulty current left the house through the mains water pipe, through the mains water network and onto the substation. Because water authorities are now using insulated pipes, the mains water system may no longer be used as the sole means of earthing in new or existing installations. Now the metallic sheathing of the Electricity Board's cable provides a continuous metallic path for the earth leakage current back to the substation. In some areas the Electricity Board also offers another system known as protective multiple earthing (PME). This takes advantage of the fact that the neutral pole of the mains electricity is solidly connected to earth at the substation and gives a first class earthing system.

Earthing terminal The Electricity Board sometimes provides a terminal in the house for earth connection, for which it may make a small charge. Where the Board is unable to provide an earth terminal – either because the metallic sheathing is not continuous or because PME has not been adopted in the area – the consumer must find an alternative, since he is responsible for earthing.

For direct connection of an earthing circuit to earth, the impedance (AC equivalent of DC resistance) of the earth connection must not exceed 4 ohms to enable it to carry the 60amp or more current which may result from a leakage. Earth terminals provided by the Electricity Board meet these requirements; but alternative systems provided by the consumer are unlikely to do so. For example, simply installing an electrode in the ground to provide an earth terminal would result in fuses failing to blow should an earth leakage fault occur; the installation would be dangerous with a high fire and electrocution risk. The solution here would be to install an earth leakage circuit breaker in conjunction with an earth electrode.

Installing earth electrode The copper or copper-sheathed electrode must be a minimum of 1200mm (or 48in) long and it should be driven vertically into firm soil so the clamp terminal is just above ground level. Firm soil is essential to provide good electrical conductivity between the electrode rod and earth; the moisture content of the subsoil will further improve conductivity. When deciding on a suitable position for the electrode, bear in mind the concrete foundations of a house wall are probably not more than 300mm (or 12in) below ground level and they protrude between 75 and 100mm (3 and 4in) beyond the faces of the wall. If your consumer unit is situated in a cellar, you can drill a hole larger than the electrode in the wall, drive the electrode horizontally through this into the subsoil and seal around it with mastic; or drill a hole in the floor and insert the rod, but in either case beware of the presence of a damp proof membrane which would be punctured by this process and

500 V 50 Hz
60 A
OFF
PRESS TO TEST
IMPORTANT
INSTALLATION METALWORK MUST BE CONNECTED TO TERMINAL f
EARTH ELECTRODE MUST BE CONNECTED TO TERMINAL e
YELLOW BUTTON
TEST OFTEN. IF BREAKER DOES NOT SWITCH OFF INFORM YOUR ELECTRICAL CONTRACTOR IMMEDIATELY

Above Voltage-operated ELCB
Left Current-operated high sensitivity ELCB
Below Earth electrode

WARNING
You should consult the Electricity Board before undertaking any protective installation since there are now new regulations on earthing circuits.

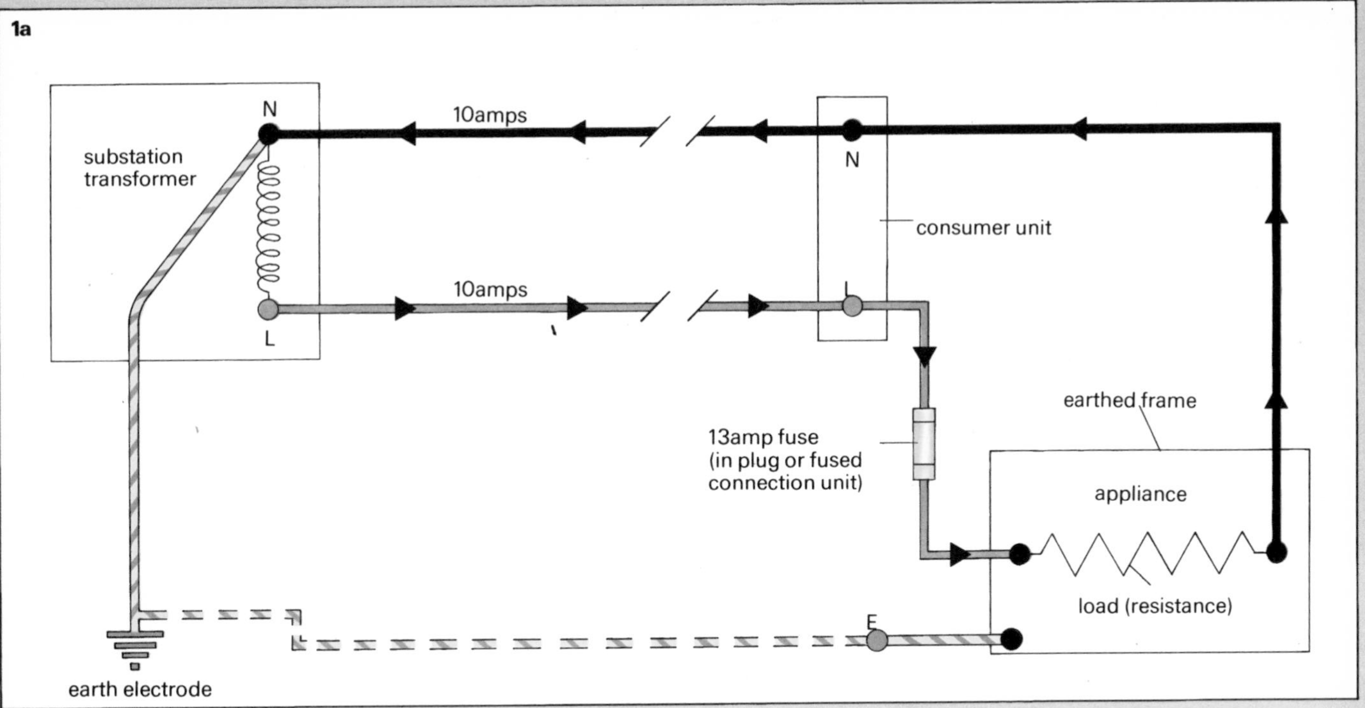

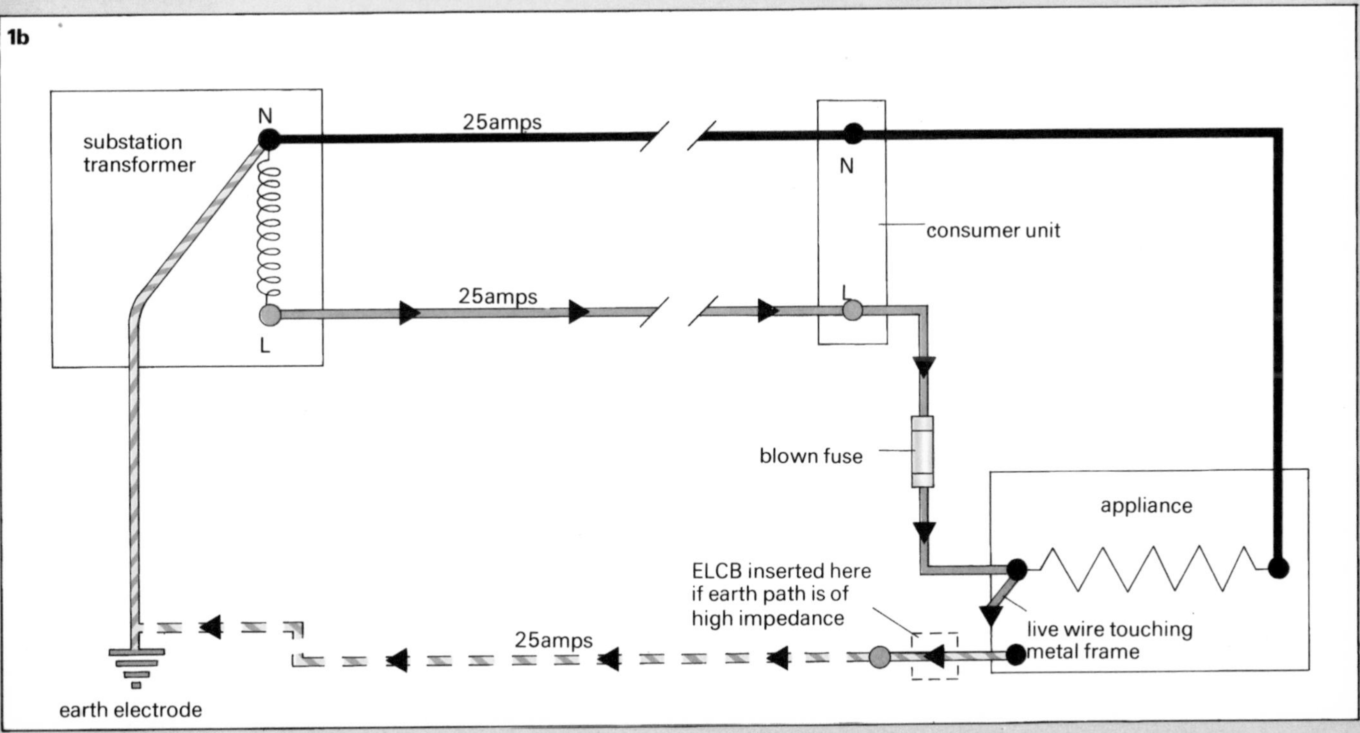

allow damp to penetrate. Connection to the terminal clamp should be with 2.5sq mm single core green/yellow PVC-insulated cable; at the connection point fix an indelible label stating: 'Safety Electrical Earth – Do Not Remove'.

Types of ELCB

There are two main types of ELCB installed in the home: one is voltage-operated and the other current-operated. The current-operated ELCB should be your first choice, but if the product of the operating current and the impedance of the earth loop (as measured on an impedance tester by the Electricity Board or an electrical contractor) exceeds 40, you must use the voltage-operated type.

Voltage-operated This is the cheapest ELCB and is simply a double pole circuit breaker with trip coil and tripping mechanism. The circuit breaker section has four main terminals – a conventional double pole mains switch and two subsidiary

1a The normal current path from the substation to an appliance via the consumer unit
1b The current path where current from a short circuit, caused by the live wire in an appliance touching an earthed frame, returns to the substation via earth

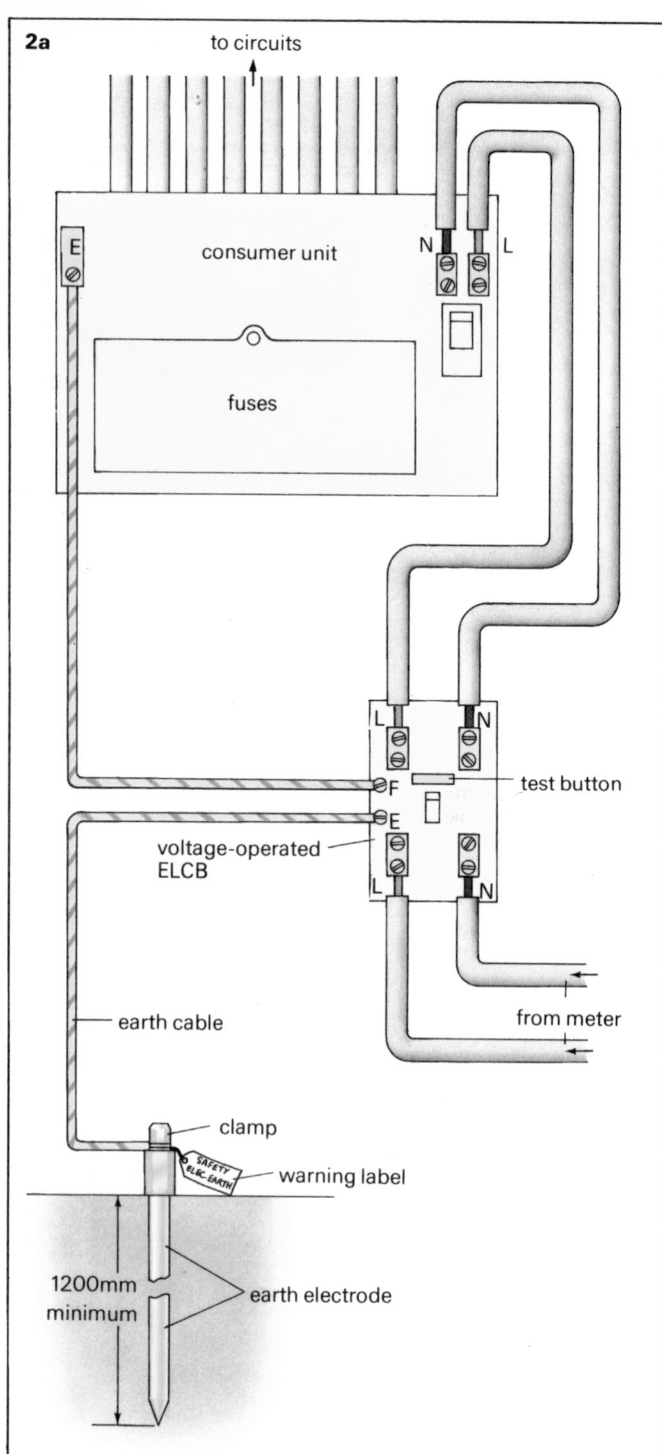

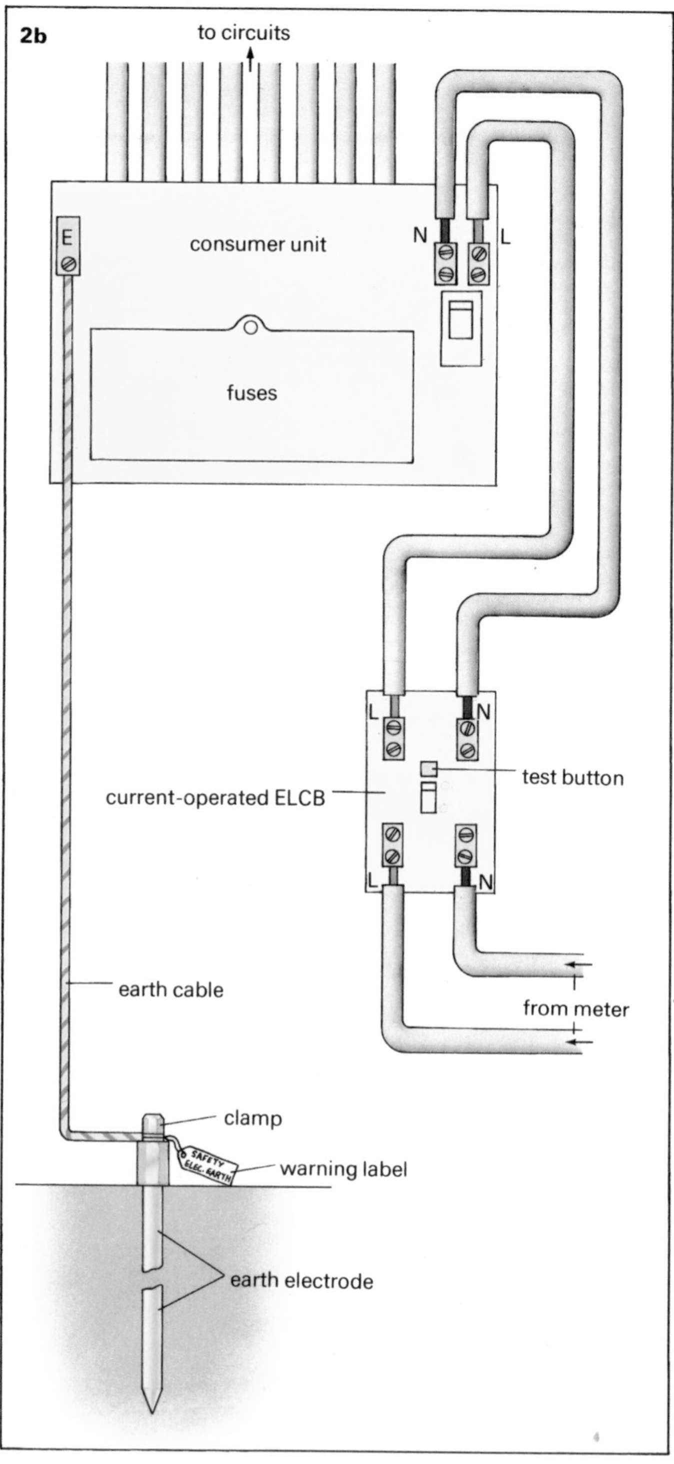

terminals. The mains leads from the meter are connected to one pair of live (L) and neutral (N) terminals; the other pair are load terminals which feed the installation and are normally connected by two leads to the mains terminals of the consumer unit. The subsidiary terminals are marked 'F' and 'E'. The F terminal is connected to the earth terminal on the consumer unit; the E terminal is connected to the earth clamp terminal of the earth electrode in the soil. Any leakage of current to the earth conductor in the main circuit passes through the tripping coil of the ELCB, energizing the electro-magnet which trips the circuit breaker. About 40 volts is needed to operate the tripping device and the current required to produce this voltage is very small.

Since the leakage current in the earth conductor must flow through the tripping coil to operate the release mechanism, this type of ELCB is not wholly reliable. For example, if fault current flows to earth via another path, such as a gas or water pipe (called a parallel earth path), it bypasses the ELCB and the ELCB does not trip. If this parallel earth path is satisfactory, sufficient current will flow to blow the fuse. If not, the gas or water pipework indoors will remain live and be dangerous.

Warning It is not a good idea to install two or more voltage-operated ELCBs to protect different sections of the installation, unless the respective earthing rods are at least 2.5m (or 8ft) apart and are 2.5m (or 8ft) away from buried water or gas pipes.

Current-operated This has been developed to over-

2a The wiring of a voltage-operated ELCB to the consumer unit and an earth electrode

2b The wiring of a current-operated ELCB to the consumer unit; the earth lead from the consumer unit goes directly to the earth electrode

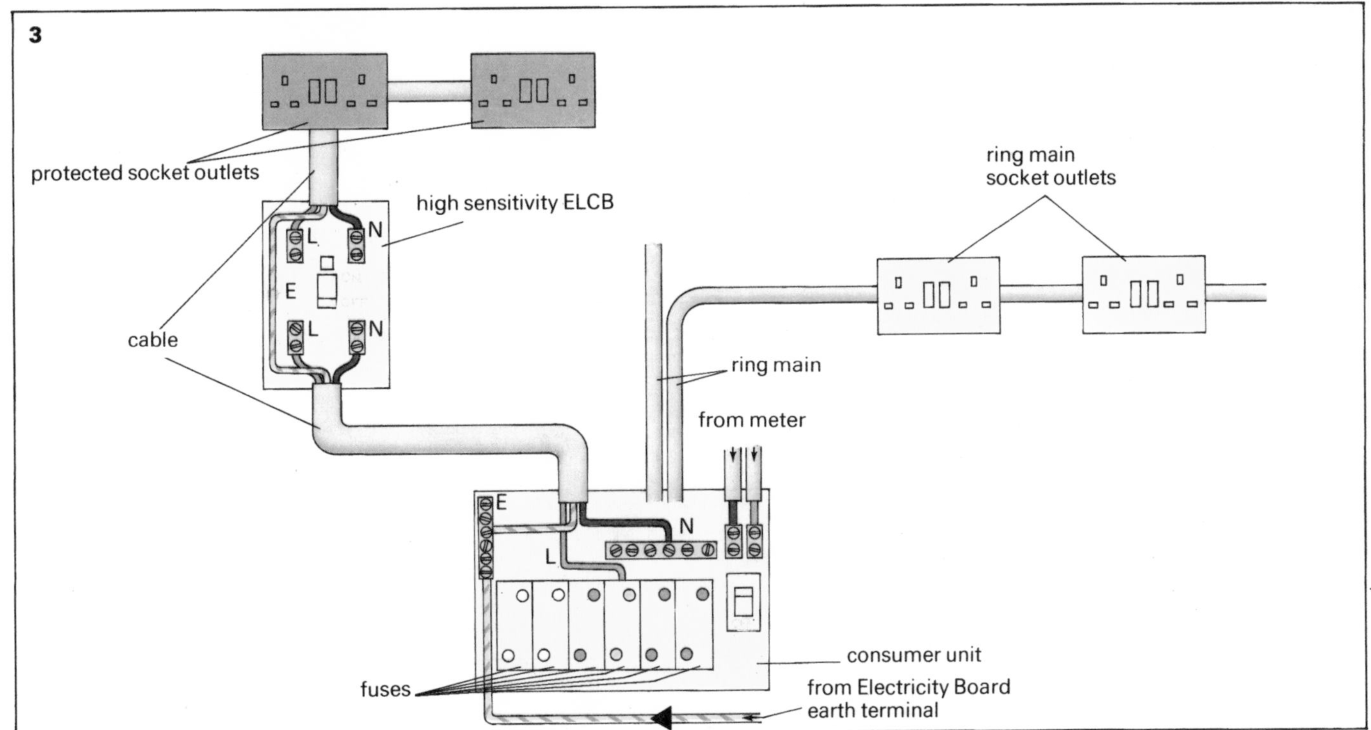

3 The wiring of a high sensitivity ELCB to the consumer unit, using 4.0 or 2.5sq mm cable, and to the socket outlets; use different coloured fittings to distinguish protected sockets from ring main sockets. There are now consumer units that incorporate an ELCB (current operated)

come the disadvantage of the voltage-operated ELCB. Although similar in style to the voltage type, its tripping coil is not energized directly by earth leakage current and has no earth conductors connected to it. There are four terminals – L and N mains terminals and L and N load terminals. The earthing lead from the consumer unit in this case goes direct to the earth electrode.

This type of ELCB works on the current balance principle – that current flowing into a circuit is equal to the current flowing out. For example, if 10amps flow into a circuit through the positive or live wire, you can expect 10amps to return via the negative or neutral wire. However, if a live wire touches earthed metal, some of the return current is diverted from the main circuit into the earth circuit; this causes an out-of-balance current in the main conductor. At the instant of the fault, the live pole of the mains switch will be carrying a lot of current and the neutral pole less, since some will be leaking to earth. By having an out-of-balance current sensing device and by connecting this to a tripping coil, you have a current-operated ELCB. No matter which path the earth leakage current takes, the sensing device will detect the out-of-balance in the mains lead and operate the tripping coil. The normal current-operated ELCB of 60–100amps switch rating needs about ½amp of out-of-balance current to operate, which means the earthing system needs to carry only that amount of current for the ELCB to work.

High sensitivity ELCB An ordinary ELCB gives no protection from direct electric shock, which is generally caused by touching a live wire or contact when also touching earthed metal or standing on the ground. With a normal current-operated circuit breaker this is because the amount of current required for it to operate is more than that required to electrocute someone; with a voltage-operated type it is because the current flowing to earth via another path (through the human body) does not flow through the ELCB trip coil. There is, however, a current-operated high sensitivity ELCB which will protect you against electrocution if you touch a live wire while in contact with the ground either directly or via earthed metal.

It must be emphasized, however, that neither this ELCB nor any other device installed in the home will prevent you being electrocuted if you come into contact with both live and neutral poles of the 240V supply, even if you are standing on an insulated surface or wearing rubber boots in the garden. But if you are in contact with the ground at the same time, there is just a chance the high sensitivity ELCB will trip before you are electrocuted.

The high sensitivity ELCB, which trips at 30 milliamps in a fraction of a second, is especially useful for selective circuits such as those used for power tools, hedgecutters, mowers and other appliances where shock risk is fairly high. It should not be inserted in the main house circuits because, if condensation or some other small earth leakage current causes it to trip, it will cut off the power to the whole house. This is called nuisance tripping and is not only inconvenient, but it could also cause a serious accident.

A consumer unit is now available in which an ELCB protects some socket outlets and a conventional mains switch controls other circuits including lighting. Where a circuit is installed to supply a few socket outlets, it is best to use fittings of a different colour for the protected ones, so only these are used with high shock risk appliances.

A high sensitivity ELCB is available for plugging into a 13amp socket, from which you can run high risk power tools. Similar to an adaptor but larger, it is a useful safety device for the home.

High sensitivity ELCBs are fitted into some special consumer units in place of the usual mains switch. Although these give additional personal protection, however, they cannot be expected to prevent electrocution when handling live wires.

The ELCB should be tested regularly using the test button.

Wiring fittings and appliances

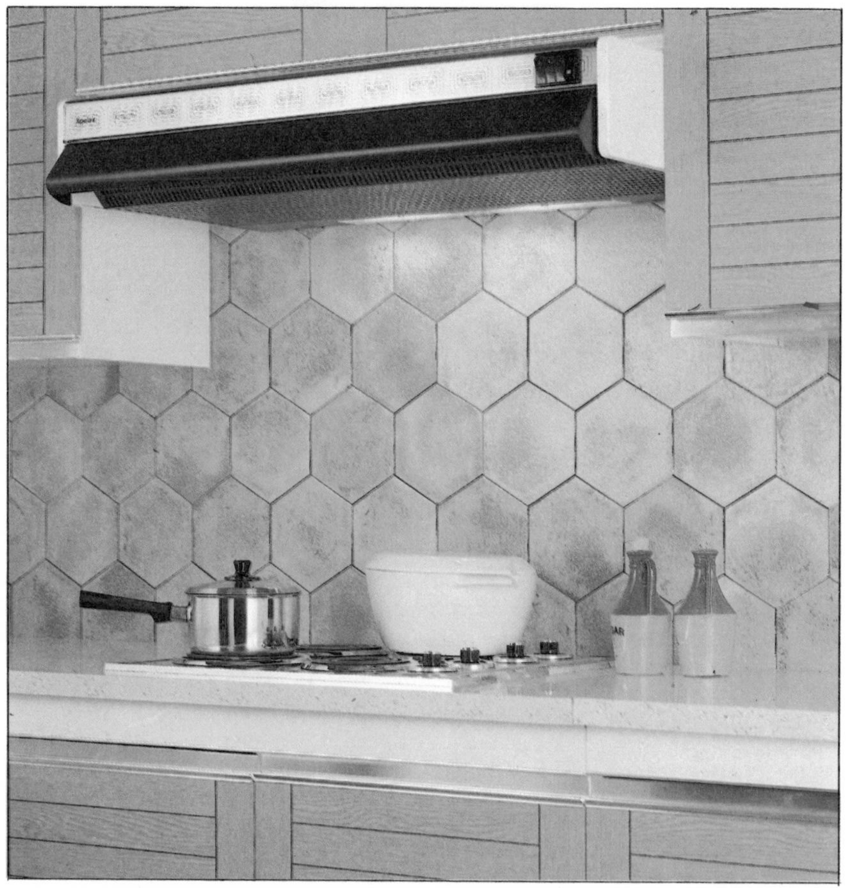

You may decide to add fittings and appliances to your existing home – or find that the power outlets in a new home are inadequate for your needs. You can do this work yourself, whether it involves putting in wall lights or spotlights, bells, buzzers, chimes, a TV aerial, a cooker or cooker hood, an immersion heater or night storage heaters. Sometimes it is possible to adapt existing circuits; alternatively you may have to run a new circuit to feed the equipment, such as with an electric cooker when the previous owners used a gas one. If the instructions are followed carefully, your home will function more smoothly.

Wiring in an electric cooker

The average domestic electric cooker consists of an oven, a hob containing three or four rings and a grill. The conventional position for the grill is below the hob and usually built into it, although with some models it is positioned at eye level. Some models have a double oven.

The majority of cookers are compact, self-contained, free-standing units positioned against the wall and connected to a wall-mounted control switch by means of a trailing cable to allow the cooker to be moved forward when you want to clean behind it; a lockable bogie placed under the cooker will make it easier to move. Other models are built into the kitchen units; these usually have separate hob and oven sections and are termed split-level cookers, the oven being raised to a more practical height for cooking.

Circuit rating

Electric cookers are heavy current-consuming appliances, having loadings of up to 12kW (12,000 watts) for medium size cookers and even higher loadings for large, family size cookers including the double oven models. Cookers with loadings up to 12kW are usually supplied from circuits of 30amp current rating, while those in excess of 12kW are usually supplied from circuits of 45amp rating.

Although the maximum current demand of a 12kW cooker on a 240v supply is 50amps with everything switched on, allowance in rating the circuit has been made bearing in mind that rarely in the average home are all the rings, the grill and the oven in use at any one time. This means the circuit rating need only be 30amps. Even if everything is in use at one time, the current demand on the circuit at any one moment is still probably less than 50amps. This is because the rings, the grill and the oven are thermostatically controlled or include a simmering device which reduces the total current demand. In rating the circuit, allowance has also been made for an electric kettle plugged into the socket outlet of the cooker control unit and therefore taking current from the cooker circuit. Although a high-speed electric kettle takes up to 13amps from the circuit, kettles are assessed at only 5amps.

There is an official formula for arriving at the circuit requirements of an electric cooker, based on the average use when cooking for a family. The first 10amps is estimated at 100 percent and the remaining current at 30 percent; 5amps is allowed for an electric kettle plugged in the cooker control unit. If the current demand of a 12kW cooker is 50amps, the first 10amps is included, the remaining 40amps is estimated at 12amps and there is a 5amp allowance for a kettle. The total assessed load is 27amps and the circuit required is therefore 30amps.

Although the regulations permit a 12kW cooker to be supplied from a 30amp circuit, it is always worthwhile considering installing a 45amp circuit, provided the consumer unit will accept a 45amp fuse unit; most will not. If there is no spare fuseway for an electric cooker circuit in the existing consumer unit and a separate switch fuse unit has to be installed, it is worth fitting one with a 45amp rating. A 45amp circuit means a larger size cable, but the extra cost is comparatively small and the work involved is the same as for a 30amp circuit.

Top A free-standing electric cooker needs a 30 or 45amp circuit, depending on its loading; a microwave cooker, however, simply runs off a 13amp fused plug and socket outlet

Above A split level cooker requires the same circuit rating as an ordinary cooker

Cooker circuit

A circuit for an electric cooker consists of a two core and earth flat PVC-sheathed cable starting at a fuseway and terminating at a 45amp cooker control unit or cooker switch. From the control unit or switch the same size cable runs through a cable entry into a terminal block in the cooker. Where the oven and hob are separate, one cooker control unit and switch can be used for both provided neither is more than 2m ($6\frac{1}{2}$ft) from it.

Cooker control unit This is a double pole switch and a switched 13amp socket outlet mounted on one panel. It is made with or without neon indicators and is available in either surface or flush-mounted versions.

Cooker switch This is simply a 45amp double pole plate switch without a kettle socket outlet, with or without a neon indicator and available in surface or flush-mounted versions. The cooker switch is cheaper than a control unit since it has no socket outlet; it can be fitted when you do not want to operate the kettle from the control unit, which can often be a disadvantage and also potentially dangerous. If the control unit is fixed in the traditional position above the cooker, the kettle flex could trail over the rings; if these are switched on, the flex will burn and could start a fire or give an electric shock before the fuse blows.

With the introduction of the ring circuit, the traditional single utility plug and socket in the kitchen has largely been replaced by numerous socket outlets; this means a socket on the control unit is unnecessary, since the kettle can be used from one of these extra socket outlets.

Cable sizes

For a 30amp cooker circuit, you should use 6sq mm cable and 10sq mm cable for a 45amp circuit. Cable is available in grey or white sheathing; white is usually preferred, especially if part of the cable is fixed to the surface and if the trailing section between the control unit or switch and the cooker is visible.

Cable route

Having decided on the position for the control unit or switch, which must be within 2m (or 6ft) of the cooker so it can quickly be reached by someone using the cooker, choose the route for the cable. Where the consumer unit is on the same floor as the control unit in the kitchen (as in the conventional house), the simplest route is under the ground floor – assuming this is of timber construction. Run a cable down the wall below the consumer unit and pass it behind the skirting (if any) and into the void of the suspended floor. Feed it under the joists where it can lay unfixed on the sub-floor, and up through a hole drilled in the flooring immediately below the position of the control unit or switch.

If you have a solid ground floor (as in many modern houses), you will have to find an alternative route. This usually means running the cable up the wall above the consumer unit and into the void above the ceiling, under the upstairs floorboards and down through a hole in the ceiling above the control unit or switch. If you adopt this route, you will have to lift floorboards and probably drill through joists.

Where the bathroom – and particularly a combined bathroom/WC – is above the kitchen, you may have problems raising floorboards and the

1

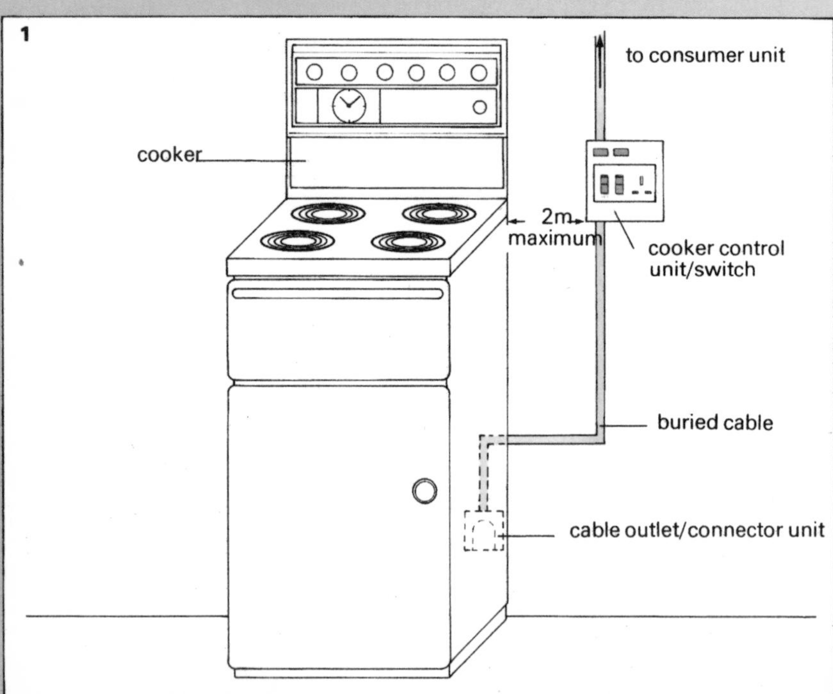

2

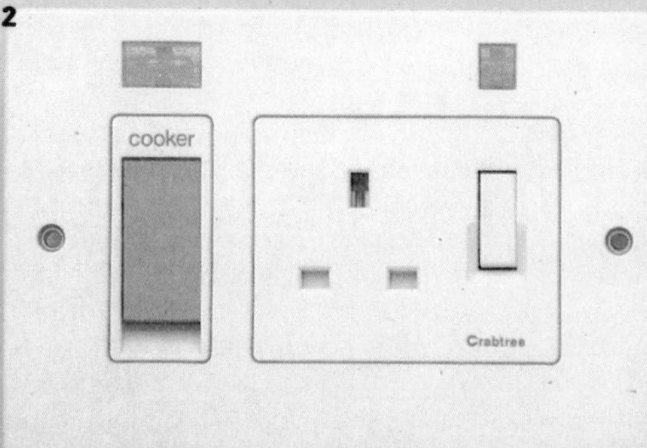

3

4

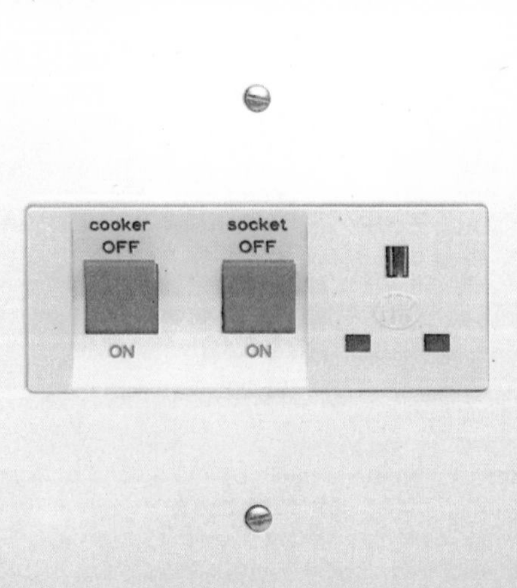

1 The wiring layout for a free-standing cooker. The cable outlet or connector unit is hidden when the cooker is in position against the wall; make sure there is sufficient cable between the cable outlet or connector unit and the cooker to allow the cooker to be pulled forward

2 & 3 Cooker control units (45amp double pole switch and 13amp switched socket outlet) with neon indicators

4 Cooker control unit

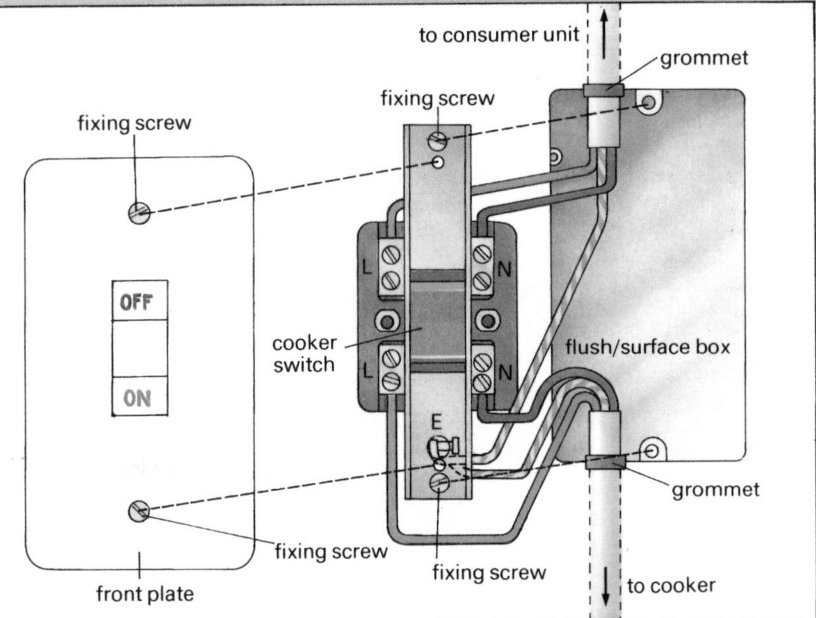

5 Wiring a cooker switch; with the type shown you must remove the front plate from the switch before connecting the cables
6 Cooker control unit
7 45amp double pole cooker switch
8 Cooker control unit (30/50amp)
9 Connector unit

cable route will have to be diverted. Under these conditions it is best to prepare the route before buying the cable, so you can measure the exact length required and save buying too much of this relatively expensive material.

For a single-storey building with a solid floor, the cable can readily be run in the roof space. In a flat which has solid floors and where there is no access to the ceiling above, surface wiring will be necessary. Here the cable can be enclosed in conduits which can be in the form of hollow skirting.

Fitting control unit

Surface-mounted control units are available in two versions. One is all-plastic, with an enclosed back and thin plastic sections which are knocked out to provide entry holes for the cable; it is fixed to the wall with a couple of screws. The second type consists of a square plate, usually metal, which is mounted on a metal box; both are finished in white and the box is fixed to the wall with screws. The box has a selection of knock-out holes fitted with blanks, two of which are knocked out for the cables and fitted with PVC grommets to protect the cable sheathing. A range of smaller, oblong plastic control units is also available; these are mounted on plastic surface boxes or metal flush boxes.

The standard flush-mounted control unit is also of square plate design, mounted on a matching metal box sunk into the wall so it sits flush with the plaster. This box also has knock-out holes for the cable and these must be fitted with PVC grommets. This type is suitable where the cable is buried in the wall; where it is not possible to bury all the cable – such as with a tiled wall – you will have to cut short channels above and below the box to feed in the cable.

A cable trailing down a wall from the control unit to the cooker is not only unsightly, but can also be an obstruction. It can be fixed to the wall with cable clips for most of its length provided the final loop is left free in case you want to pull out the cooker from the wall. However undue strain is likely to occur on the bottom clip and to overcome this you can fit a connector unit.

Connector unit This consists of a terminal block fitted into a metal flush box and a moulded plastic cover plate with an entry hole for the cable. The connector unit is fitted about 1200mm (or 2½ft) above the floor or lower if necessary; the cable running down from the control unit is connected to the terminals, the cable preferably being buried in the wall. The trailing length of cable running from the cooker is also connected to the terminals on the connector unit and the sheathing is clamped to prevent any strain being exerted on the terminals when the cooker is moved out from the wall. If the cooker is changed or temporarily removed, you can disconnect it easily by releasing the cooker cable from these terminals.

Cable outlet unit An alternative arrangement is a cable outlet unit. Here the cable between the control unit and the cooker is not cut, but merely passes through, and is clamped in, the outlet box, which should be positioned behind the cooker.

Connecting control unit

Having fixed the box to the wall with about 200mm (or 8in) of each cable within the box, strip the sheathing off the end of each cable, leaving about 25mm (1in) within the box; strip about 8mm (⅜in) of insulation from the ends of the four current carrying conductors. Slip green/yellow PVC sleeving over the bare earth wires, leaving about 8mm (⅜in) exposed. Connect the red circuit conductor to the mains terminal marked L and the black to the mains terminal marked N. Connect the red conductor of the cooker cable to the load terminal marked L and the black to the load terminal marked N. Connect the two earth conductors to the earth terminal of the control unit. Arrange the wires neatly in the box, fix the switch to the box and screw the cover and

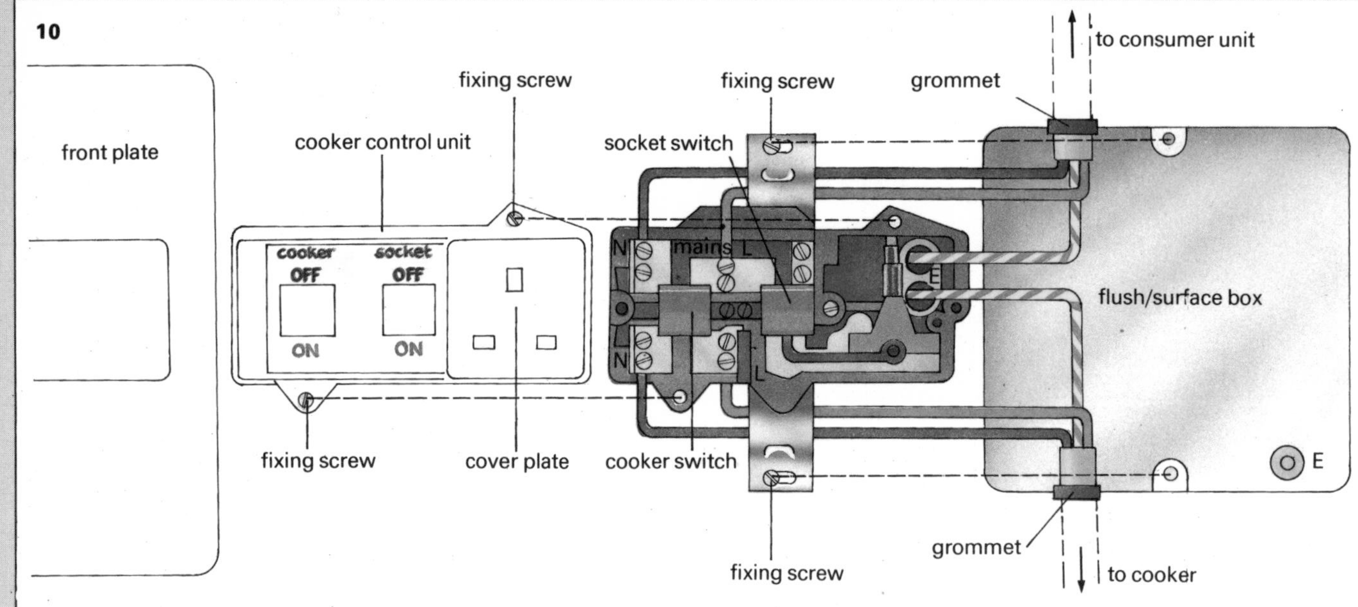

front plates to the switch assembly. Separate cables are not required for the socket outlet since this is connected internally to the cooker terminals.

The method of connection is the same for a cooker switch. With a unit made entirely of plastic, the cables are threaded into the unit with the cover removed and the unit fixed to the wall. The cable connections are then made and the cover replaced.

Connecting to consumer unit

With the mains switched to OFF, remove the consumer unit cover, run the cable into the unit and prepare the end of the conductors as before. The red wire is connected to the fuseway terminal, the black to the neutral terminal bank and the green/yellow PVC-sleeved earth wire to the earth terminal bank. Insert and fix the fuse unit, replace the cover and put the main switch back to ON.

Switch fuse unit Where there is no spare fuseway, you will have to install a separate switch fuse unit consisting of a double pole 60amp mains switch and a fuse unit of 30 or 45amp current rating. Fit the unit near the consumer unit and connect two 3m (or 10ft) lengths of 10sq mm PVC-sheathed cable – a red insulation cable to the L terminal and a black insulation cable to the N terminal. Also connect 6sq mm green/yellow insulated earth cable to the E terminal. The cooker circuit cable is wired to load or circuit terminals as for the consumer unit.

The mains leads are connected to the mains by the Electricity Board. You may also have to fit a two-way service connector box for the two pairs of meter leads you will now have.

Connecting split-level cooker

The same circuit cable from the 30 or 45amp fuseway to the cooker control unit or switch is required for a split-level cooker; the one control will serve both sections provided each is within 2m (or 6ft) of the control unit. If the control unit is fixed midway between the two units, they can be spaced up to 4m (or 12ft) apart, which is adequate for most kitchen layouts. Otherwise a second control unit is required, one being linked to the other using the same size

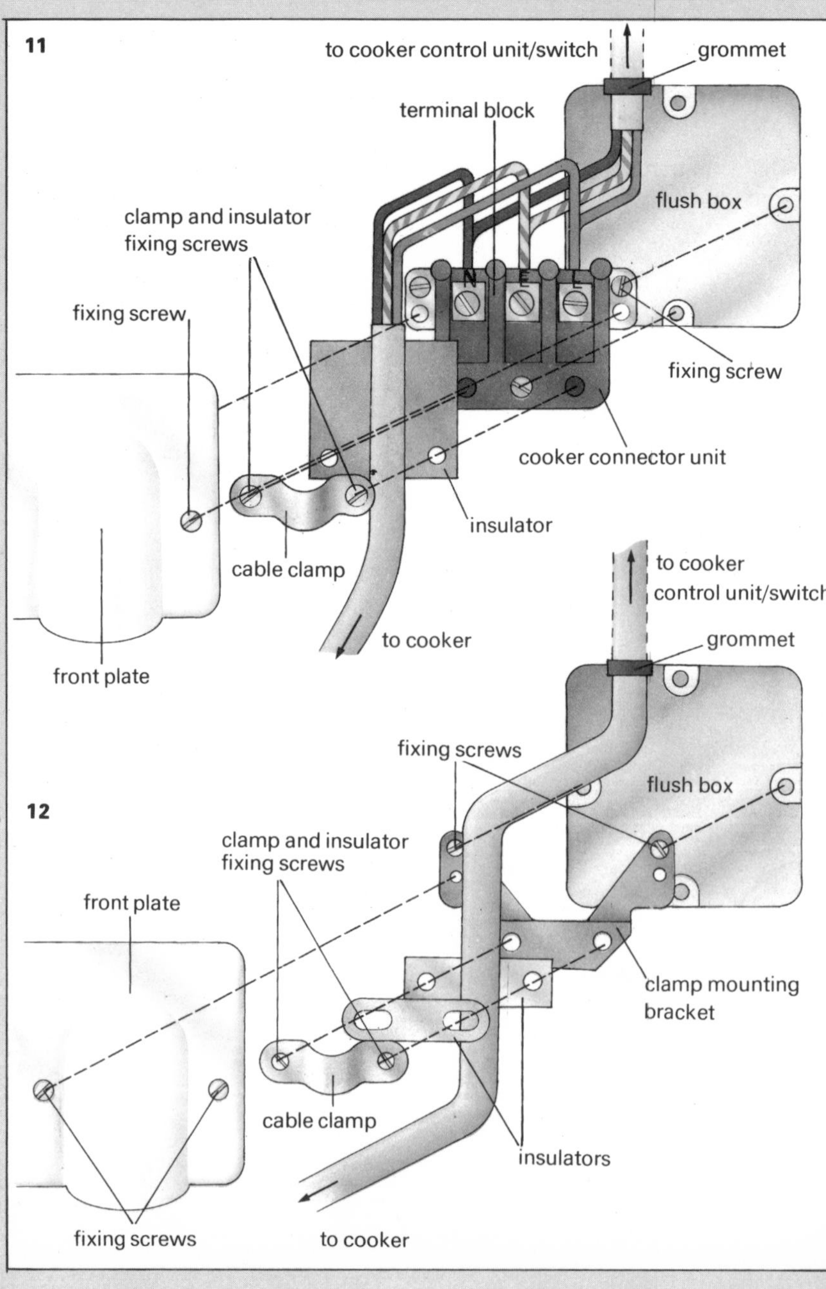

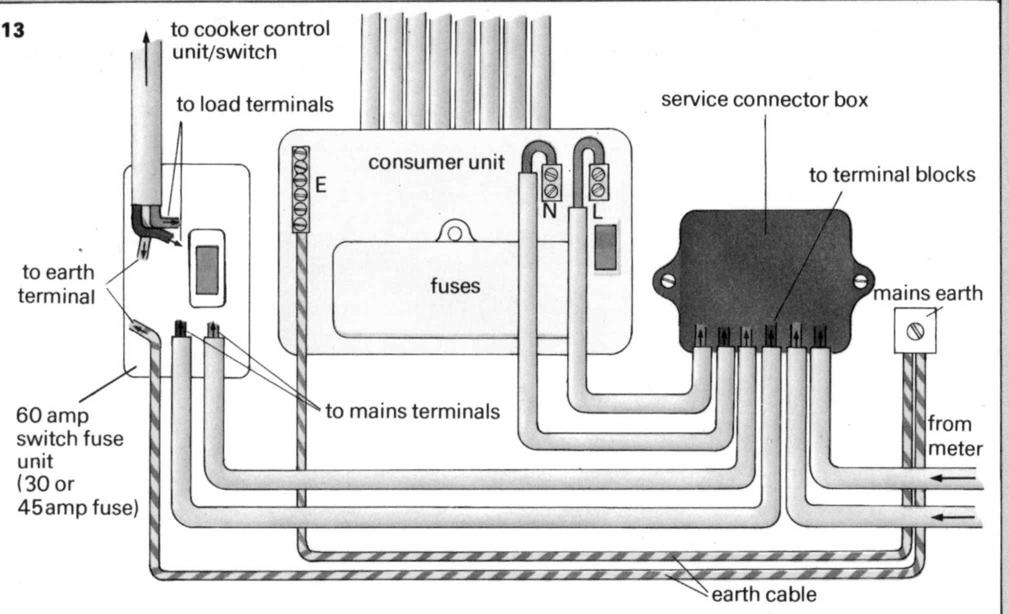

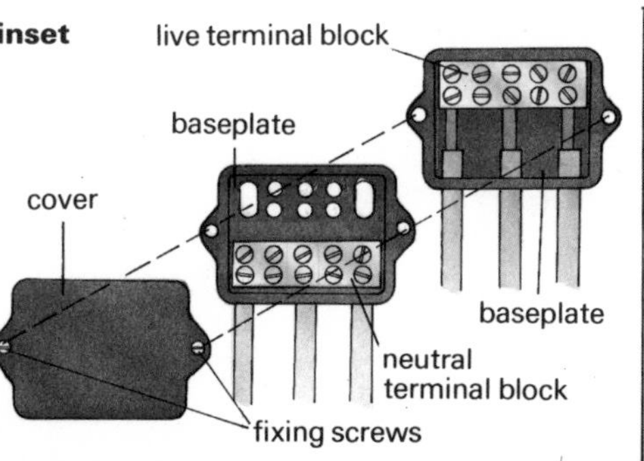

10 Wiring a control unit; remove the front and cover plates before connecting the cables. **11** Wiring a connector unit; use a box with four mounting lugs. **12** Connecting a cable outlet unit. **13** Connecting to the mains if there is no spare fuseway in the consumer unit; the wiring at the service connector box (**inset**). **14** The wiring for a split level cooker supplied from one control unit or switch between the two sections. **15** The wiring for a split level cooker supplied from one control unit or switch at one side of the two sections. **16** The wiring for a split level cooker supplied from two control units or switches looped together by the circuit cable

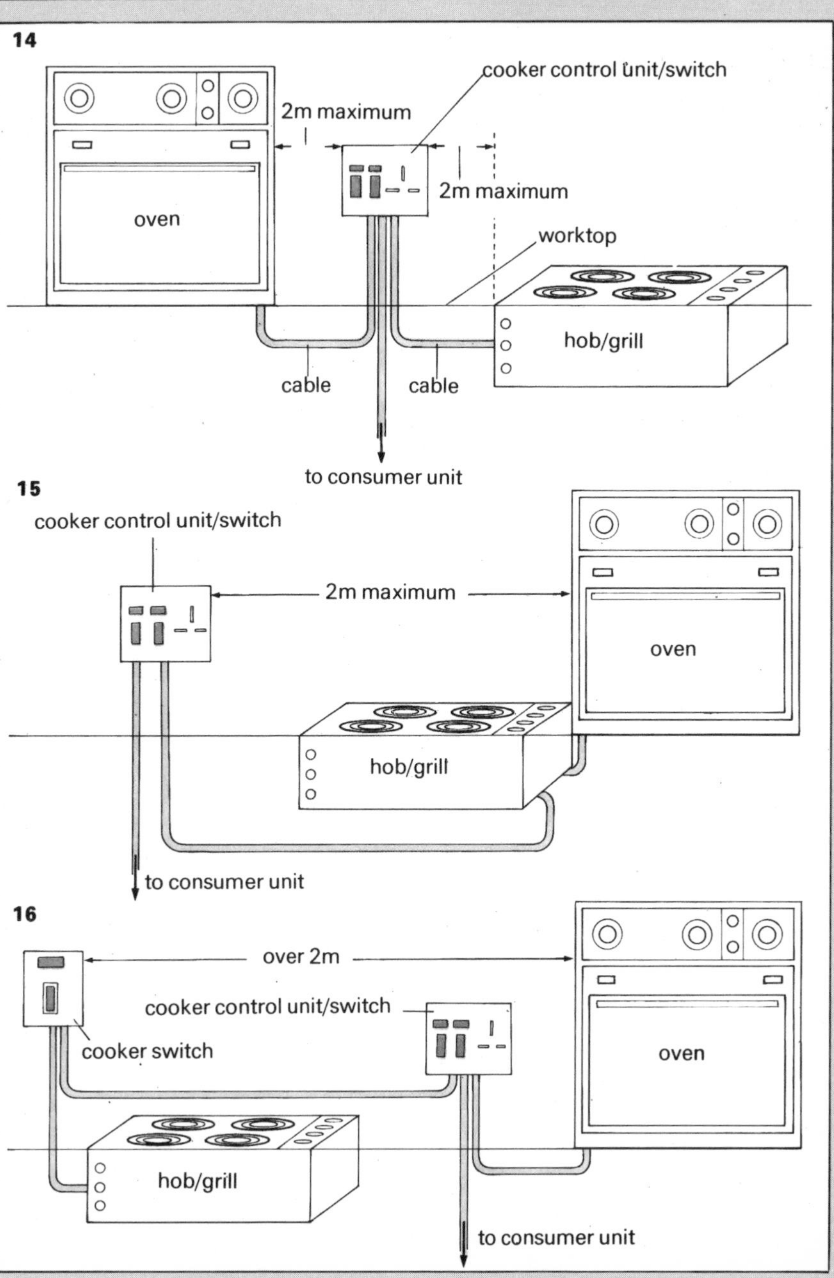

:able as for the circuit.

Where, as in most cases, the one control unit is to erve both sections of a split-level cooker, you can either run two cables from the load side of the control unit – one to each section – or, depending on he relative positions, you can run one cable to the nearer of the two sections and then run a cable from he terminals of the nearer one to the other section.

Every cable must be of the same size as the main circuit cable, even though one or both may carry ess than the total current. The reason for this is hat, with no intervening fuse, the cable rating is determined by the rating of the circuit fuse.

The cables being run direct to the sections of a split-level cooker can be fixed to the surface or buried in the wall to suit individual requirements.

Connecting small cookers

Microwave cookers, which are becoming increasingly popular in the home, have loadings around 500 watts and are fitted with flex to be run off a 13amp fused plug and socket outlet. These, therefore, need no special circuit. The same applies to baby cookers, which have a maximum loading of 3kW.

Choosing and fitting cooker hoods

There are basically two types of cooker hood – recirculating and ducted. There are also models which are suitable for either recirculation or for direct extraction from the rear or top via ducting to the outside air. With one make of this type there is a wall grille as an optional extra. Each hood is fitted with a fire shield which is kept open during normal use by a fusible cord; this 'fuses' in the event of a cooking fat fire and releases the shield.

Apart from a filter to catch dust and grease and, in the case of a recirculating hood, a charcoal filter to catch smells, cooker hoods contain one or more fans and most models incorporate one or more electric lamps to illuminate the hob during cooking. Fans can be either two-speed or three-speed where there is an extra boost speed besides low and normal. Switches, together with a neon indicator, are positioned in front of the hood for easy access and operation.

Buying cooker hoods

The position of the cooker hood and the amount of trouble to which you are prepared to go in installing it are among the factors which you should consider when buying a hood. A recirculating hood is simply screwed to the wall or underside of a kitchen cabinet; since no outlet to the outside air is required the hood can be fitted to any wall providing a suitable fixing, giving scope for planning. Where smells and steam are particularly troublesome, a ducted hood is preferable; but ideally this type of hood should be positioned against an outside wall using a short length of ducting which passes through a hole cut into the wall behind or just above the hood. An inside wall, however, should not be completely ruled out; although the ducting should be as short as possible, lengths up to 6m (or 20ft) can be installed with the ducting fixed to a vertical exhaust in the hood and run up and over to a hole cut in the outside wall. In this case bear in mind you will have to conceal the ducting.

Cooker hoods must be positioned at the correct height for efficient and safe operation. It is generally recommended the hood is positioned 600–900mm (or 24–36in) above a hob or 400–600mm (or 16–24in) above an eye-level grill or top oven; but always follow manufacturer's instructions on this. The hood should be positioned as near as possible to the minimum height for maximum efficiency in operation.

When fixing a cooker hood above an eye-level grill if a special mounting bracket is not provided, it is an advantage to use a mounting block 100–125mm (4–5in) thick to site the hood further away from the wall and prevent the airflow being obstructed by the grill.

Warning Remember, where your cooker has an eye-level grill, the cooker hood should be operated at all times when the grill is used; otherwise the heat from the grill could damage the hood.

Size of hoods Cooker hoods are made in a number of sizes and your choice will depend upon the width of the cooker, since the hood must give adequate cover of the hob. A size which covers most British made standard cookers is 600mm (or 24in); for wider cookers there is a 900mm (or 36in) hood.

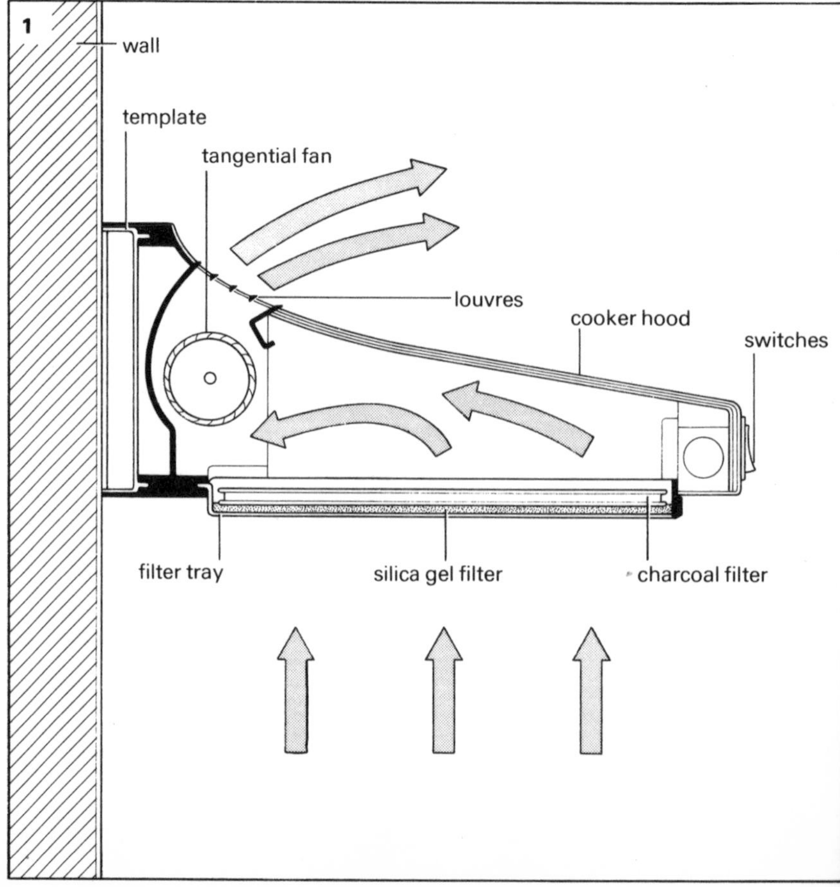

Besides these two sizes, at least one make of cooker hood is available in smaller and intermediate sizes of 550mm (or 22in) and 700mm (or 28in) as well.

Fan and lights Two-speed models have a single tangential fan located at the rear of the hood to give maximum stability and are powered by a two-speed motor; three-speed models have two tangential motors which provide three-speed facilities. Lighting may be with a single lamp which is sometimes fluorescent; some models have two lamps. The fans and lights are switched independently with the fans having multi-switch controls.

Hood finishes White and brushed aluminium are the most popular finishes, but hoods are also available in a variety of other finishes including stainless steel, teak veneer and oak veneer.

Installing cooker hoods

The type of installation work required will depend on the model you have chosen. General guidance for fitting typical models is given below, but you should always check with the manufacturer's instructions.

Fitting recirculating models

A template with relevant fixing instructions is usually provided with each hood. A hood can be screwed directly to the wall or fitted to the underside of a kitchen cabinet. It is sometimes necessary to reinforce the cabinet fixings; so if you decide to fix the hood to a cabinet, first check these fixings. Also make sure the wall construction will provide proper support for the hood fixing screws.

Fitting ducted models

These can also be fixed directly to the wall and some models can be fixed to the underside of a suitable cabinet using the template where provided. Check the cabinet fixings before fitting the hood.

You will need a ducting kit and a length of ducting. One typical kit contains a rectangular-to-round adaptor to connect the rectangular outlet in the hood to the round ducting, a louvre flap for the outside and duct sealing tape. The items in this kit are designed for attaching to 125mm (5in) diameter flexible ducting, although the size of ducting required varies; for example, another type of hood requires 100mm (4in) ducting. When ordering ducting from your supplier, buy it slightly longer than required.

The duct is fitted to the rearwards exhaust in the hood or to the vertical exhaust, depending on the location of the outlet hole cut in the outside wall and the route of the duct. To fit a duct to the rearwards exhaust of a hood which is either wall or cabinet-mounted using the ducting kit described above, first make a hole in the wall on the centre line of the hood outlet to take the 125mm (5in) diameter ducting. Open up the hood, remove the back blanking plate and fit the outlet in position. Connect one end of the ducting to the circular side of the adaptor and tape the joint to ensure an air-tight seal. Push the ducting into the hole in the wall so the fixing plate on the adaptor is flush with the inside wall surface. Make good the plaster and cement round the ducting on the outside wall surface. Fit the foam seal onto the adaptor, locate the cooker hood outlet on the adaptor and fix it to the wall or cabinet. Fit the louvre onto the outside end of the ducting and seal round the joint with mastic or putty. Fit the louvre flaps where relevant.

To fit a duct to the vertical exhaust of a hood which is either cabinet or wall-mounted, using the same type of kit, first make a hole suitable for the ducting on the centre line of the vertical outlet. The

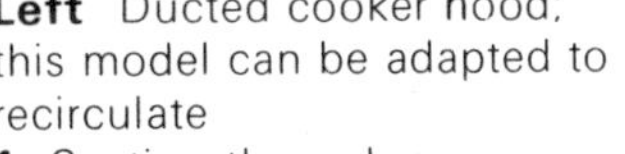

Left Ducted cooker hood; this model can be adapted to recirculate
1 Section through a recirculating cooker hood, showing the tangential fan, different filters and the direction of air flow
Below Recirculating cooker hood

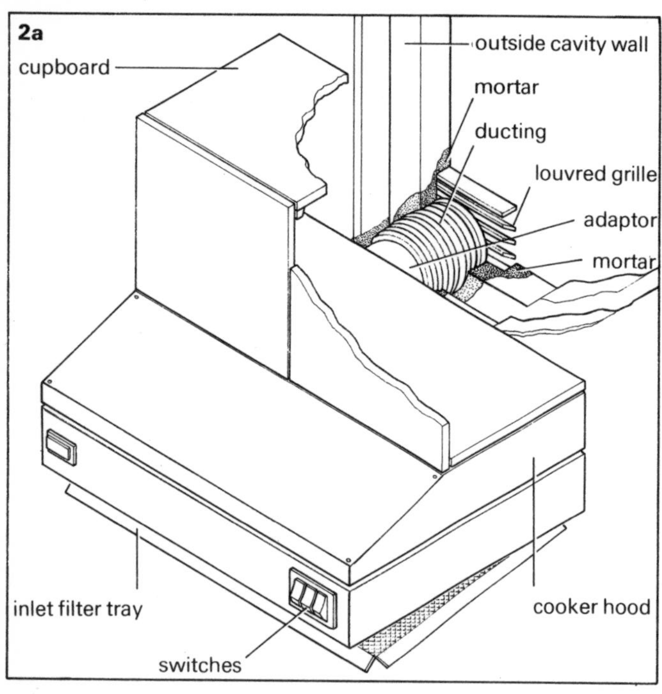

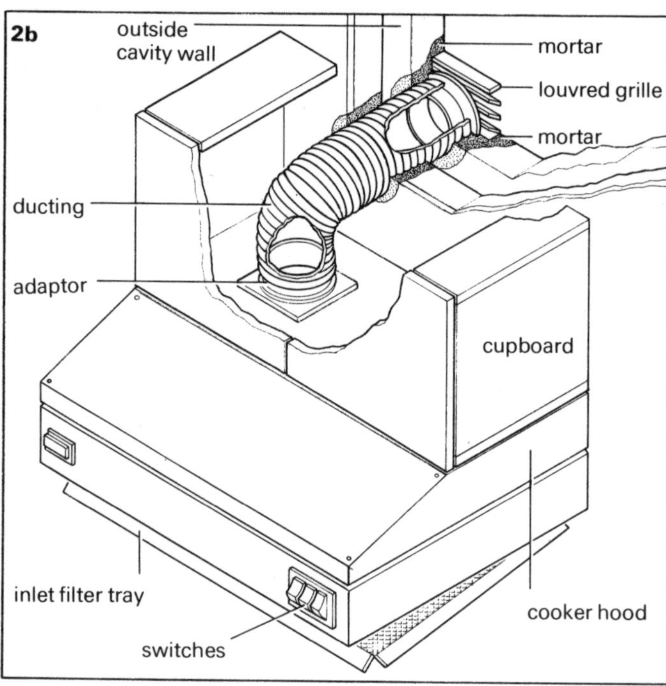

2a Fitting the duct to the rear exhaust of a cabinet-mounted cooker hood
2b Fitting the duct to the vertical exhaust

hole should be at least 200mm (8in) above the top of the hood so the bend in the ducting will not be too tight. When mounting on a cabinet, cut a hole in the cabinet base using the hood or template (if supplied) as a guide. Remove the top blanking plate and fit the outlet in place. Connect the adaptor to the outlet and fix the hood to the wall or cabinet base. Push one end of the ducting through the hole in the wall and bend the other end down onto the adaptor, making sure the bend has a minimum inside radius of 125mm (5in). Tape the joint, make good the wall and fit the louvre in place as before.

Warning Make sure you do not kink flexible ducting since this will restrict the air flow and could fracture the walls of the ducting; keep the number of bends to a minimum and make them with as large a radius as possible. Take care to seal all joints well and keep the length of ducting to a minimum – in any case below 6m (or 20ft). Whenever possible don't exhaust into a prevailing wind or into existing flues if there is any danger of fumes re-entering the house at another point.

Assembling the hood

To assemble the hood and fit the filters on a typical model, you should first remove the filter tray according to the manufacturer's instructions. Make sure the grease filter completely covers the holes in the grille, remove all internal packing pieces and refit the filter tray. Detach the outlet grille and remove any packing pieces and the plastic bags from the charcoal filter(s). Shake the filter(s) to remove any loose dust generated during transit. When refitting the filter(s) and grille, make sure the filter completely covers the holes in the grille and the charcoal is evenly distributed within the filter(s).

Wiring up the hood

The electrical loading of a cooker hood ranges from about 80 to 220 watts depending on the size and number of fans and lights; but the loading is never more than 250 watts for a domestic model, which means a hood can be supplied from a 5amp circuit or a spur from a ring main with a 3amp fused outlet.

A suitable outlet is a 13amp switched fused connection unit, fused at 3amps, fixed close by the cooker hood and connected to it by 0.75sq mm three core PVC circular sheathed flexible cord. The fused connection unit can be supplied from a spur cable looped out of the ring main at the terminals of a nearby 13amp socket outlet using 2.5sq mm twin core and earth PVC-sheathed cable. Replace the 13amp cartridge fuse in the connection unit by one of 3amp rating. You could supply the cooker hood from a lighting circuit, providing an earth connection is available, but this is not recommended since it can cause an overload.

Cooker hoods have neon indicators to show when they are switched on, so an indicator on the connection unit is not necessary. A 13amp fused plug and socket outlet may be fitted in place of the connection unit.

Warning On no account put articles on a cooker hood and don't leave the cooker rings on when not covered by pans, since this may impair the efficiency of the filters and the cooker hood.

Maintaining cooker hoods

Make sure the cooker hood is switched off before cleaning it with warm water containing a mild detergent such as washing-up liquid; don't use too much water. Activated charcoal filters are effective for 12–18 months depending on use and replacements are available from the hood manufacturer. When renewing them, take the opportunity to wipe clean the inside of the cooker hood. The grease and foam filters should be washed about once a month; allow them to dry before replacing in the hood. Use a soft, short-haired brush to clean the impeller and the outlet grille, together with the circular motor cooling vent.

Before replacing any parts on a cooker hood, disconnect it from the electricity supply by removing the circuit fuse. To replace a lamp, follow the manufacturer's instructions and use the same type and size of lamp or tube as the original. Faults occurring in a cooker hood should be repaired by a qualified electrician or the hood returned to the manufacturer for repair.

Installing night storage heaters

Storage heaters are a relatively efficient method of supplying heat in the home; because heat is stored, you do not have to provide a continuous supply of energy. After the initial supply needed to provide the heat for storage, the electricity can be switched off and heat will still be emitted. There are various makes of storage heater available and these are of two types: storage radiators and storage fan heaters.

Storage radiators

The storage radiator is simply blocks of heat storage material into which is inserted a spiral element; the blocks are enclosed in a metal casing which comes in various finishes. Traditionally, concrete bricks have been used for the heat storage material, but now other lighter, more efficient materials are used. There are layers of insulation material between the storage blocks and the metal casing to control the amount of radiant heat emitted from the casing; this ensures the output is extended over many hours instead of being expelled in a short time.

During the day the rate of heat output gradually drops, although many models of storage radiator have a mechanical boost device which when opened (manually or automatically) in the evening lets out more heat until most of the heat has been transferred from the storage blocks into the room. Once the storage blocks have received their full charge of heat, there are no means by which you can control the output. You can, however, vary the quantity of heat charged overnight by adjusting an

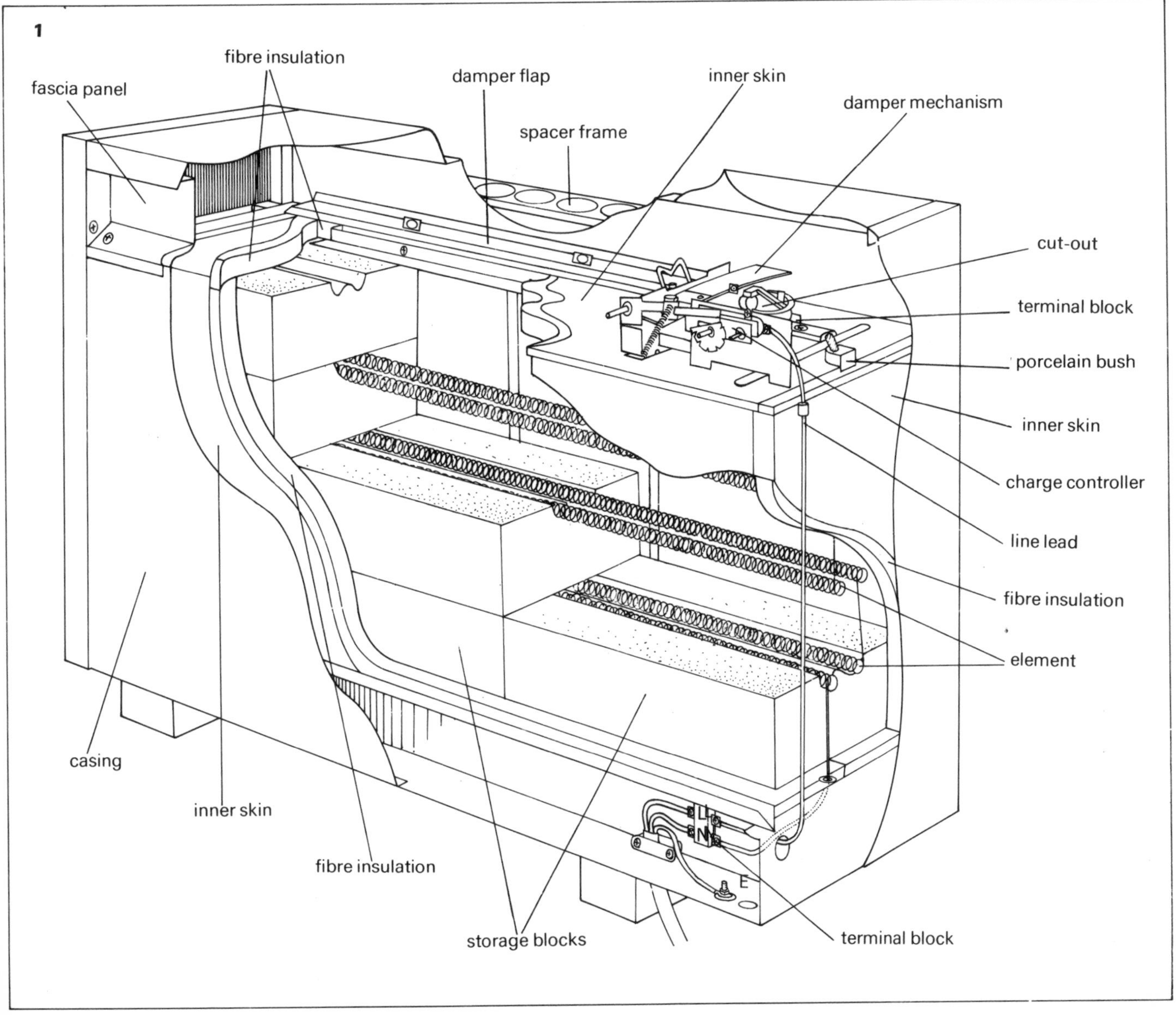

1 Cut-away of a night storage radiator, showing the relevant component parts

input control. In colder weather the input control can be left at its maximum setting, while in milder weather the input control can be turned down to reduce the heat output and save electricity.

Storage radiators are made with a number of electrical loadings ranging from 1.2kW to 3.3kW. The loading represents the amount of heat stored and therefore the number or size of storage blocks and the overall dimensions of the casing; but it is not the rate of heat output. Stored heat is conveniently quoted in kWh (kilowatt hours). A heater of 1.2kW loading can store up to a maximum of 9.6kWh in eight hours (1.2 × 8) and a 3.3kW heater can store up to 26.4kWh in an eight hour switch-on period. Smaller size heaters are suitable for the hall or small rooms and the larger sizes for larger rooms; for an average size room a 2kW storage radiator which can store up to 16kWh is suitable. The heat output rate is about half the charge rate; this is because the heater is off-charge for 16 hours.

Radiator circuit wiring

Because all the storage radiators in the house are generally switched on at the same time with no diversity of use, they are not supplied from plugs and sockets like direct acting heaters. Instead they are supplied from separate circuits switched by the Board's time switch. These are run from a separate consumer unit from that which supplies general services such as lighting, socket outlets, cooking and water heating. A separate unit is necessary because it has to be time-controlled so the circuits to the heaters are energized only during the overnight off-peak period.

The size, or number of fuseways, of the consumer unit depends upon the number of storage heaters installed, the number of radial circuits and, in some cases, the number of heaters connected to one radial. It should be at least a four way unit and preferably a six way unit, since even if you are starting with two storage radiators you may wish to add more later. Also, if you have an immersion heater, it is usually financially worthwhile to connect this to one fuseway in the time-controlled consumer unit to take advantage of the cheaper rate of electricity overnight. You should, however, make arrangements for an optional daytime boost, which normally means you will need a second immersion heater or a dual immersion heater with one element connected to the 24-hour supply.

Each single storage heater circuit is wired in twin core and earth PVC-sheathed cable, fused and rated according to the heater loading, and terminating at a 20amp double pole switch fixed about 300mm (or 1ft) above floor level near the radiator controls. It is common practice to use 2.5sq mm size conductors protected by a 15amp fuse and taking a load of up to 3kW. The radiator is connected to the switch by three core flex passing through a cord outlet. The switch is of the same dimensions as a one gang socket and needs the same depth of box. It can be either surface-mounted, using a plastic surface box, or flush-mounted on a one gang box sunk into the wall flush with the plaster.

Connecting the box and switch Remove a cable knock-out blank; if it is a metal flush box, you will need to fit a PVC grommet to protect the cable from rubbing against the metal. Run the cable into the box and fix the box – if it is flush-mounted, you will have to cut out the wall to sink the box flush.

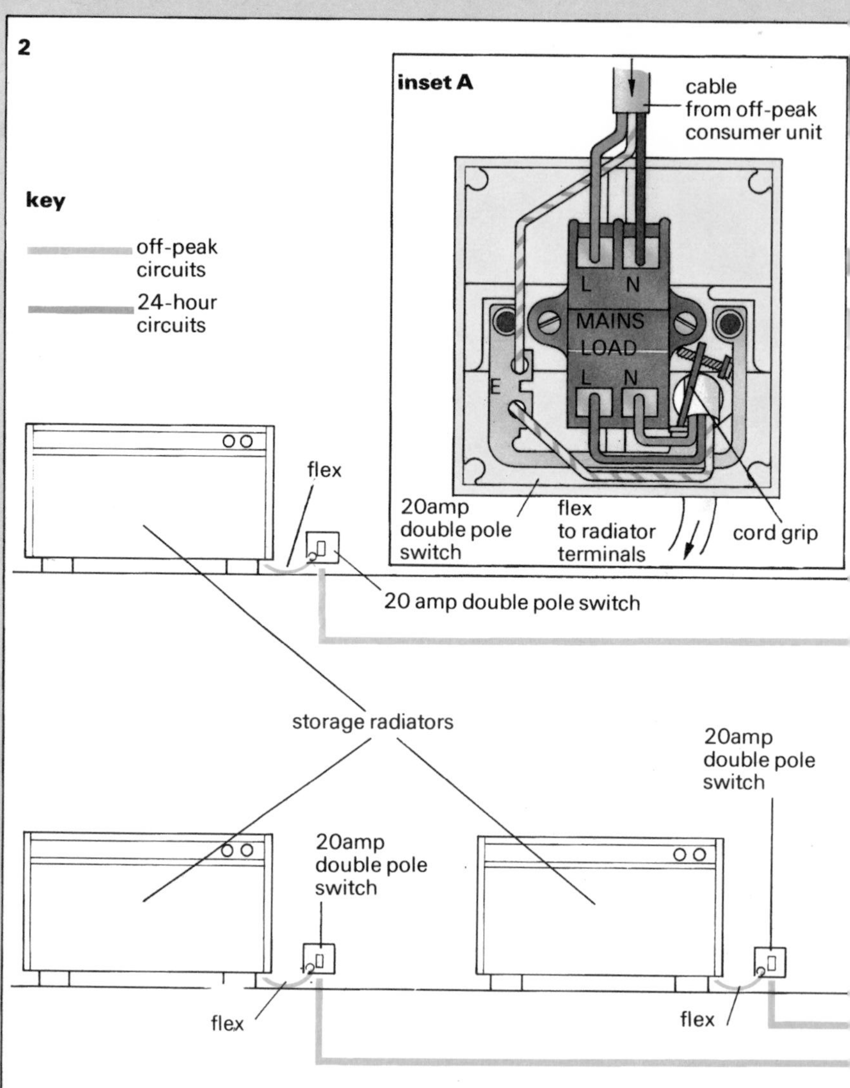

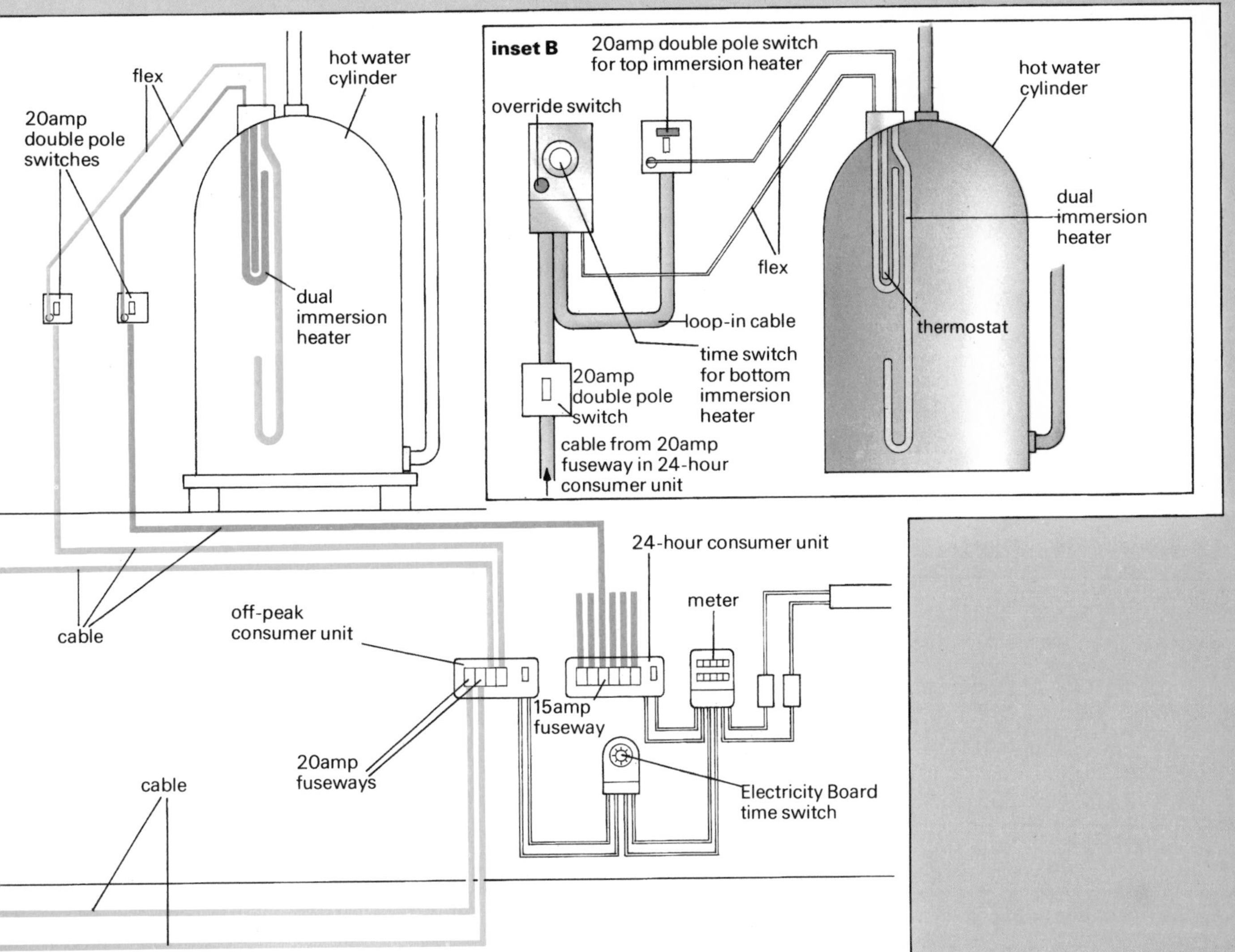

2 Circuit diagram for storage radiators and an immersion heater; the immersion heater switches are wired in the same way as the radiator switch (**inset A**). The bottom immersion heater is connected to the off-peak circuit and the top one to the 24-hour circuit. Alternatively, for large quantities of hot water during the day, the time switch can be set to the off-peak period and connected to the bottom immersion heater. The override switch can be used to heat up the entire contents of the cylinder during the day. The 20amp double pole switch is wired to the top immersion heater and can be used as a daytime booster for small amounts of hot water (**inset B**). **Above left** 25amp twin double pole switch. **Far left** 20amp double pole switch with flex outlet. **Left** White meter

Prepare the ends of the cable by stripping off the sheathing and about 9mm (or $\frac{3}{8}$in) of insulation from the two current carrying conductors and slipping green/yellow PVC sleeving over the bare earth wire. Connect the red insulated conductor to the mains terminal L, the black to the mains terminal N and the green/yellow sleeved earth wire to the earth terminal E in the box. If at this stage the storage radiator is in position, you can also connect its flexible cord to the switch; if not, fix the switch to the box using the screws supplied.

When you connect the flexible cord to the double pole switch, thread it into the flex outlet hole with the switch removed from its box and strip about 100mm (4in) of sheathing from its end, exposing the three cores coloured brown, blue and green/yellow. Strip off about 9mm (or $\frac{3}{8}$in) of insulation from the exposed end of the conductors. Connect the brown wire to the load terminal L, the blue to the load terminal N and the earth to the terminal E alongside the existing earth terminal. Then fix the switch to the box using the screws supplied.

Connecting the consumer unit Install the consumer unit as already described earlier in the book. Remove the cover of the unit and dismantle as much of it as necessary. Fix the frame or casing to the wall fairly close to the existing 24-hour consumer unit and meter, using a backing sheet of non-combustible material if the unit is open-backed. Run the circuit cables into the unit and prepare the ends for connection by removing the necessary amount of sheathing and insulation. Connect the red insulated wires to the fuseway terminals, the black insulated wires to the neutral terminal bank and the green/yellow sleeved earth wires to the earth terminal bank. Connect a 1m (or 3ft) length of 10sq mm red PVC-insulated single core cable to the mains terminal L, a 1m (or 3ft) length of 10sq mm black insulated cable to the mains terminal N and a 1m (or 3ft) length of green/yellow insulated 6sq mm cable to the earth terminal bank. The Electricity Board will connect the two mains leads to a white meter and time switch and you should connect the earthing lead to the mains earth terminal.

Installing a single storage radiator Ideally, even one heater should be connected to the Board's time switch, but it can be operated from any ring circuit 13amp socket. You will, however, need a time switch to limit the charge period to eight hours. This can be a plug-in time switch, which has a socket outlet into which you plug the storage heater. You can use the white meter tariff and set the time switch to coincide with the cheap rate period. The time switch has an over-ride switch which enables the heater to be given a boost charge in the evening when needed, but at a higher rate for the electricity used. This is more satisfactory than using a direct acting heater for a short period since any heat not used goes towards the night charge.

Storage fan heaters

A storage fan heater resembles in appearance a storage radiator, but it is generally larger and has an inlet and outlet grille. The fan heater is normally of a higher loading and contains a tangential fan. This draws in cold air which passes through ducting in the storage casing and over the storage blocks, where it is heated and expelled as controlled temperature warm air into the room.

These heaters have more thermal insulation than storage radiators, so only a small proportion of heat is emitted as radiant heat via the casing. This often combats condensation without wasting a lot of heat. The heater section is energized only during the eight-hour overnight period when the cheaper rate for electricity applies. Heat is emitted only when the fan is running; to enable the fan to be switched on at any time, the fan circuit is connected to the 24-hour electricity supply. This means the supply will be at a more expensive rate (except at night); but since the fan consumes less current than the average electric lamp, this is usually not significant in terms of cost.

Fan heater circuit wiring

As with storage radiators, the heater section of this type of appliance is supplied from a time-controlled consumer unit. The circuit is wired in twin core and earth PVC-sheathed cable with each cable starting at a separate fuseway in the consumer unit; the usual cable size is 4sq mm with fusing of 20 or 25 amps. However, instead of terminating at a 20amp double pole switch, the cable terminates in a 25amp twin switch fixed close to the storage heater.

The circuit to the fan is run in 1.5 or 1.0sq mm twin core and earth PVC-sheathed cable. Where more than one storage fan heater is being installed, all fans can be supplied from one 5amp circuit. This circuit can be run separately from a 5amp fuseway in the general services consumer unit on the 24-hour supply or it can be supplied from a spur on the ring circuit via a fused connection unit connected to the ring cable and fitted with a 3amp fuse. This circuit cable also runs into the 25amp twin switch and, when supplying other fans of storage fan heaters, is looped in and out of the twin switch. For a maximum of two fans, you can run the circuit cable from an existing 5amp fuseway supplying a lighting circuit; but it is usually more convenient to run it off the ring circuit. If you decide to do this, you should locate a 13amp socket outlet fairly close to one heater.

The fused connection unit is linked to the socket outlet by a short length of 2.5sq mm twin core and earth cable and may be mounted on a one gang box

3 Cut-away of a storage fan radiator, showing the relevant component parts.
4 Circuit diagram for storage fan heaters and the connections for the 25amp twin double pole switch (**inset**)

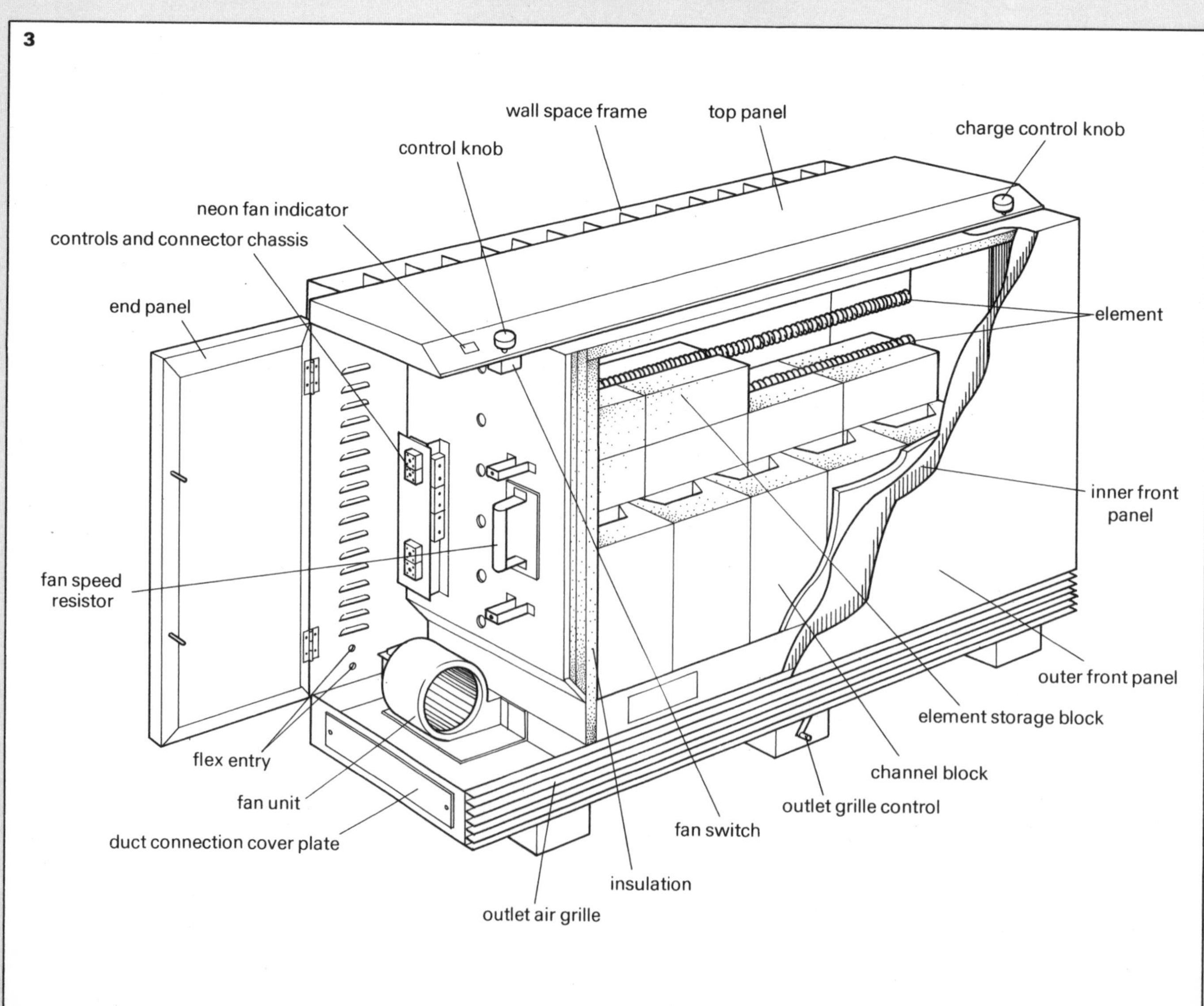

fixed adjacent to the socket outlet. Alternatively you can mount a one gang socket and fused connection unit on a dual box, which is slightly wider than a two gang outlet box and has two extra fixing lugs at the centre for the fixing screws of both accessories. If the existing socket is flush-mounted, you should remove the existing one gang box and cut out a larger chase for the dual box in the wall. If the existing socket outlet is surface-mounted, you will find replacing a plastic box presents little difficulty. If there is a two gang socket, you will have to mount the fused connection unit separately.

Installing the switch After you have run the circuit cables under the floorboards – and with two cables at each storage heater switch position – you can fix the 25amp twin switch. The unit has two separate switches both operated by a single rocker; this is so it meets safety regulation requirements that all poles of circuits at a heater must be capable of being isolated from the mains by the operation of a single switch. The switchplate has two cord outlets; one is for the heater flex which is connected to the switch marked 'heater' and the other is for the fan circuit flex which is connected to the switch marked 'fan'. There is a choice of surface or flush-mounting and the switch is available with or without neon indicators. A special flush-mounted box is required to take the switch, so buy this at the same time.

Remove two knock-out blanks for the cables; if using a flush metal box, fit the necessary PVC grommets. Thread in the two cables and fix the box to the wall using screws in plugged holes. If you are using a flush box, you will have to cut a chase into the wall so, when it is fixed, the box is flush with the plaster. Prepare the ends of the cable by removing the sheath but leave about 25mm (1in) within the box. Strip about 9mm (or ⅜in) of insulation from the four insulated wires, connect the red and black wires of the heater circuit cable to the mains terminals L and N respectively of the heater switch and the red and black wires of the fan circuit cable to the mains terminals L and N respectively of the fan switch.

Thread in the two flexible cords from the heater and strip about 150mm (6in) of sheathing from the end of each and about 9mm (or ⅜in) of insulation from the six wires. Connect the brown and blue wires of the heater flex to the load terminals L and N of the heater switch and the brown and blue wires of the fan flex to the load terminals L and N respectively of the fan switch. Connect the two green/yellow sleeved earth circuit wires and the two green/yellow insulated flex wires to the four earthing terminals. Neatly arrange all the wires in the box and fix the switch to the box using the screws supplied with the switch.

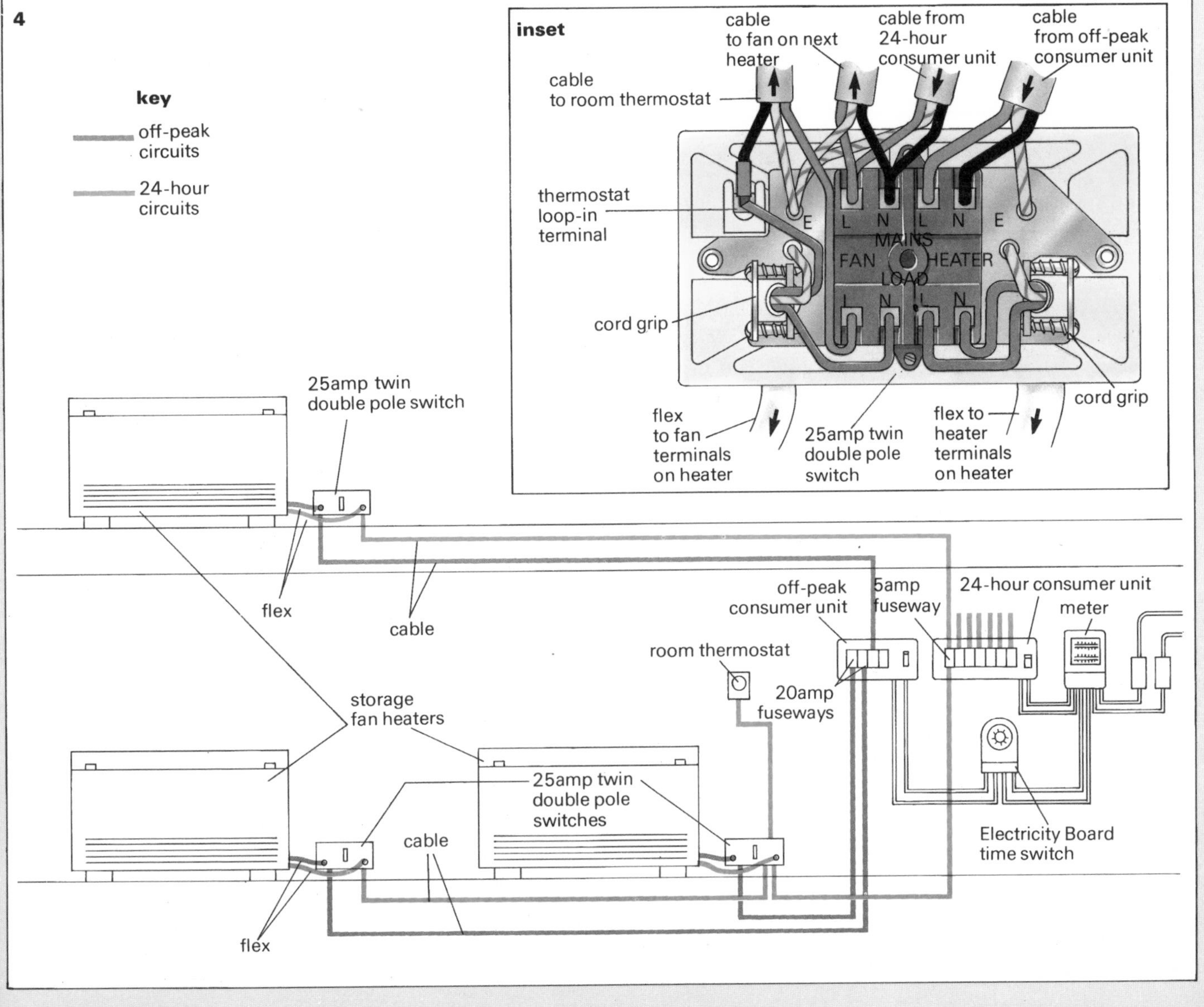

Immersion heaters

One great advantage of an immersion heater fitted to your hot water cylinder is that it can be used to supply as much or as little hot water around the home as you need at any particular time. It can also supplement other heating systems such as gas, oil or solid fuel. With care, you can fit it yourself.

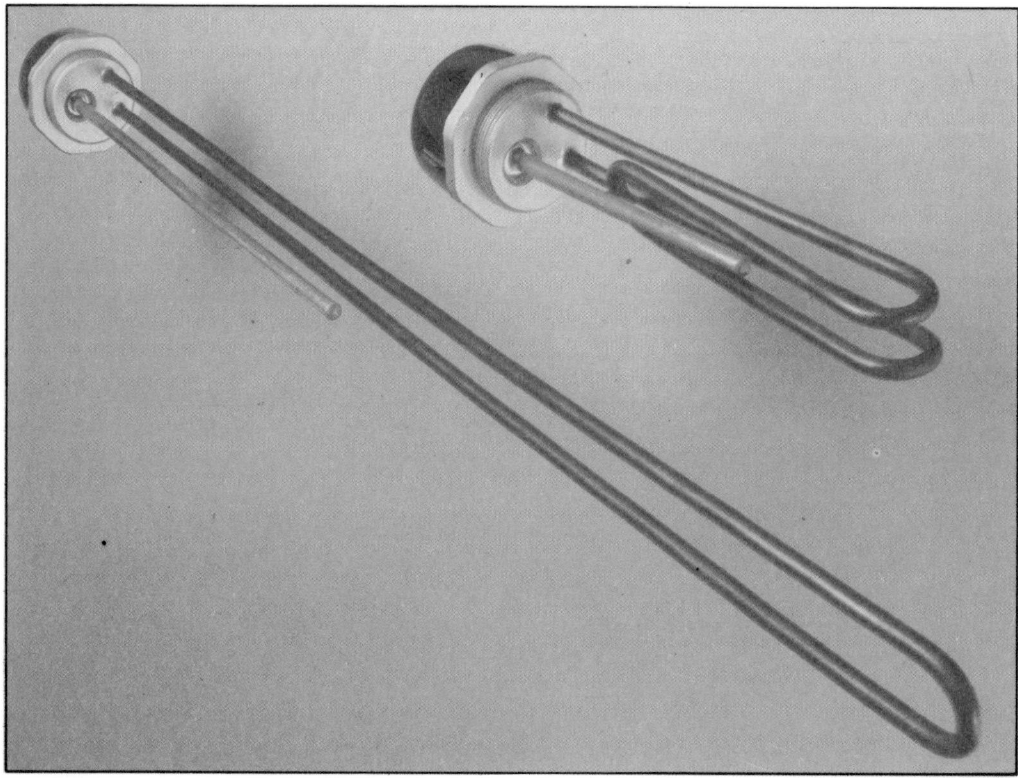

Left Immersion heaters are available in different lengths. You can buy a dual-element model, which heats either the top or all of the cylinder, or a single element one. If you decide on the single heater, you will find it is more economical to fit two, one at the top of the cylinder and the other lower down near the bottom

1 Types of immersion heater shown fitted into the hot water cylinder

1a Single element in varying lengths to suit different size cylinders

1b Separate heaters can be fitted so the top of the cylinder is heated for small amounts of water and all the cylinder heated when larger amounts are needed

1c The dual-element heater does the same job, but has the advantage of being a single fitting

1 Types of immersion heater

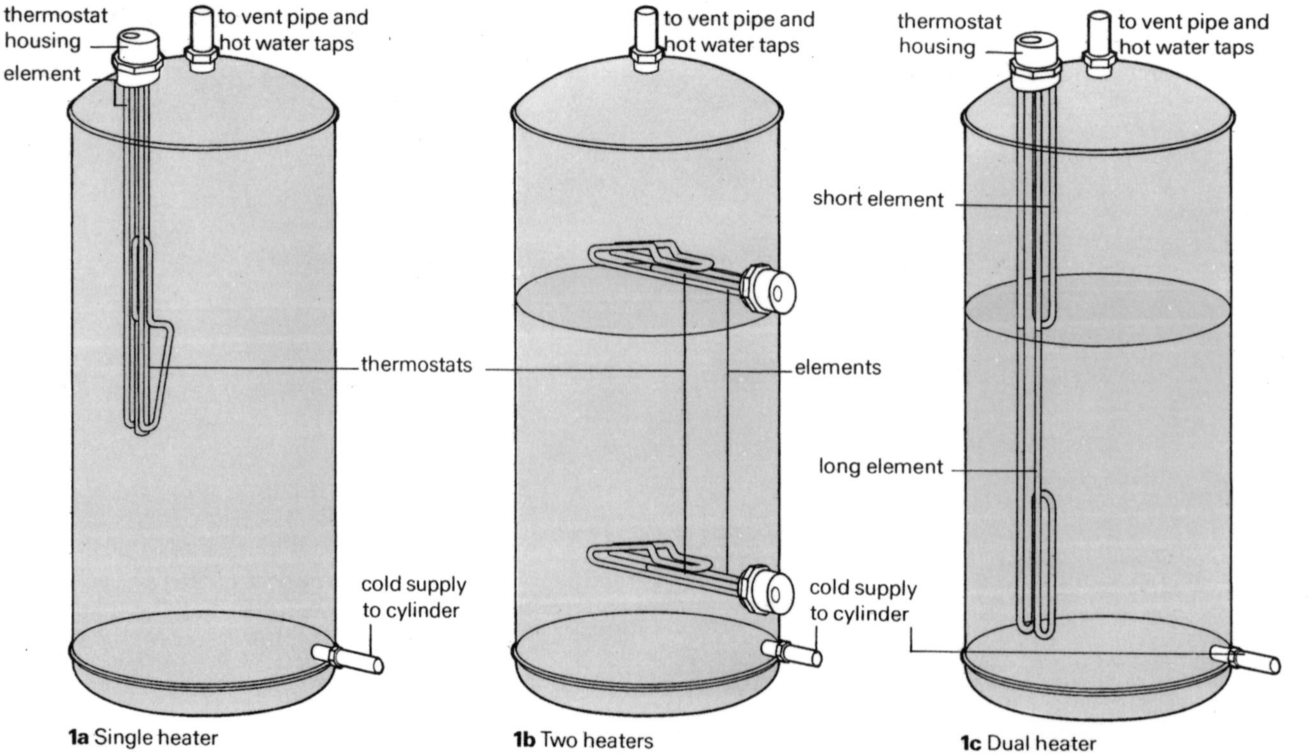

thermostat housing
element
to vent pipe and hot water taps
thermostats
cold supply to cylinder

1a Single heater

to vent pipe and hot water taps
elements
cold supply to cylinder

1b Two heaters

thermostat housing
to vent pipe and hot water taps
short element
long element

1c Dual heater

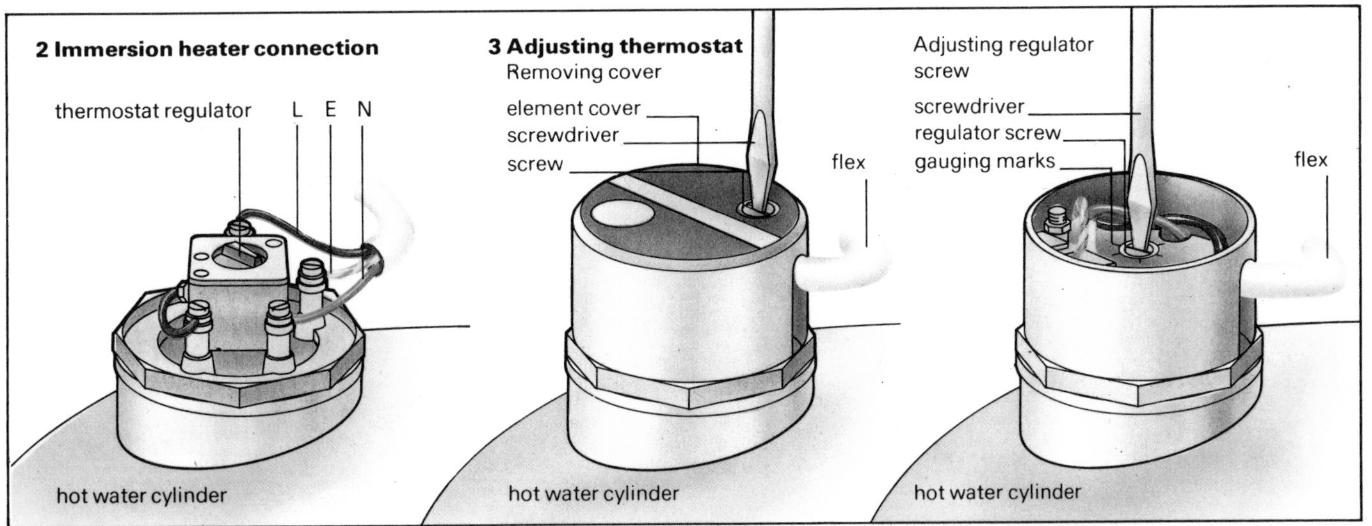

One of the most convenient methods of supplying hot water in the home is by installing an immersion heater in your hot water cylinder, although it is a fairly expensive form of heating to run if used constantly. Heaters are made in a range of lengths and loadings to suit the different types of cylinder and to give varying quantities of hot water. On some the heating element is coated with a titanium sheath; this is specially for use in hard water areas where corrosive substances in the water would adversely affect an ordinary element without a special coating.

The length of the heater can range from 245–914mm (10–36in). The type most commonly fitted is the single-element one which will heat the whole cylinder. It is, however, more economical to have two elements, one fitted near the top and the other about 50mm (2in) from the bottom of the cylinder. The top element heats enough water for hand or dish washing and the bottom one heats the whole cylinder, when for example you want a bath. There is also a dual heater, with a short and long element, which operates on the same principle. Both systems are independently switched so you can have either or both elements on at any time to suit your needs.

Special long heaters are needed for indirect and self-priming cylinders and for rectangular tanks. Hot water cylinders designed to work on the Electricity Board's White Meter tariff have either two heaters or a dual-element one to heat part or all of the water.

Wiring heaters

Common ratings for the heater are 1, 2 and 3kW, but because the immersion heater is considered to be a continuous load, whether you keep it switched on all the time or not, it must be supplied by its own circuit direct from the consumer unit using 2.5sq mm cable from a separate 20amp fuseway. The cable runs to a 20amp double pole switch (usually with a pilot light) which should be sited near the heater and close enough for anyone to operate if they are adjusting the thermostat. The wiring from the switch to the heater should be a 20amp rubber heat-resistant flex.

If you are installing two heaters in one cylinder, your double pole switch should incorporate a second switch which allows you to have either one or both heaters working. In this case a separate flex must run to each heater from the switch.

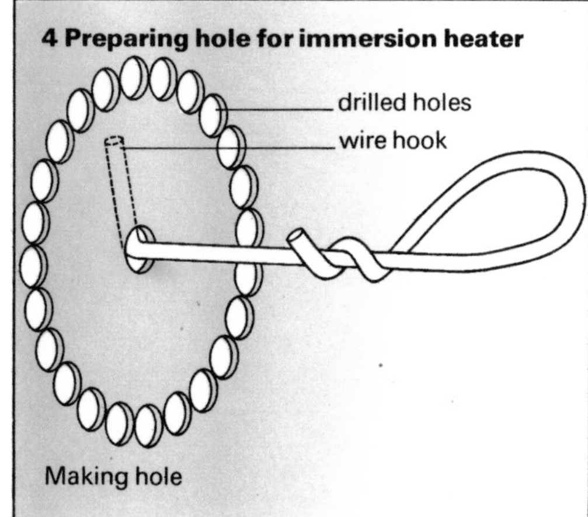

2 Wiring up the heater after removing the element cover
3 Adjusting the thermostat via the regulator screw
4 Making a hole in the cylinder to fit a heater; the wire hook is used to prevent the cut-out section falling into the cylinder

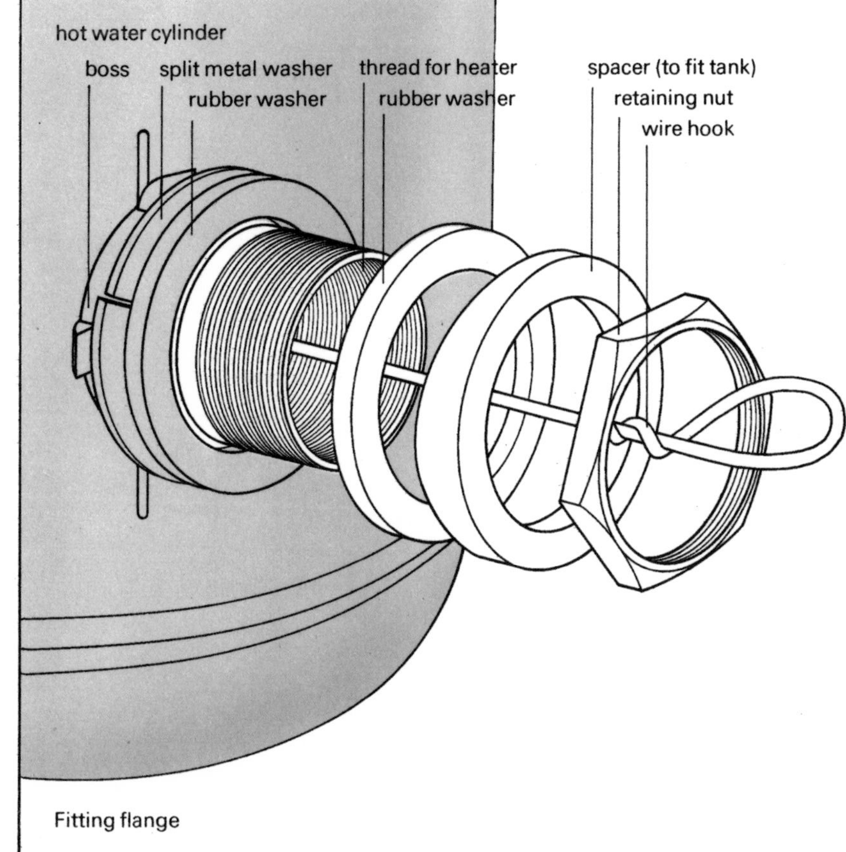

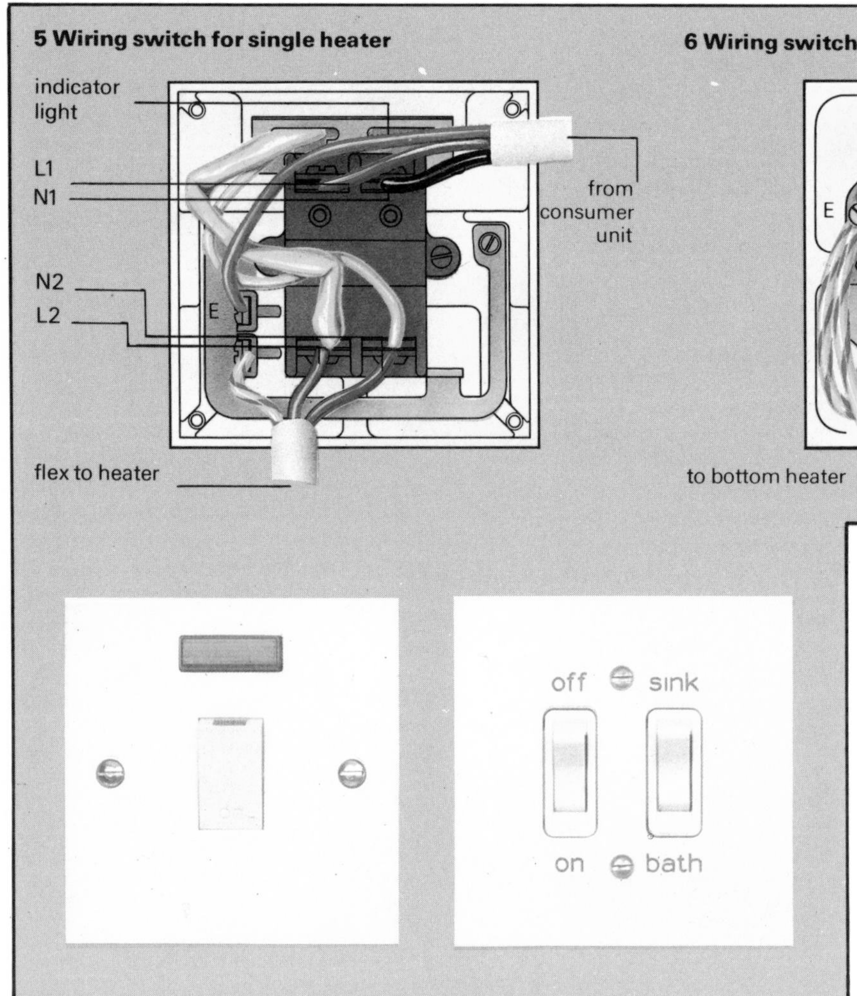

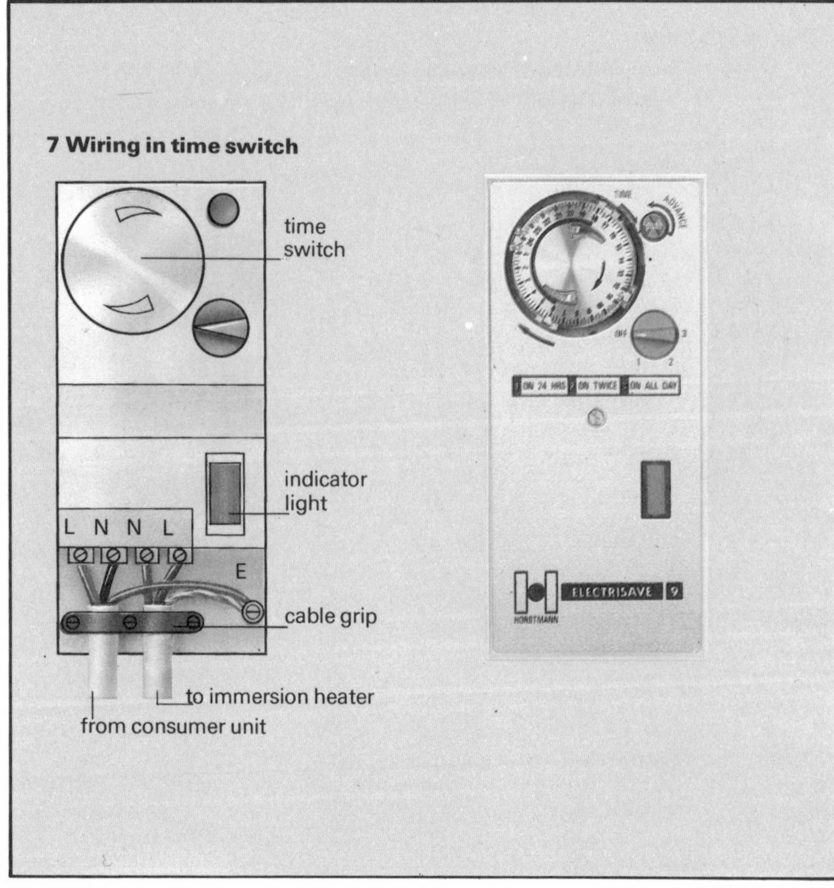

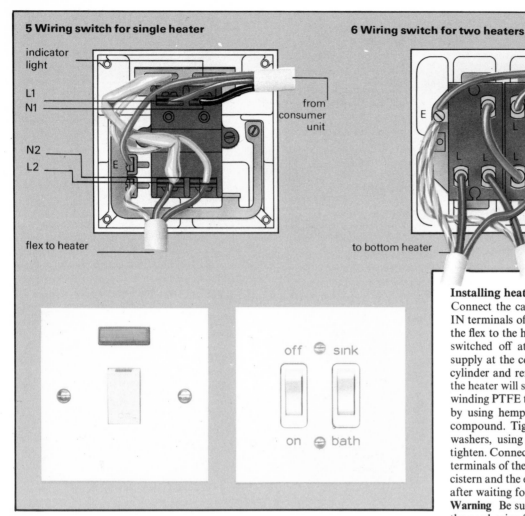

Installing heater
Connect the cable from the consumer unit to the IN terminals of the switch and connect one end of the flex to the heater, making sure the electricity is switched off at the mains. Turn off your water supply at the cold water storage cistern, drain the cylinder and remove the relevant boss, into which the heater will screw. The threads are sealed first by winding PTFE tape against the direction of turn, or by using hemp string and a non-toxic plumbing compound. Tighten the heater against its sealing washers, using a large wrench – but never over-tighten. Connect the free end of the flex to the OUT terminals of the switch, turn on the stopcock at the cistern and the electricity at the consumer unit and, after waiting for the cylinder to refill, switch on.

Warning Be sure to clamp the flex at both ends in the cord grips fitted to the heater and switch, and use the correct flex grips to secure it to the walls. Otherwise the flex might become entangled in linen (if in an airing cupboard) and be pulled away.

Cutting boss Most cylinders are now made with at least one boss fitting. However, if you have a direct copper cylinder, without a boss, in good condition you can cut a hole to take the heater. Mark out the required diameter hole and cut it with a hole saw fitted to an electric drill. Alternatively, drill a series of holes around the edge of the circle, knock out the centre and file the edge smooth. You can buy a patent fitting that includes the boss, a thread to take the heater thread, washers and a retaining nut. Don't try to cut a boss in an indirect self-priming cylinder.

Adjusting thermostat You must turn off the heater before attempting to adjust the thermostat setting. You reach it by unscrewing any screws holding the cap in place. Use a screwdriver to obtain the required setting, generally 60°, 71° or 82°C (140°, 160° or 180°F). In hard water areas scale tends to build up in cylinders at temperatures above 60°C (140°F) which is the lowest acceptable temperature for normal domestic purposes. The thermostat automatically turns off the power supply when the required temperature is reached.

Using time switch An immersion heater can be controlled by a special time switch, which offers two on and off periods in each 24 hours.

5 Wiring up switch when fitting single heater
6 Wiring up switch when fitting two heaters
7 Wiring up time switch to heater

Bathroom fittings

The bathroom can be one of the most dangerous places in the home if you don't follow the rules for electrical safety. But it can also be one of the most comfortable with the introduction of electrical fittings. As long as you install them correctly they will not only work at maximum efficiency, but need never be a cause for anxiety to you or your family.

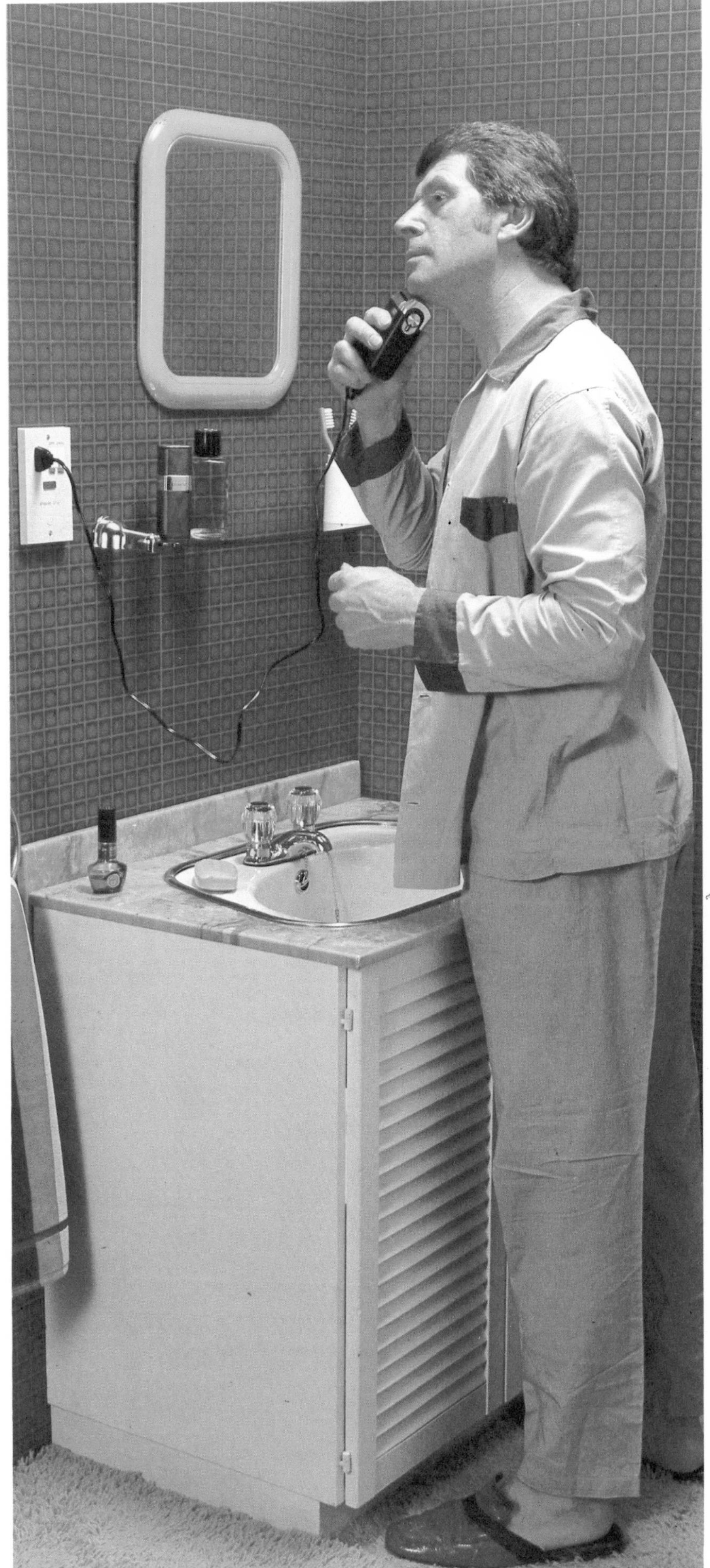

There is nothing worse than a bleak, chilly bathroom to greet you on a cold morning. Yet even the largest bathroom can be greatly improved with the addition of a wall-mounted infra-red heater for instant warmth, a small oil-fitted electric radiator, a heated towel rail (to warm towels when you have a bath and to dry them afterwards), a combined heater/light unit or a shaver socket combined with a mirror light.

Two important factors, however, must be remembered: these installations must be correctly wired and appliances must be fixed so securely that they can be removed only by using proper tools. Correct wiring means no socket outlets – except for the shaver – are permitted inside a bathroom (or washroom) and only cord-operated switches are allowed inside. And the usual general warning must be repeated: always switch off at the mains before you begin any electrical work.

Heated towel rail

A good selection of these is available, so choose the largest one that will fit in your bathroom. It is a good idea to buy one that incorporates a pilot light because this means you are less likely to forget to turn it off. Towel rails must be connected to the ring circuit through a switched fused connection unit that is sited outside the bathroom.

Decide where you are going to install the appliance, first making sure the plaster or plasterboard wall is strong enough to make a secure fixing. Use a spirit level to check the appliance is being fixed horizontally and mark with a pencil the fixing holes for the screws. Drill and plug the holes.

Prepare the route for your cable (2.5sq mm twin core and earth PVC-sheathed) from the ring circuit to the switched fuse connection unit; install the unit as close to the appliance as possible – but outside the bathroom. Decide on the route for the appliance flex to reach the connection unit. If this entails a long run you may have to install a flexible cord outlet box – linked to the connection unit with 1.5sq mm twin core and earth cable. The wires from the appliance are then connected to their corresponding terminals on the cord outlet box.

When you have completed the installation, check all terminal and fixing screws, turn on the mains and switch on the appliance to check it is working.

Oil-filled radiator The installation method for oil-filled radiators is similar to that for fitting a heated towel rail.

1

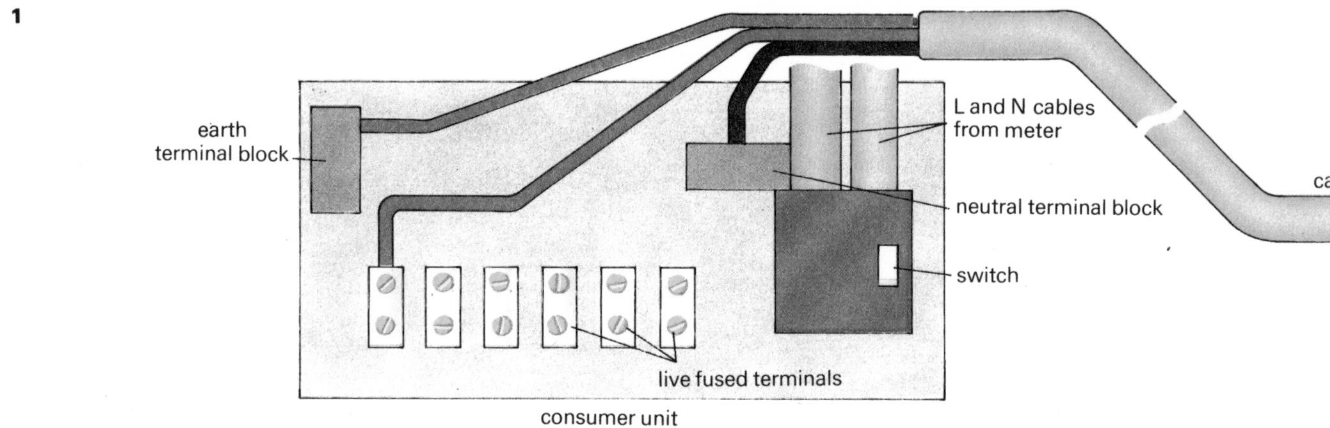

2

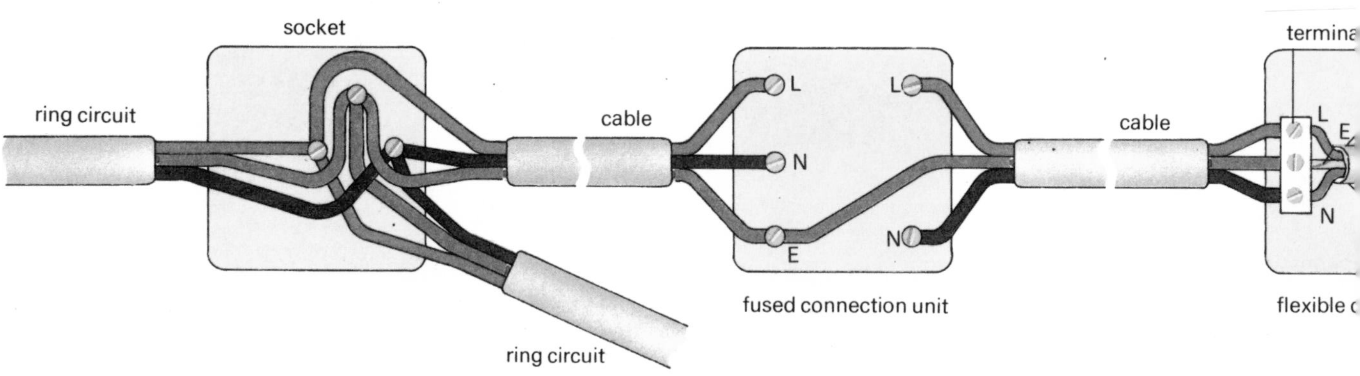

Wall heater

This must also be fed from the ring circuit, using a switched fused connection unit and a flexible cord outlet as described for a towel rail. The heater should be fixed as high on the wall as possible and preferably not above a bath or a shower. Alternatively you may connect the appliance to a cord-operated isolating switch (incorporating a pilot light) and connect the switch to the ring circuit via a connection unit as before.

The appliance is fixed to the wall with plugs and screws; always ensure it is properly secured before connecting up and switching on.

Light/heater units

The ultimate in space-saving, this unit incorporates a lamp in the centre of a ceiling fitting with a heating element around the outside. A cord-operated switch within the unit operates the heater. The master switch should be a cord-operated ceiling switch. It should not be connected to a lighting circuit because many units have a total loading of 850 watts and if used simultaneously with a number of other lights on the circuit it could overload the maximum 1200 watts capacity and cause a fuse to blow in the consumer unit – not a happy thought if you are in the bath at the time.

There are two ways of supplying such a unit. One is through a switched fused connection unit, the other by running a separate circuit from a spare fuseway in the consumer unit, using either 1 or 1.5sq mm twin core and earth cable. You must take great care in connecting up at the consumer unit; the circuit should be controlled by a 5amp fuse.

The appliance should be securely mounted to a timber batten screwed between joists in the ceiling

3

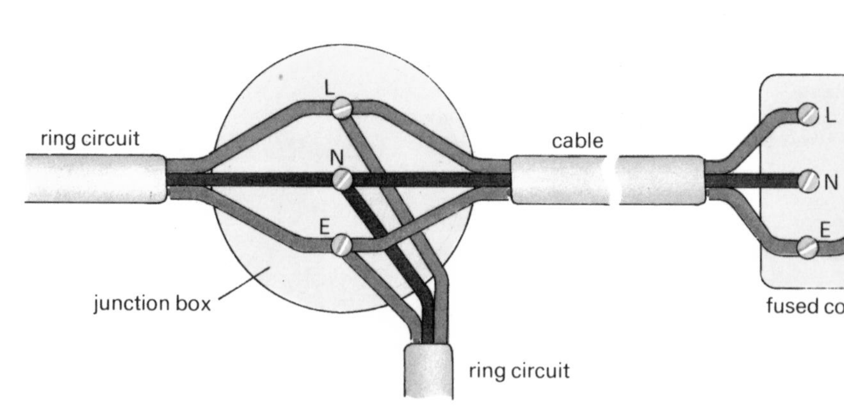

4

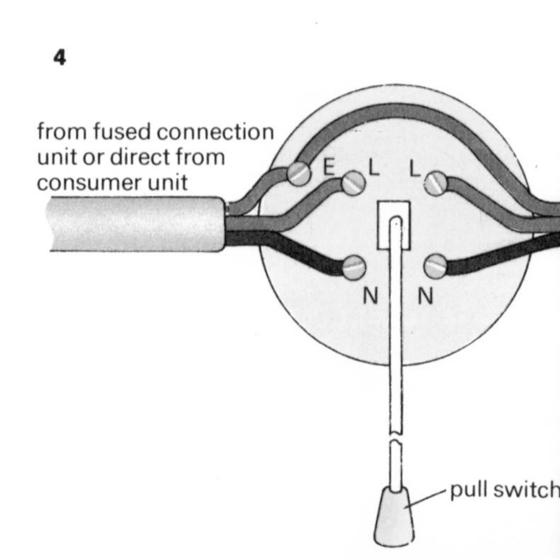

1 Wiring appliance direct to consumer unit. **2** Wiring appliance to ring circuit socket outlet via fused connection unit. **3** Wiring appliance to junction box via fused connection unit. **4** Wiring appliance to fused connection unit or consumer unit and including pull switch. **5** Wiring shaver socket to ceiling rose.

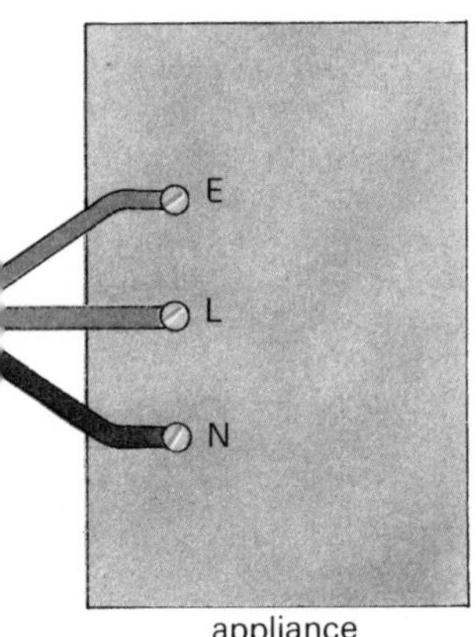

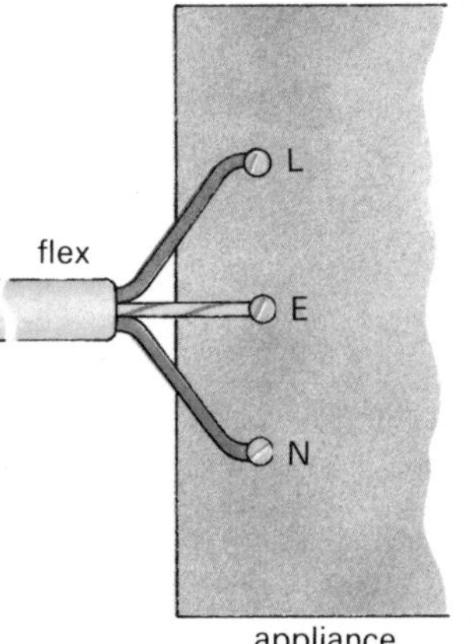

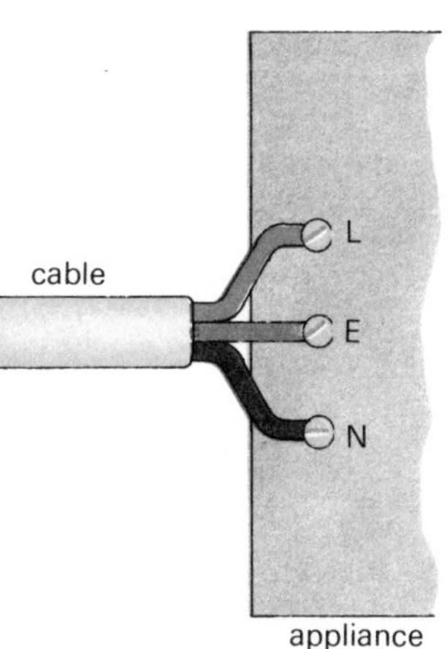

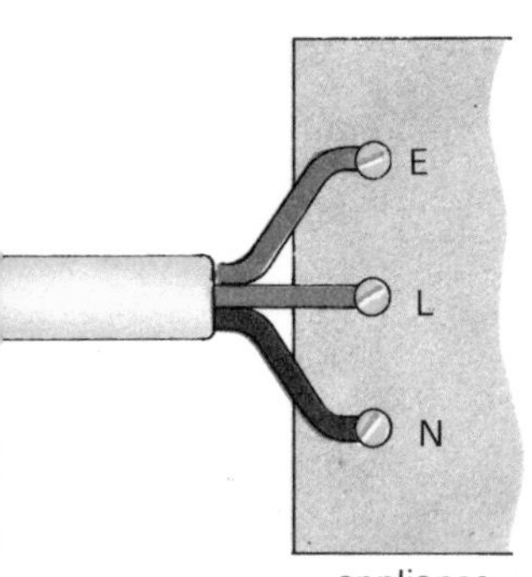

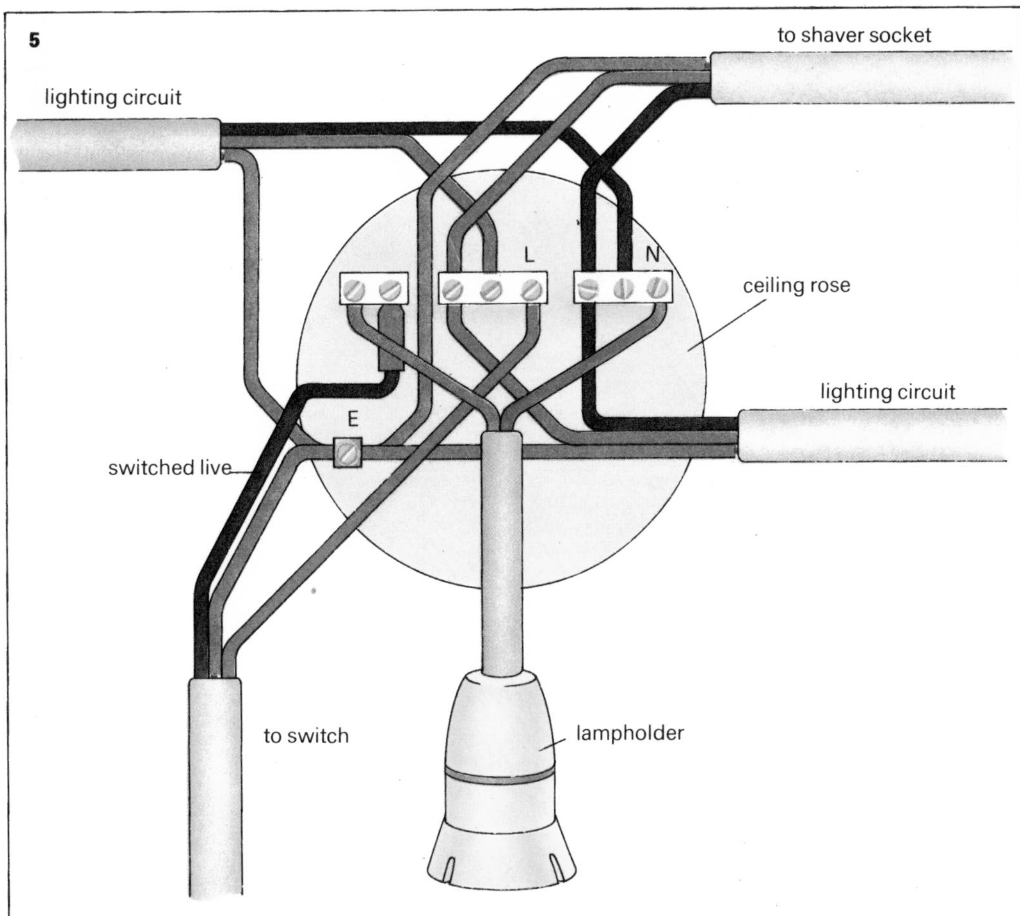

or roof space. Connect the ceiling cord-operated switch between the appliance and the connection unit; if you are running the appliance from the consumer unit, fit an isolating ceiling cord-operated switch within reach of the appliance.

Ceiling rose If by installing a heat/light unit you are making the existing ceiling rose redundant, you must remove the pendant flex, rose, switch wires and switch. Having disconnected the switch wire at the rose, disconnect at the switch or switches; pull the cable through from the ceiling space and discard it, replastering any recess where the switch was fixed.

You must install a junction box between the joists above the rose and use this to seal off (or terminate) the cables that run to the rose. You will have to take great care doing this, ensuring the conductors fitted to the rose are connected to their corresponding terminals in the junction box. With an older installation, earthing was probably not used; if earthing is used, connect the earth to its proper terminal in the box. With an older installation you may have difficulty identifying all the cables. If you have any doubts, always seek expert advice – don't trust your own judgement.

Shaver sockets

The specially designed shaver socket for use in the bathroom is available in several types: some come complete with a mirror light. The shaver supply unit can be connected directly to the lighting circuit without using a fuse in the spur, because it contains an isolating transformer. The unit has a two-pin socket that accepts British, Continental and American standard round and flat-pin plugs. It is possible to buy a dual voltage socket outlet for 240 or 115 volts in cases where the shaver does not adapt. Shaver sockets are also made without isolating transformers for use in other rooms.

It is impossible to run other appliances off a shaver socket because a thermal unit will cause them to cut out.

Remember when installing a shaver socket that anyone who is short-sighted needs to get quite close to a mirror with their spectacles off. So avoid placing it over a deep sink or cupboard that forces them to stand and peer. If you have a rechargeable electric razor, make sure there is a shelf near the socket where you can leave the shaver to recharge.

Mirror light This is a boon when you are making-up, or shaving with an electric or wet razor. Units are available which combine a striplight and a shaver socket at the end.

Having decided the position of the shaver and/or mirror light unit, trace a pencil outline round the box (available flush, semi-flush or surface-mounted) or mark the securing screw holes. Thread your cable through a hole drilled in the wall through the back of your surface-mounted box or through knock-out holes. Secure the box. Trim the cable sheath, strip the insulation material and connect up in the normal way to the correct terminals. The earth terminal is generally riveted in the base of the box; the live and neutral conductors go to terminals on the reverse side of the socket unit. Then secure the unit to the box with the screws provided, turn on the mains and test the light.

Warning If you have any doubts about the safety or suitability of a product, don't buy it. The yellow and blue label of the British Electrotechnical Approvals Board attached to a product proves it has been tested to the British Standard for electrical safety.

As an alternative to making the existing wiring and ceiling switch redundant, you may decide to alter your lighting by converting them to operate a wall light suitable for use in a bathroom.

Replace the rose with a junction box, as already described, and reconnect the ceiling switch wires to the switched live, live and earth terminals in the junction box. Measure a length of 1sq mm two core and earth cable (which is standard for lighting circuits) to run from the junction box across your roof or ceiling space and down the wall to the new light position. You should channel the cable into the wall and then replaster. Connect the cable to the switched live, neutral and earth terminals in the junction box and the corresponding terminals on your wall light, which will have been fixed to the wall.

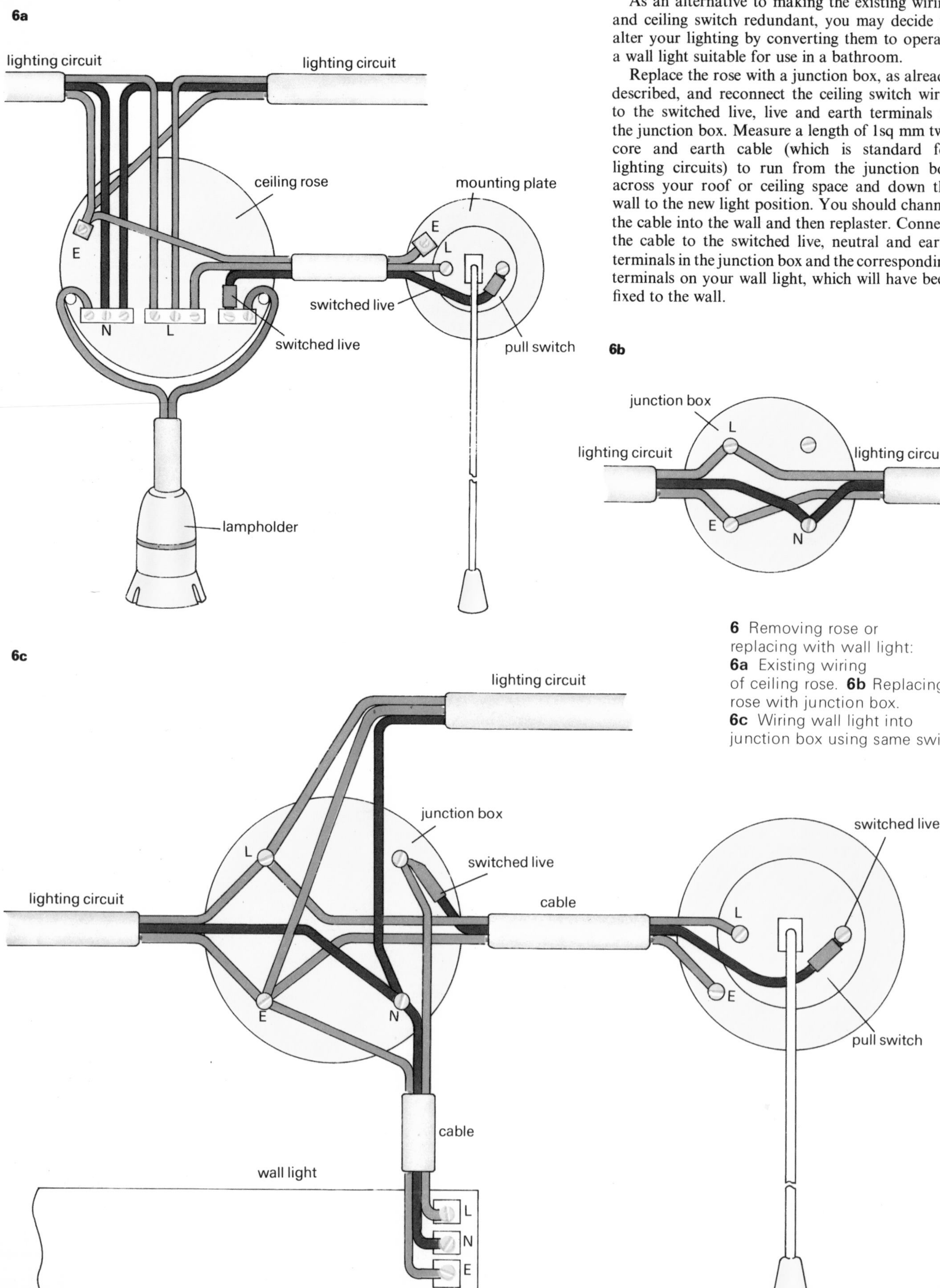

6 Removing rose or replacing with wall light: **6a** Existing wiring of ceiling rose. **6b** Replacing rose with junction box. **6c** Wiring wall light into junction box using same switc

Installing spot and wall lights

Wall-mounted lights and spotlights offer wide scope for lighting arrangements since they can be installed in any room as the main lighting or to supplement existing lighting, which is usually supplied by a conventional ceiling rose. If you have individual lighting, such as a rise and fall pendant over the dining table, wall lights can be used to provide general illumination.

Spotlights are particularly versatile since they can be fitted on the wall or the ceiling and can be used to highlight particular features of the room such as pictures, displays or even curtains. Spotlights are particularly useful for providing local lighting for reading, sewing and other similar activities since they are available with swivel brackets which allow the light to be directed as required. Wall lights or spotlights are also very useful in a double bedroom since light can be localized, causing the minimum disturbance to the other occupant.

Types of lamp Spotlights use two principal kinds of lamps: a reflector lamp of 75 watts is available in clear (white), blue, green, red and yellow; the PAR 38 sealed beam spotlight and floodlight (100 and 150 watts) is available in the same range of colours. The latter is suitable for both indoor and outdoor use, the floodlight version giving a wider beam of light suitable for illuminating outdoor areas. When buying fittings for spotlights, check which size and type of lamp it will accept; on some models the wattage is stamped inside the holder.

Fittings These are usually made of either polished or matt aluminium or finished in enamel in a variety of colours including white and pastel shades of green, yellow and mauve. Lighting track is particularly useful for holding spotlights. Available in various lengths, this can be fixed to the ceiling or wall and will take a number of spotlights which can be locked in position on the track.

Wiring wall lights

New wall lights may well need wiring extensions from the existing circuit, unless you are fortunate enough to move into a new home where wall lights have already been installed by previous owners or decide to fit wall lights with a flexible cord from a plug and socket outlet. In the case of new circuit wiring, the power may be run from three sources – from an existing lighting circuit, from a ring circuit via a fused connection unit or from a new lighting circuit in the consumer unit.

The lights are usually added to the circuit supplying the same floor, although there is much to be said for using a different circuit – from another floor, if it is a two-storey house, or from a circuit supplying other rooms, if a bungalow. A different circuit will mean the lights in the room will be supplied from more than one circuit, preventing a blackout should a fuse blow. This will also ease pressure on the ground floor or main living area lighting circuit, which tends to become overloaded if extra lights are added. There are regulations covering the maximum number of lights on one circuit – 12 lamps not more than 100 watts each on one circuit and fewer when one or more 150 watt lamps are fitted. Where added wall lights – especially those having two lamps, even if they are only 40 or 60 watts – will exceed the regulation number, use another circuit or install a new circuit, which can be a fused spur from a ring main.

Wiring from existing circuits Although wall lights are more conveniently controlled independently from the other lighting, wiring can be simplified by connecting to the existing fittings and using the existing light switch by the door. In this case the wall lights should have their own switches so they may be turned off if you want just a main light.

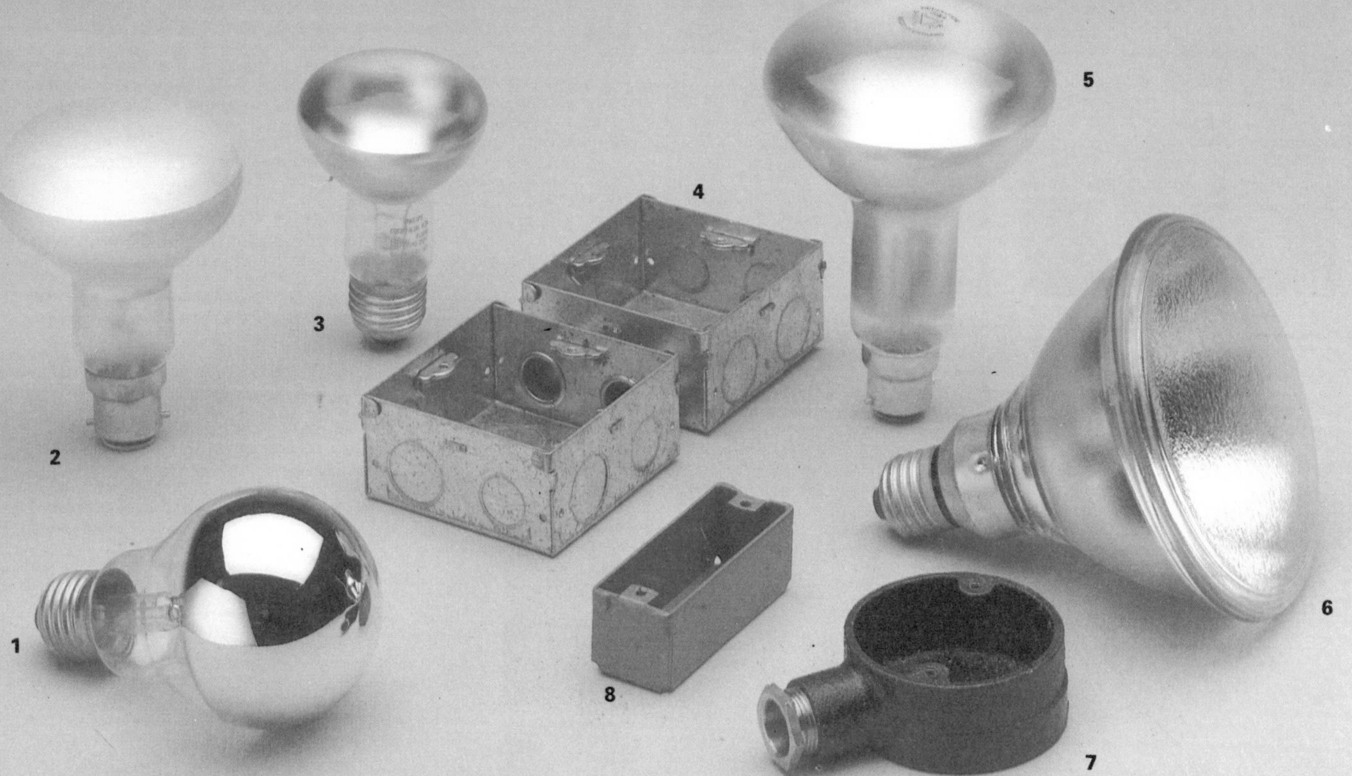

1 Screw cap crown-silvered spotlamp
2 Bayonet cap reflector spotlamp
3 Screw cap reflector spotlamp
4 Dual box
5 Bayonet cap reflector spot lamp
6 Screw cap sealed beam PAR 38 lamp
7 BESA box with brass bush
8 Architrave box

9

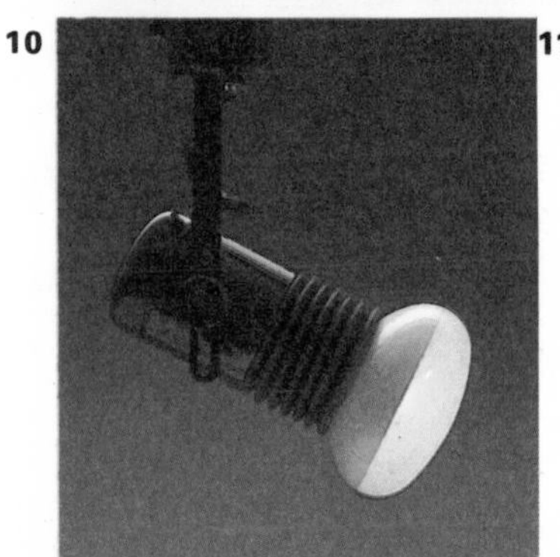
10

11

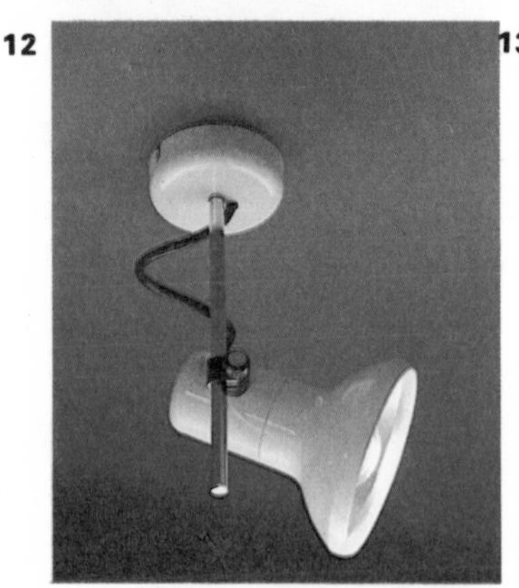
12

13

14

15

The problem with this arrangement is that to have the wall lights on you must also have the main light on. This can be overcome either by fixing a cord-operated ceiling switch or by replacing the lampholder in the ceiling with a switched version if it has an open shade. A more satisfactory solution is to connect to the neutral terminal on the existing light and replace the existing one gang switch with a two gang switch; the second switch will be for the wall lights. Mount the new switch on the same box and use the existing unswitched live to supply both switches. This technique has been covered earlier in the book.

Where, however, the existing circuit is wired on the loop-in ceiling rose system, as most modern circuits are, there will be a live terminal as well as a neutral one at the rose; this is the ideal source of electricity for the wall light circuit. If not wired on the loop-in system and if the ceiling light switch is located in the wrong part of the room, it will be necessary either to locate a junction box on the lighting circuit to allow access to a live terminal or to run a cable from the lighting circuit fuseway in the consumer unit.

Whichever method you use to obtain the source of electricity, you will need a four terminal 15/20amp plastic junction box – the basic accessory for the wiring – and flat 1.0sq mm twin core and earth, PVC sheathed cable.

The junction box is fixed under the floor to a piece of timber between the joists, roughly equidistant from the wall lights and the wall switch position. A convenient position for the box is above the existing ceiling light, if the light is used for looping. Run a length of cable from the junction box to each wall light, preferably a separate cable to each. This will save you having to run two cables down the wall to all but the last wall light and having to house two cables and the connectors in the confined space behind the backplate.

Run a cable from the junction box to the switch position; if this is the same as the existing switch a two gang unit replaces the one gang switch. Run a final cable from the junction box to the source of supply – the ceiling lighting point, a junction box or the consumer unit. When making the connections at the junction box, ensure the ends of the sheathing terminate within the box and all earth conductors are enclosed in green/yellow PVC sheathing.

Wiring from ring circuit In this case it is necessary to insert a fused connection unit into the 30amp ring main and fit a 3amp fuse in the unit to protect the lighting wiring, which has a lower current rating. The simplest method is to loop out of a convenient 13amp socket outlet connected to the ring cable and not fed from a spur cable.

The socket outlet you choose should be on the first floor, if in a two-storey house, so cable may be run under the floorboards; this will save having cable running up walls and will also normally mean the lights are on a different circuit than, for example, table lamps, which will be on the ring circuit in the ground floor rooms.

Turn the power off and remove a socket outlet to check it is not a spur, as described earlier in the book. A single socket box can be replaced by a dual box which is slightly longer than a two gang box and has two extra screw-fixing lugs for mounting two single accessories side by side (in this instance one will be the fused connection unit). If connecting the fused connection unit to a double socket, you will need a separate single box for the unit alongside he socket box. The fused connection unit must be onnected to the socket outlet terminals by .5sq mm twin core and earth PVC-sheathed able.

From the fused connection unit run a length of .0sq mm twin core and earth PVC-sheathed able to the junction box feeding the wall lights and witch. Connect the 2.5sq mm cable to the mains erminals of the fused connection unit and the .0sq mm cable to the load terminals.

9 Track-mounted spotlights. **10** Track-mounted spot with reflector lamp. **11** Track-mounted spots. **12** Spotlight for wall or ceiling mounting. **13** Clamp-on fitting. **14** Sealed beam spot for wall or ceiling mounting. **15** Outdoor sealed beam spot. **16** Wiring a cord-operated switch to a ceiling light. **17a** The wiring system for the existing junction box and ceiling rose. **17b** Wiring a two gang switch from the junction box system. **17c** Wiring a separate switch from the junction box system

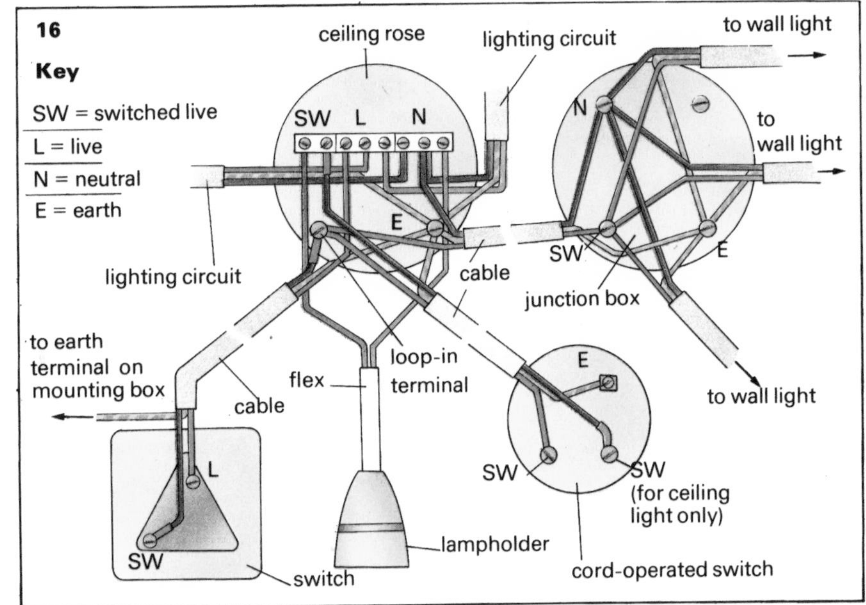

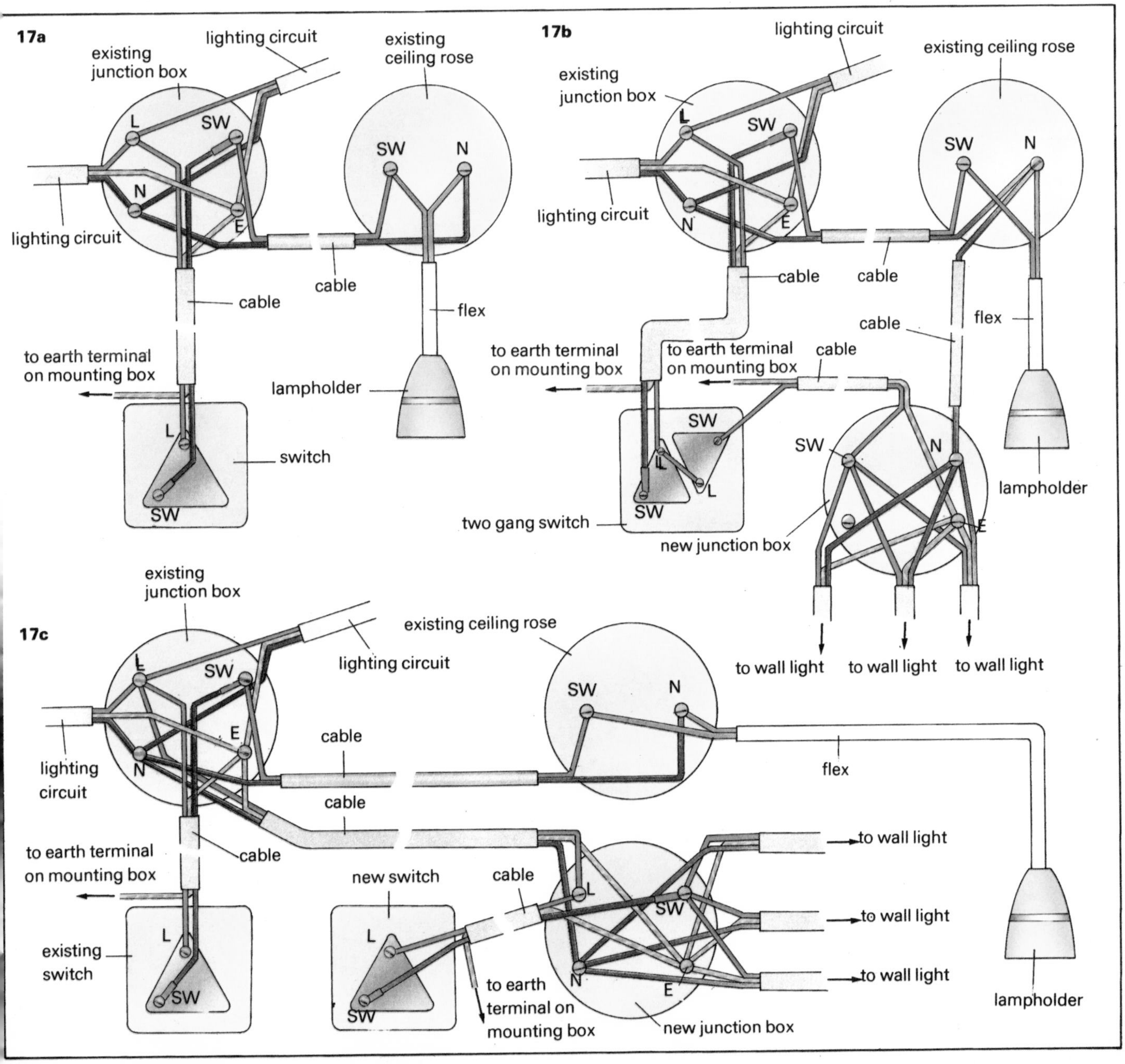

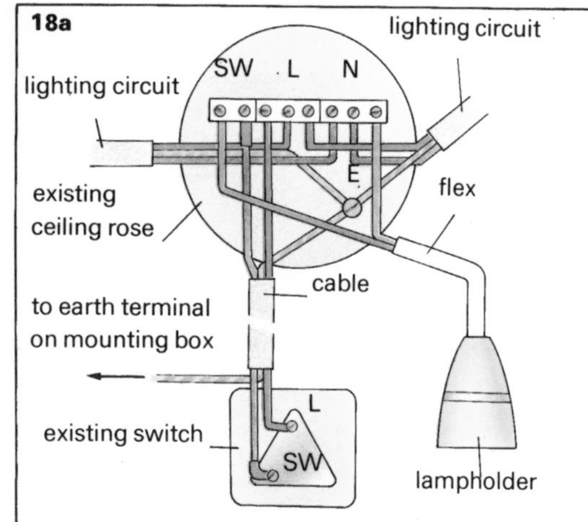

Mounting wall lights

Most wall light fittings are situated at the traditional height of 1.8m (6ft) above floor level; they can be fitted at any preferred height, depending upon the height of the ceiling and the style of the fitting.

Usually they have a backplate or base which has an open back. Regulations require the ends of cables, cable connectors and fitting flex to be totally enclosed in non-combustible material; a plastic or metal box is usually sunk into the wall and covered by the backplate of the fitting. Often the wall lights will have a circular backplate with two fixing holes drilled at 50mm (2in) fixing centres which match the standard 'BS' circular conduit box (termed BESA).

A plastic box can be used for all but very heavy fittings. If a metal box is used, fit a male brass bush into the threaded conduit entry in the edge to prevent the cable chafing as it enters the box. The metal version is also used for lights having a rectangular backplate with drilled fixings, made of wood, metal or plastic. Many wall lights, however, have no BESA plate and some are very narrow and of shapes unsuited to the BESA box. These require a narrow metal knock-out box (half the width of a socket outlet box) called an architrave box and designed for use with an architrave plateswitch. Remove the knock-out disc from the box and fit a PVC grommet to protect the cable.

The box is sunk into a chase cut into the wall, fixed with screws in plugged holes. Thread in the circuit cable, dropping it down from the ceiling; the cable may be clipped to the wall or buried in the plaster as desired. Trim and prepare the end of the cable in each box by stripping off the sheathing down to about 19mm ($\frac{3}{4}$in) and remove about 9mm ($\frac{3}{8}$in) of insulation from the two insulated conductors; slip green/yellow PVC sleeving over the bare end of the earth conductor. Using a two way insulated cable connector (already connected to the fitting wires in some wall light fittings), connect the red circuit wire to the brown wire of the fitting, the black to the blue and the earth wire of each to the earth terminal in the box. If there is no earth terminal, as in a plastic box, terminate the earth with a one way cable connector.

With a BESA box, secure the fitting to the box lugs with M.4 metric (2BA) screws (usually supplied). With an architrave box, the fitting can be fixed directly to the wall using screws in plugged holes. Should one of the fixing holes coincide with the box, it will be necessary to fix a drilled metal cover to the box using M3.5 metric (4BA) screws; drill another hole in the cover for a self-tapping screw to hold the fitting. Run cable down to the switch and fit as described earlier in the book. Check the power is still turned off and connect the cable to the existing ceiling fitting, junction box or fuseway as relevant.

Mounting spotlights

Spotlights can be mounted at any height on a wall or in any position on a ceiling. Wiring is the same as for wall lights, except when the spotlights are to be ceiling-mounted; here a cable is passed through a hole pierced in the ceiling as for a conventional ceiling rose.

Most spotlight fittings have a circular base drilled for 50mm (2in) fixings and are therefore suitable for mounting on a BESA box. Many are sold ready wired with a short length of three core

18a Existing loop-in ceiling rose system. **18b** Wiring a two gang switch from the loop-in system. **18c** Wiring a separate switch from the loop-in system. **19a** Wiring a new circuit from the consumer unit. **19b** Wiring a new circuit from a ring circuit. **20a** Mounting a wall light on a BESA box. **20b** Mounting a wall light on an architrave box; where it cannot be screwed both sides of the box, fit a metal cover and hold the fitting with a self-tapping screw

19a

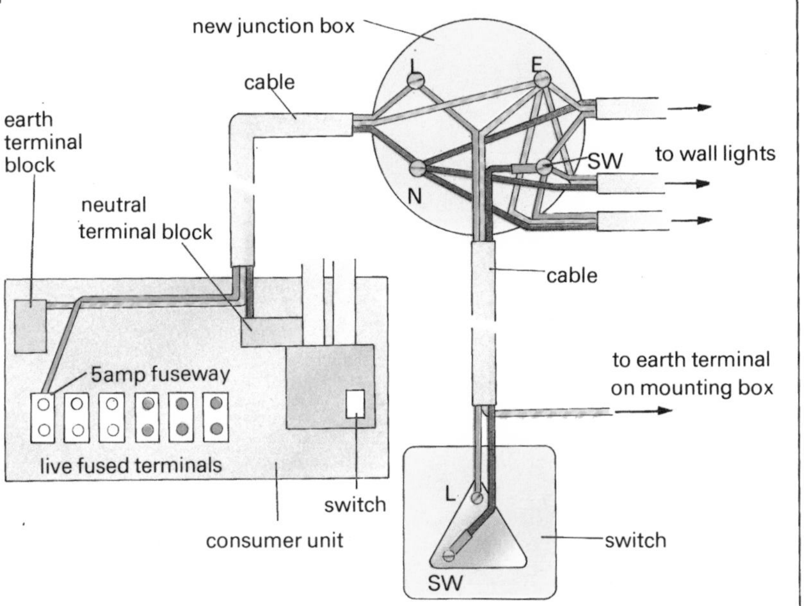

new junction box
cable
earth terminal block
neutral terminal block
5amp fuseway
live fused terminals
switch
consumer unit
L
E
N
SW
to wall lights
cable
to earth terminal on mounting box
L
SW
switch

19b

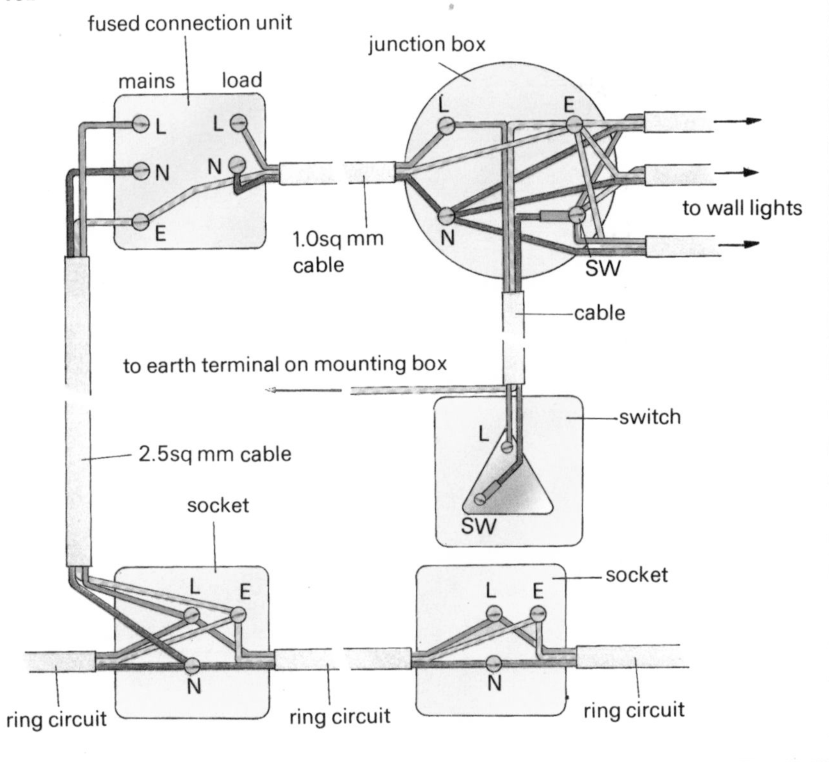

fused connection unit
mains
load
L
N
E
1.0sq mm cable
junction box
L
E
N
SW
to wall lights
cable
to earth terminal on mounting box
switch
L
SW
2.5sq mm cable
socket
L E
N
socket
L E
N
ring circuit
ring circuit
ring circuit

circular sheathed flex passing out through a small hole in the baseplate edge. This means instead of being mounted over a BESA box, the base can be fixed directly to the wall and the flex connected to a plug and socket outlet, ceiling rose or switched fused connection unit.

Lighting tracks enable one or more spotlights to be mounted in line on a ceiling or wall. Lighting pendants and the occasional small appliance may also be plugged into a lighting track. Domestic tracks come in standard lengths and couplers enable you to extend the track to any length. The tracks have a current rating of 16amps, although in practice the load is limited to the current rating of the circuit feeding the track. From a 5amp circuit the limit is 1200 watts; from a 3amp fused spur it is 720 watts; from a 13amp fused spur up to 3120 watts may be run off. The last is necessary when appliances such as toasters or irons are used from the track.

A lighting track is basically a PVC extrusion containing two bare conductors (live and neutral) with an earth strip, enclosed in an anodized aluminium track. Spotlights fitted with track adaptors clip into the track and will slide along until locked into position. Flexible cord adaptors may be fitted to the track to operate a lighting pendant or an appliance fitted with the adaptor in place of a conventional plug. A cord-operated 2amp switch to control up to 480 watts is available, which may be clipped into the track if required. A track can be connected directly to fixed wiring either at a wall lighting point or at a ceiling point in place of a ceiling rose and operated by conventional wall switches. Alternatively flexible cord can be connected to the track terminals, which in turn are connected to a ceiling rose, cord outlet or to a plug and socket outlet.

Warning Every spotlight and wall light must be under the control of an isolating switch, such as a conventional wall switch, even when the fittings have their own integral switches. This is to ensure the lampholder and other live parts are dead whenever you attend to the fitting. A cord-operated, or push-button, integral switch does not indicate whether the fitting is on or off. Spotlights are made in the 100–150 watt range, so check the lighting circuit will not be overloaded; if the circuit would be overloaded, a ring circuit spur should be used to supply the power.

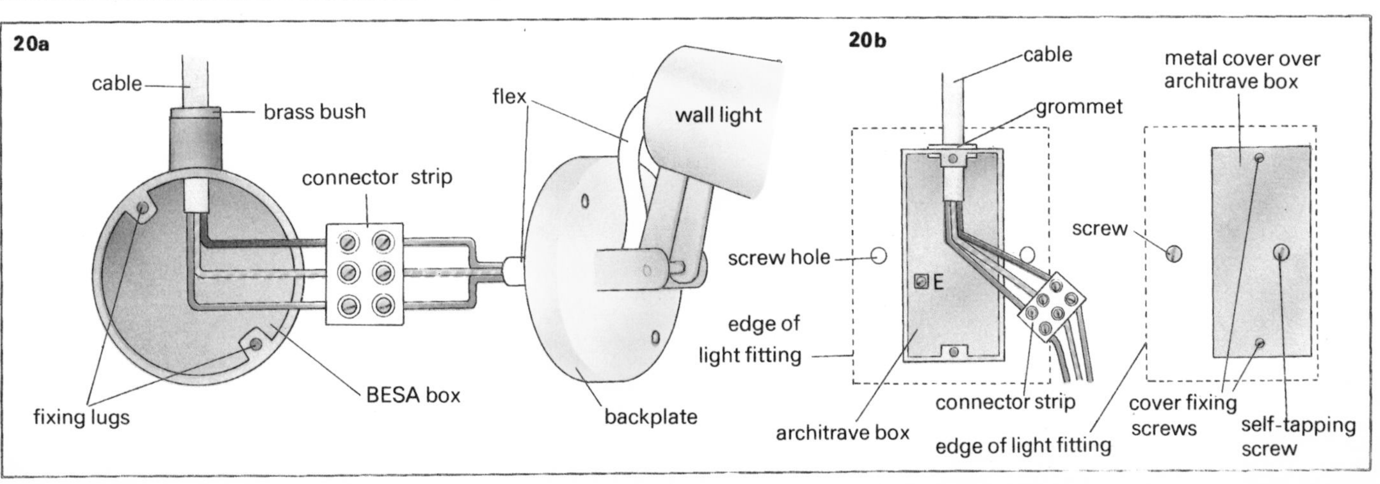

Bells, buzzers and chimes

Fitting a bell, buzzer or door chime is a simple job, since many are sold in kit form specifically for DIY installation. All work off a low voltage supplied by dry batteries or a small safety transformer which is permanently connected to the mains and reduces your 240 volt household supply to 3, 5, 8 or 12 volts. You will need a transformer system for a bell push with a light; if you just want a bell or chime without illumination, a system operated on dry batteries is easier and cheaper to install. Batteries normally last for about 12 months, depending on the amount of use. Prices vary considerably according to the signal which is produced and the kind of external fitting used.

Trembler bells An electro-magnet causes a hammer to vibrate against a metal gong (or dome) and produces the familiar clear ringing tone.

Buzzers An electro-magnet causes a diaphragm to vibrate. Pitch and volume can be varied and some produce a tone similar to a fog horn.

Chimes These have a double-ended plunger, mounted on a spring drawn through an electro-magnet, which strikes the metal chime bars and produces a double note. Some can be wired to a second bell push on another door, which will produce a single note so you will know which door to answer.

Sonic musical signals Produced in a variety of pre-programmed tunes, this type gives an individual touch to surprise any caller.

How they work

Bells, buzzers, chimes and sonics may be operated by battery or transformer (in some cases either), but check first with the manufacturer's installation instructions. Some are specially made so they do not cause interference on a television set or radio. The bell push is a spring-loaded switch; as it is pressed two contacts join to complete the circuit.

Usually manufacturers supply installation instructions and wiring diagrams with their kits, but the basic principle is a simple circuit which is completed when the bell push is operated.

Batteries are often fitted inside the case of the bell or chime and connection to the push is by twin core flex usually called bell wire. This is often sold in white or cream; you can paint over it to match your existing wall colour. Since domestic fittings are operated off a low voltage, there is no danger of getting a shock or of causing a fire with this wire. It can be left exposed along the edge of skirting, round

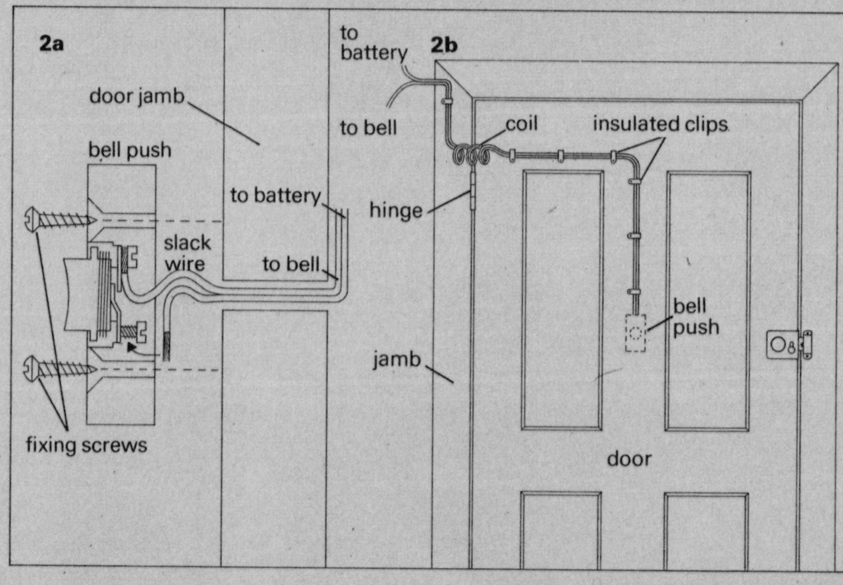

Top A DIY battery-operated bell kit
1 Basic wiring for a bell and bell push powered by a battery
2a Installing a bell push in a door jamb; connect the two terminals before securing the bell push
2b Installing a bell push in the centre of a door; secure the bell wire with insulated clips and leave a coil of slack wire on the hinge side to reduce bending when opening

Above A small buzzer unit; this can be battery-operated or connected to the mains via a transformer
You can connect two bells to one bell push; use the parallel system (**3a**) for two bells with the same resistance and the series system (**3b**) for bells with a different resistance – here you must increase the voltage to get an effective signal
4 To operate a bell from the mains, connect it to the consumer unit via a transformer or to the ring main via a transformer and fused connection unit (**inset**)

door frames or even along the edge of coving. Small insulated fitting clips secure the wire to the surface, but take care not to sever the wire when nailing. Bell wire should be clipped to the surface at about 300mm (or 12in) intervals.

How they are installed
The hall is the best site for the sounding unit, but this will obviously depend on what sort of accommodation you have. Many people have them in the kitchen, but there is a risk of steam corroding both batteries and sounding unit.

If the distance between bell and push is more than about 9m (30ft) you may need to increase the voltage of the battery or the thickness of the wire because the resistance of the wire reduces the effective voltage. The loss of about ½ volt for every 9m (30ft) of wire may not be noticeable when the batteries are new, but after a while the bell or chime signal will weaken and then stop altogether.

It is a simple matter to install a bell push at the front and back doors to operate one sounding unit; you can also fit a second sounding unit to work from the same push – this is useful in a large house or where the occupant has hearing difficulties. Two methods can be used to wire a second bell or set of chimes.

Parallel This method is for bells or chimes which have the same resistance.

Series This system is for bells or chimes which do not match. Here increased voltage is necessary, otherwise either only one bell will work or neither will give a loud enough sound. The series system cannot be used for trembler bells.

If you fit a transformer, you must connect it to the mains using 1sq mm twin core and earth cable. It can be connected as a spur from a ring circuit, but most consumer units have a 5amp fuseway designed for this connection. If you take a spur from the ring circuit, use a fused connection unit with a 3amp fuse.

Transformers usually have three connections on the output side. If you take the bell wire to the outer connections, this gives an 8 volt supply; taken to the middle and one of the outer connections, it gives a 5 volt supply; and taken to the middle and the other outer connection a 3 volt supply. Transformers are also available which give a 12 volt supply for use when two fittings are run in series or for long wiring runs. All this is clearly marked on the transformer case, so you should have no difficulty selecting the right connections.

To fix the unit you have chosen, drill a hole through your door jamb to run the bell wire from the bell push to the battery and sounding unit. The bell push must be wired to its two terminals before it is screwed into the jamb. You should leave a loop of wire inside the push so it can be removed for

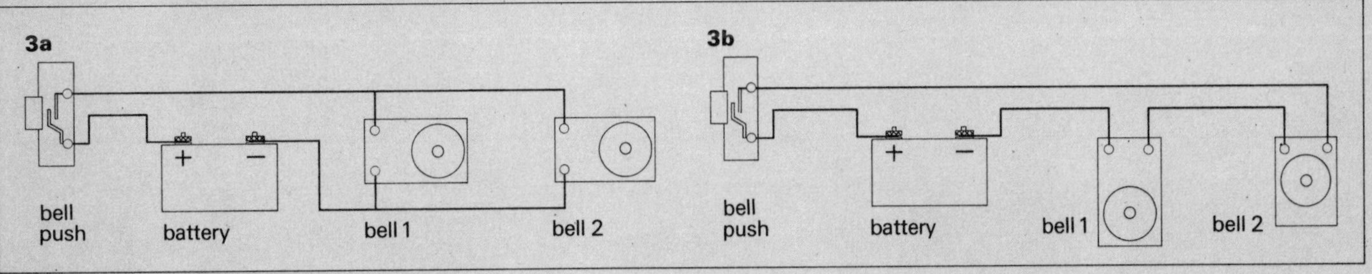

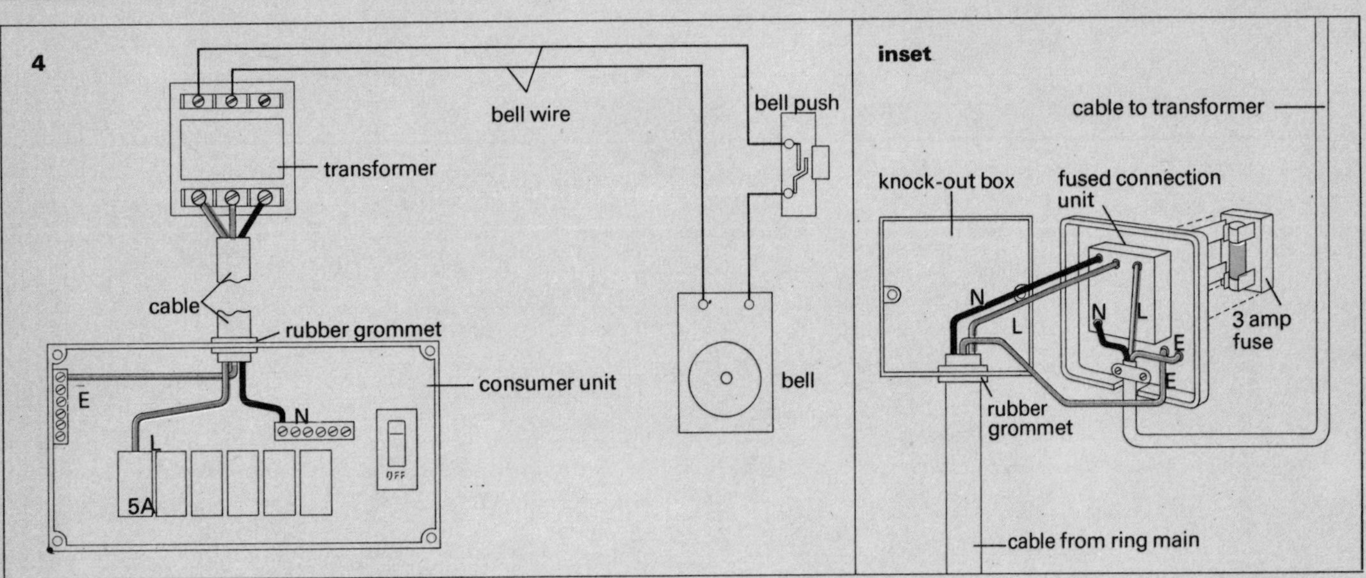

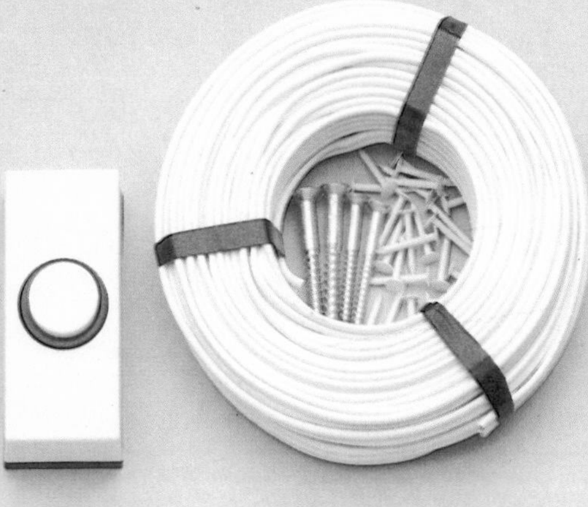

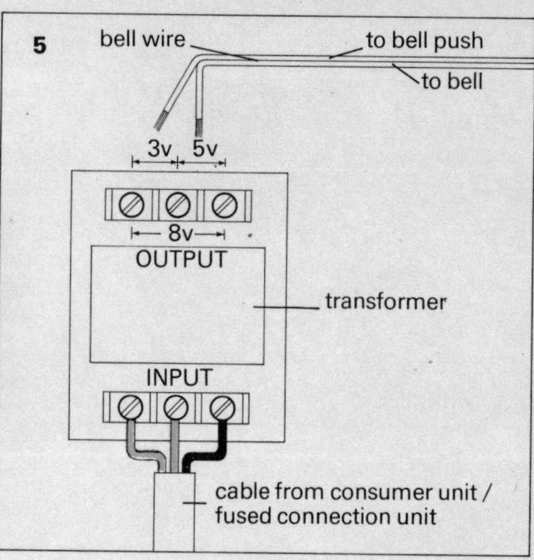

Far left A DIY chimes kit operated by battery and containing a chime, push button, bell wire, fixing screws and enamelled wiring nails

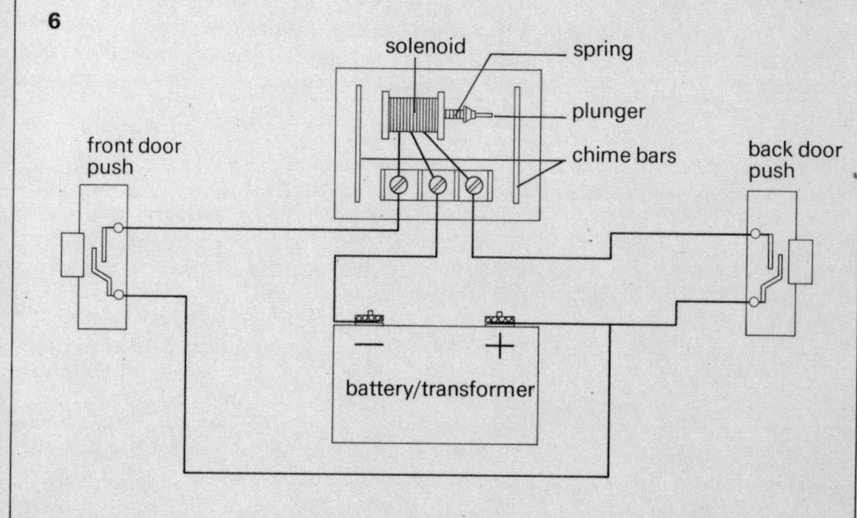

inspection. Alternatively fix the bell push to the door and run the wire from the push through a hole in the door to the hinged side and onto the jamb, leaving some slack wire between the door and the jamb to prevent excessive bending when the door is opened and closed; otherwise the bell wire will very quickly break. Ideally, form the slack wire into a small coil by wrapping a few turns round a pencil before attaching the wire to the jamb. Continuous conductor hinges are available which overcome the need for slack wire, but these are expensive.

Attach the housing of the sounding unit to the wall with plugs and screws, and clip or screw the cover over it. Usually the cover is made of plastic or wood, but some manufacturers make more decorative ones in such materials as ceramic. Make the electrical connections according to one of the circuits illustrated.

How to correct faults

If your bell stops working, it may be due to a flat or damaged battery, a loose connection, faulty bell push or dirt in the sounding mechanism.

Any contact in a bell or buzzer can be cleaned by rubbing a piece of card between the contact and screw, but don't use abrasive material. You need a soft brush, dipped in lighter fuel, to clean the solenoid spring and plungers on a chime to ensure the plunger can move freely.

Warning Always disconnect the fitting before servicing any unit.

5 By varying the wiring to the connections you can get an output of 3, 5 or 8 volts from your transformer; the connections are clearly marked to make selection easy

6 Chimes wired into two push buttons – one at the front and one at the back door – via a battery; alternatively you can wire them through a transformer connected to the mains circuit

Fitting TV aerials and sockets

The television set is now a standard fixture in many homes, providing hours of entertainment. But a poor picture can spoil this fun. Depending on the area in which you live, there is a range of aerials to cope with the quality of reception – and various devices that enable you to enjoy your favourite programmes anywhere in the home.

There are three normal positions for a television aerial: on the roof, in the loft or placed on top of the set or elsewhere in the room. A roof fitting, sited as high as possible, is the most satisfactory method, although this job is probably best left to a professional. You can keep down the bill by laying the special coaxial cable yourself and getting the rigger to connect up after he has completed the installation on the roof. An aerial on top of the set is only really satisfactory where there is outstanding reception, whereas an aerial in the loft can provide excellent viewing, if you are not too far away from one of the broadcasting authorities' transmitters.

If you move into a new area and notice few rooftop installations, you can usually assume the area has good reception. It may mean there is no

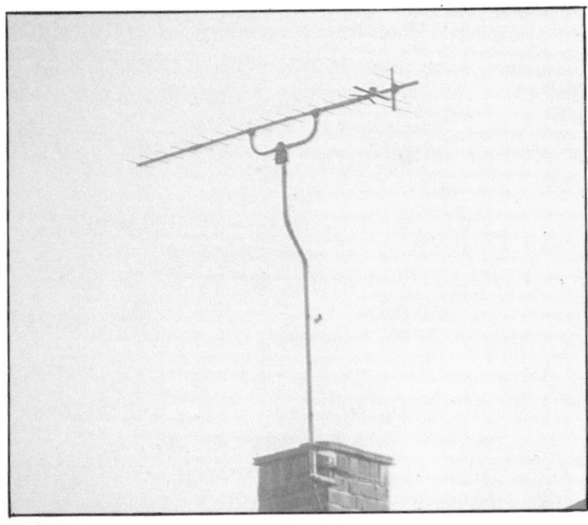

Top When you move into a new area it is worth checking to see how good the television reception is. If the signal is poor, you will have to fit a roof aerial
Centre An indoor aerial which sits on top of the set: this type is only suitable for use where the reception is outstanding
Bottom left A rooftop aerial gives the best results in any area
Bottom right An aerial fitted beneath the eaves of the house can provide good reception and is not as conspicuous as a rooftop installation

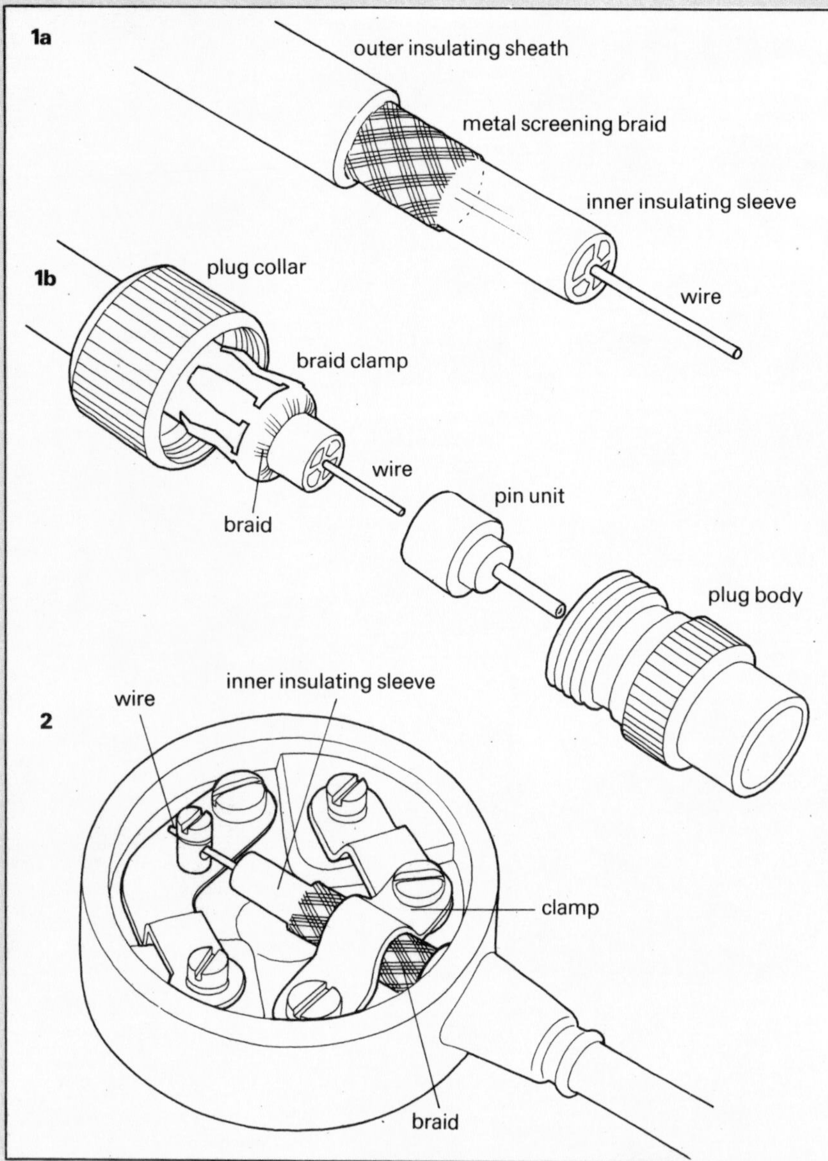

1a When connecting the aerial to the set make sure you use the right cable – a low-loss coaxial type
1b Using the correct plug – a coaxial type with special braid clamp – is vital for a sound connection
2 Wiring the coaxial cable to the set from a junction box on the aerial

reception, so check with the BBC and IBA engineering information services and see a local dealer. He usually will not mind you doing the job yourself because, like some television rental companies, he probably contracts his aerial work out to someone else anyway.

Television aerial installations are becoming more sophisticated and, by using a combination of the most sensitive roof aerial and masthead amplifiers, you can pick up distant TV stations.

Connecting cable

Use low-loss coaxial cable to connect the aerial to the set. This is expensive to buy and you should take the shortest possible route when you lay it, not only for economy's sake but because a short run helps to maintain the signal's strength. The cable consists of an outer insulating sheath, a metal screening braid (which stops unwanted signals being picked up), an inner insulating sleeve and a final inner wire which actually carries the signal. Avoid bending it sharply as this can seriously affect reception.

You can run the cable in plastic conduit, bury it in plaster or fix it to your walls with cable clips. In some modern homes you may be able to run it from the roof or loft, through the roof space and down the cavity in your walls to an aerial socket outlet (which can be either flush or surface-mounted) or direct to the plug which connects at the back of the television set.

If you run the cable externally, either from a roof aerial or through the eaves in the case of a loft aerial, you must check it periodically to see whether it is being chafed by the wind rubbing it against roof tiles or brickwork. If you bury it, you cannot take the aerial with you when you move; this need not be particularly inconvenient, since when moving from one area of the country to another, you may well need a different aerial because different channels are used in different areas and signal strengths vary considerably. So it is as well to include the aerial in the fixtures and fittings when you sell.

Wiring up

When wiring the cable either to the plug or in the weatherproof junction box on the aerial, remove 38mm (1½in) of outer insulation and loosen and fold back the braid to leave about 20mm (¾in) of inner insulation clear; then remove 6–13mm (¼–½in) of the inner insulation from the braid.

The cable is fed through an access hole (and protected by a grommet) at the junction box, the inner wire connected to the terminal and the braid clamped down with a metal clamp. The junction box is generally covered with a clip-on PVC cover.

When wiring up the plug, slip on the plug collar and the braid clamp, tighten the screw on the clamp, thread the inner wire into the pin unit and screw the collar onto the plug body. Unless the screening braid is properly clamped it will not do its job effectively.

Fixing the aerial

The aerial should now be screwed into the highest possible point in your loft and as far away from galvanized steel water tanks as possible, since the metal may deflect the signal. When you have done this, point the aerial so the shortest element or cross piece is nearest to the transmitter and, by trial and error, establish the best position (by going down to the set to check the pictures on the different channels or getting someone else to look for you) before bolting the aerial into its optimum position. Your dealer should have sold you the appropriate UHF aerial for your district and this may have from five to up to 21 elements (or cross pieces).

Amplifier If your signal is particularly weak and needs boosting, you will have to install an amplifier close to the aerial. A number of manufacturers produce these and in the case of a roof aerial the fitting should be left to the rigger. If you are fitting one to your loft aerial, you will need an amplifier and accompanying power unit. The amplifier is bolted to the aerial masthead and the coaxial cable enters and leaves this (the method of connection depending on the type of amplifier), runs into and out of the power unit and then into the set in the normal way. The power unit, which should be connected to a fused connection unit with 2.5sq mm twin core and earth cable, contains a transformer which sends 18 or 24 volts output into the amplifier along the coaxial down cable.

An amplifier will not alter the quality of the signal, only its strength, and may exaggerate any faults caused by an inadequate aerial.

Aerial sockets The neatest way of connecting your aerial to the set is via a specially designed aerial socket, which eliminates trailing cable across the floor. These are connected in the way described for the aerial junction box. You will, of course, need another length of cable and two plugs to connect from the socket to the set. Sockets are available which also provide a connection for your FM radio (from a separate VHF aerial).

Fitting an extra outlet

If you wish to run a second set off the same aerial but in another room, you will need a splitter unit; this can be fixed to a skirting board with countersunk screws. Generally this has a socket outlet for the set in the same room and the usual terminal and braid clamp for the cable from the aerial and for the cable that carries the signal to a second set elsewhere in the house. Adding an extra socket may reduce picture quality in areas where the reception is already below par.

Another method is to use a combined splitter-amplifier which contains its own power unit and is connected to the mains, via a fused connection unit, using 2.5sq mm twin core and earth cable. This has an input coaxial socket to take the cable from the aerial and up to four output sockets for sets in different parts of the house.

Extending cable The cable connector is a simple device that enables you to extend existing cable. It has female sockets at both ends and these take the standard coaxial plug. Again it will further diminish the quality of the picture if you are already suffering from a poor signal.

3 A combined splitter/amplifier strengthens the signal and provides outlet sockets for sets in different parts of the house
4a Wiring up an aerial socket to provide for both television and FM radio
4b The front plate of a TV/FM radio aerial socket
5 A splitter unit enables you to run two sets off the same aerial
6 If you need to extend cable, always use a proper cable connector

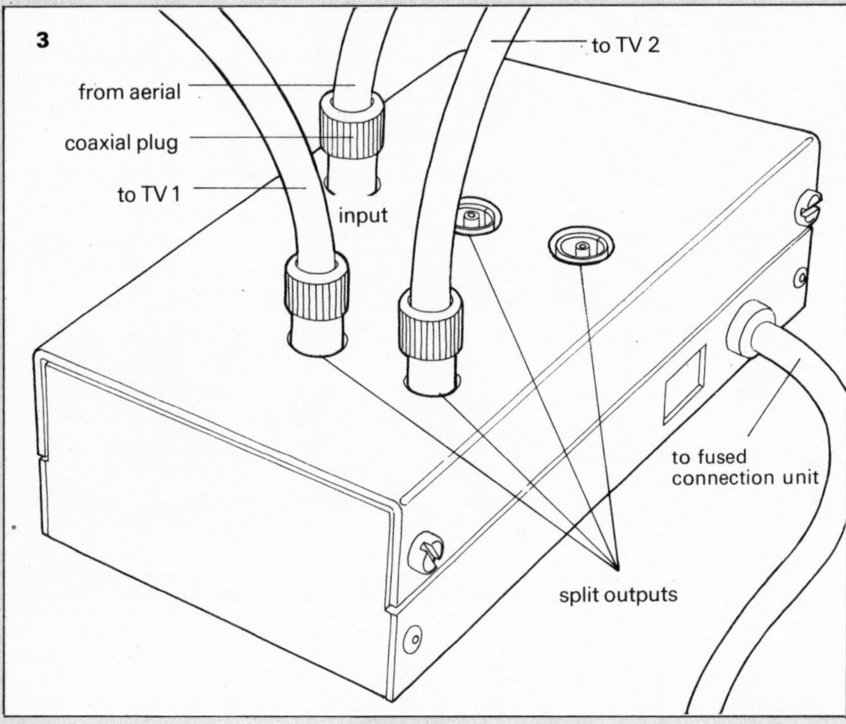

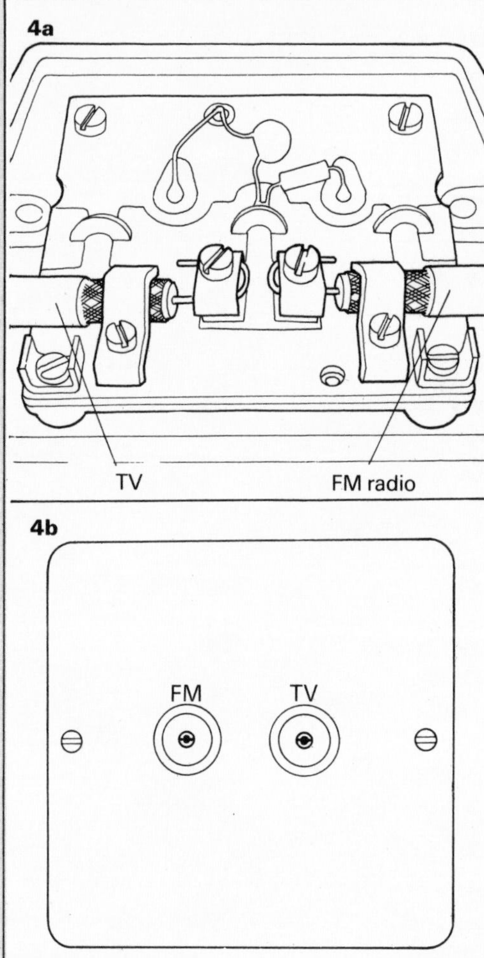

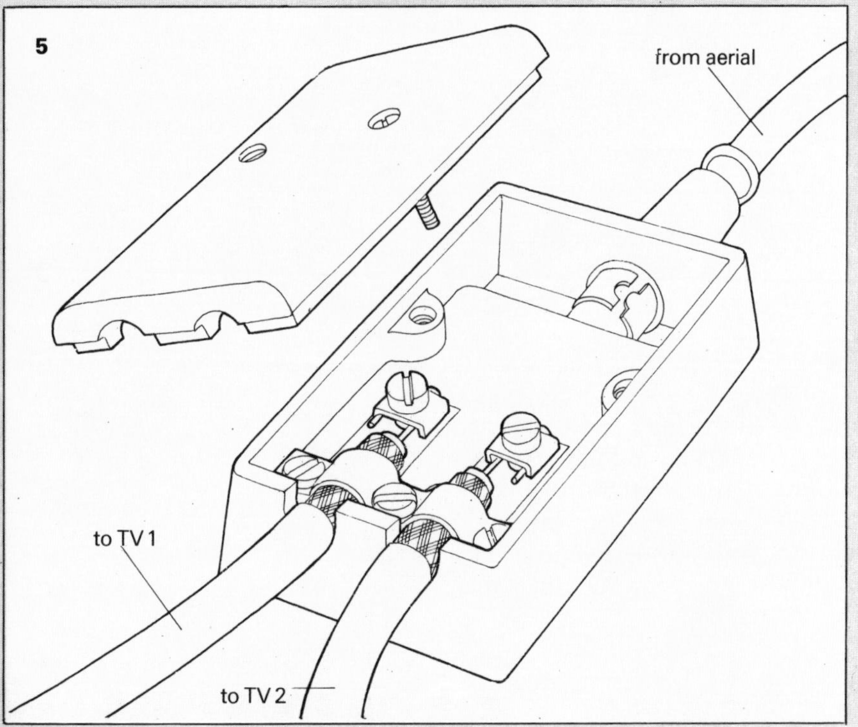

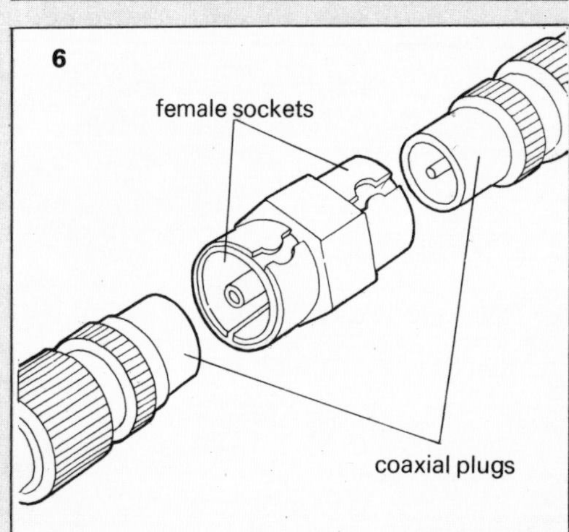

Repairing appliances

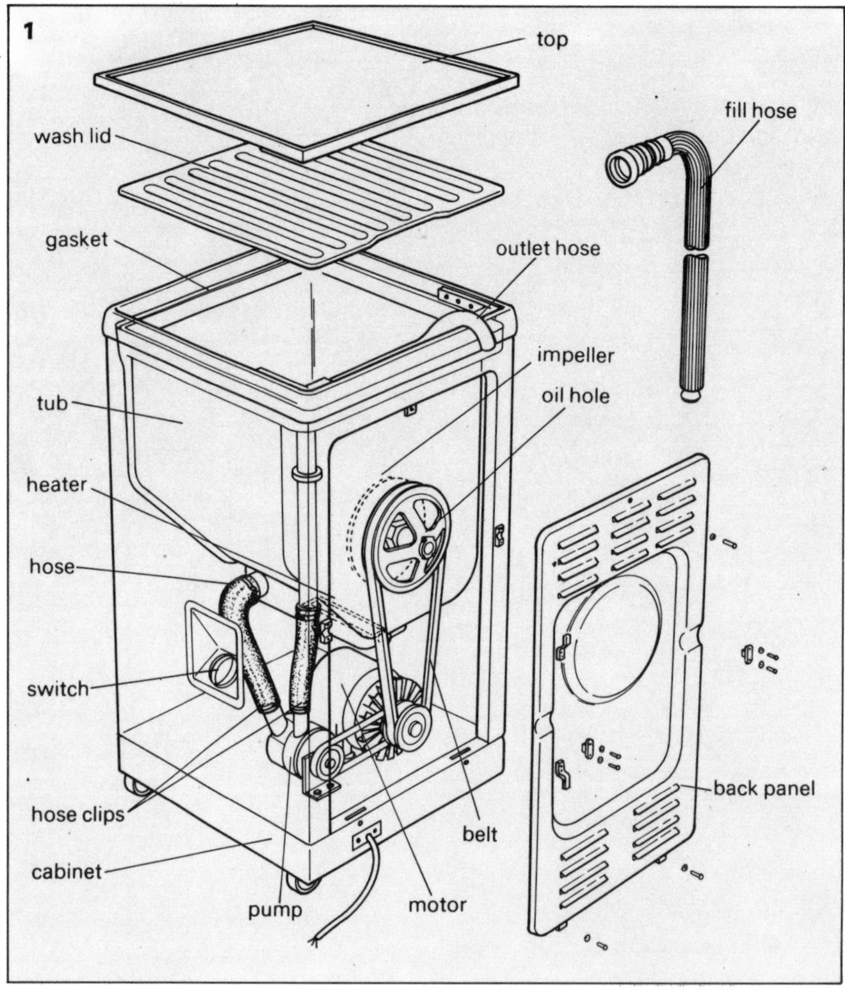

There is nothing more aggravating than to have an appliance fail on you just when you are using it and to have to wait to have it repaired. There are many small jobs you can do yourself to keep appliances working efficiently and the major ones are included here. Remember that in each case typical examples have been included, which may not match exactly the specifications of your own machine. Always check with the manufacturer's manual or instruction booklet first; if in doubt, seek professional advice before tackling the work. And always check you are not invalidating an existing guarantee.

Light 'n' Easy vacuum cleaner

In this section on home appliances we will be covering some of those more commonly used and start with the Parry Light 'n' Easy vacuum cleaner (model 3227). Before attempting any work, always check on the safety requirements to prevent injury to yourself – and damage to the machine.

Always fit genuine spare parts, obtainable from your local service centre – identified by this sign

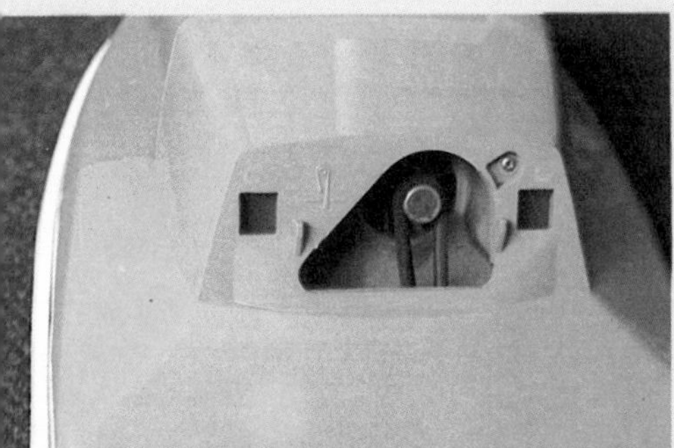

As its name suggests, the Parry Light 'n' Easy vacuum cleaner is both light in weight and easy to handle, making it one of the popular models in the home. For the best results it must, as with all cleaners, be regularly and correctly maintained and any worn or defective parts replaced immediately with genuine spare parts.

Warning Before attempting any work on your machine, always make sure the power is turned off and the plug removed from the socket; and check any job you do tackle does not invalidate any existing manufacturer's guarantee.

Roller brush assembly

To release the roller brush assembly you will first have to take the belt off the drive nut, which you reach by removing the front cover plate (**see 1**). Turn the cleaner upside down and unclip the metal shoeplate with a coin or screwdriver; the assembly, including the belt, can be pulled out (**see 2**). The end caps can be pulled off for cleaning and light oiling (**see 3**). Check the roller spindle is not scored due to a loose fitting cap: this can cause the roller to tilt and reduce brushing power. You will see the roller spindle is set slightly off centre in the end caps, so make sure these are correctly aligned when refitting. There are four numbered slots on each cap (**see 4**) to allow for roller brush adjustment. As the brushes wear down, the caps can be rotated one slot at a time to compensate for wear; but make sure you make the same adjustment on both caps. When you have reached the fourth position, you will need to replace the roller. The roller has a red mark on one end (**see 3**) to correspond with the end cap marked RED, which fits on the right-hand side of the front body (as seen from the front); so make sure the roller is positioned the correct way round when you reassemble it in the cleaner.

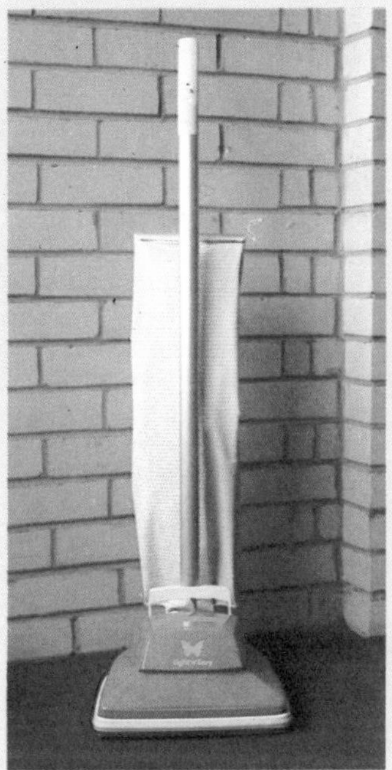

5

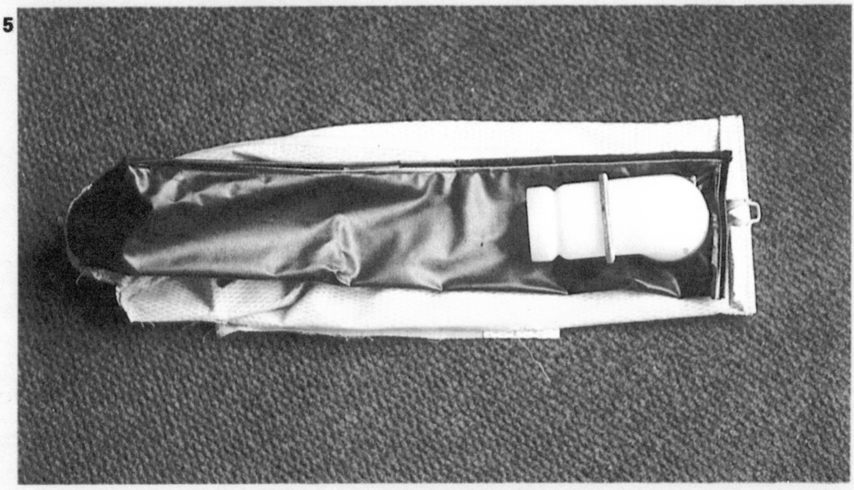

6
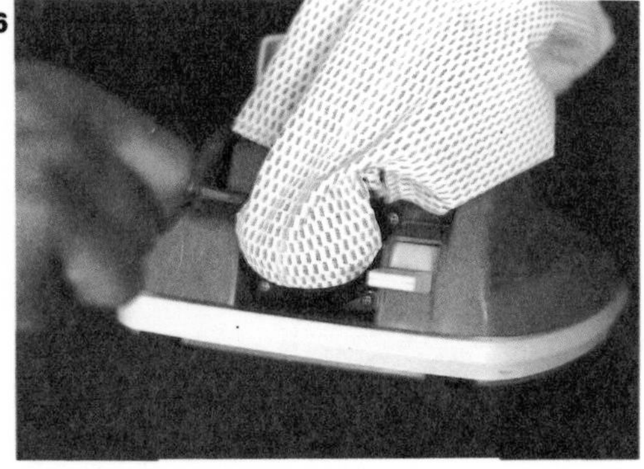

7

8

Inner sleeve

Inside the cloth bag is an inner plastic sleeve (**see 5**) which carries dust from the motor exhaust to the disposable paper bag. Any defect in the sleeve will cause the dust to blow around inside the cloth bag. To replace a damaged sleeve, first release the bag from the bag lever assembly. Undo the four retaining screws in the bag connector (**see 6**), unzip the bag and turn the neck inside out to reveal the outer bag clip (**see 7**). Release this clip from the sleeve by squeezing the clip indentations, using a pair of long-nose pliers. Remove the inner bag clip (**see 8**) in the same way. You can now remove the damaged sleeve and insert a new one, replacing the bag assembly in the reverse order. When reassembling, make sure the elbow of the nozzle attached to the inner sleeve faces the pocket used for cable storage, otherwise the inner sleeve will be wrongly positioned. When refitting the outer bag, make sure no more than 13mm ($\frac{1}{2}$in) is pulled through the clip and take care not to twist the inner sleeve when placing the clip round it.

Handle switch assembly

One part of the machine that is susceptible to damage if roughly treated is the handle switch assembly. This can be dismantled to locate the affected area. Release the two lowest screws that fix the assembly to the handle tube (**see 9**). Ease the handle up and clear of the aluminium tube. The handle is in two parts (**see 10**), held together by one screw which must be undone. Remove the mains flex by undoing the terminal screws and unscrewing the clamp that secures the flex; keep the grommet safe and remember to refit it on reassembly. The switch connections are soldered, so in the event of a faulty switch it is best to replace the handle front and switch assembly complete. To do this, release the inner handle flex connection from the suppressor (**see Motor assembly**). Note carefully which way the flex was fed through the motor compartment and to which terminals the live and neutral wires were connected. Unscrew the bag lever and pull the flex up the handle tube. You may have to feed a length of spare wire up from the bottom of the handle tube and connect it to the new lead in order to pull the new lead back through. The brown core of the inner handle flex will have to be soldered onto the spare switch terminal; the blue core is connected to the neutral screw terminal.

Mains flex

You can test for a fault in the mains flex by replacing it with a length of test flex. Remove the flex from the handle assembly as already described, carefully fix your test flex in its place, connect it to the supply and switch on. If the machine runs, your

9
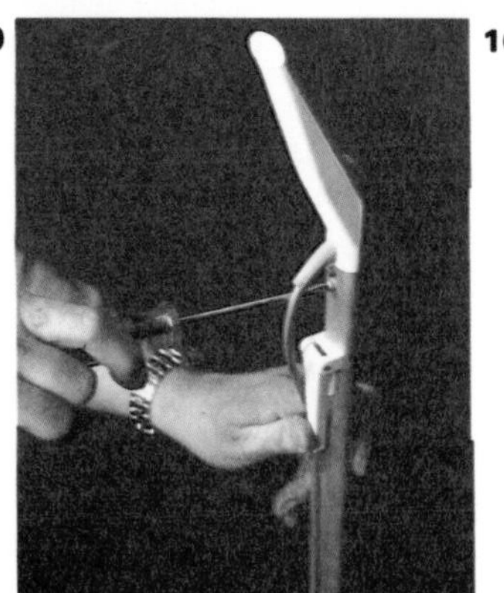

10
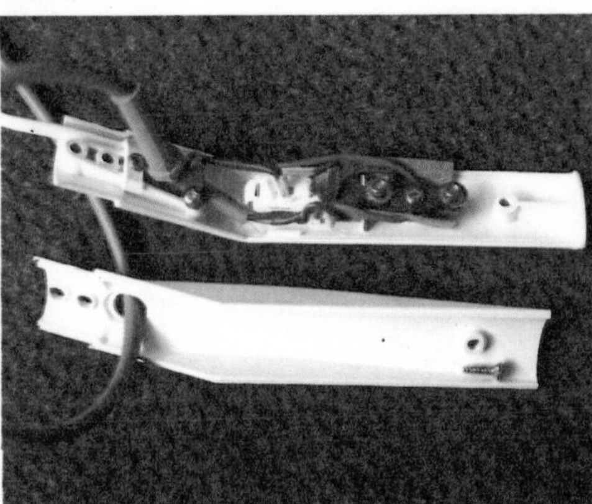

Handle front wiring

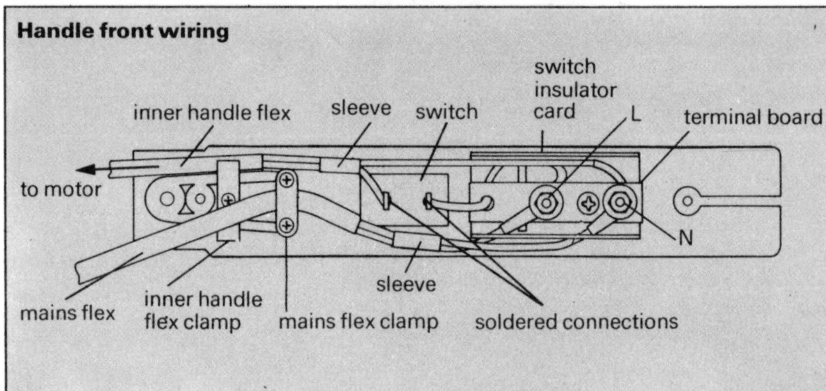

11
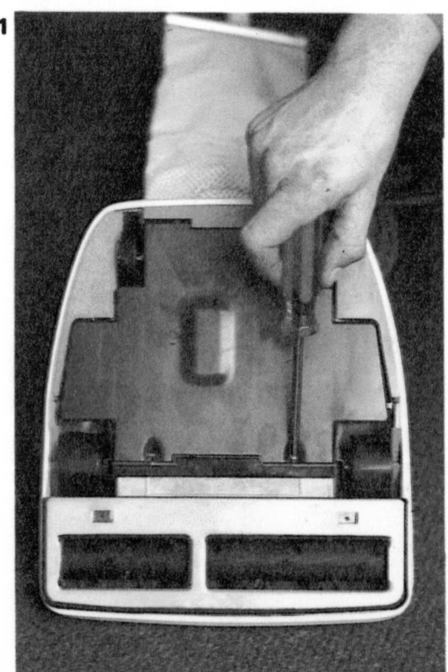

12

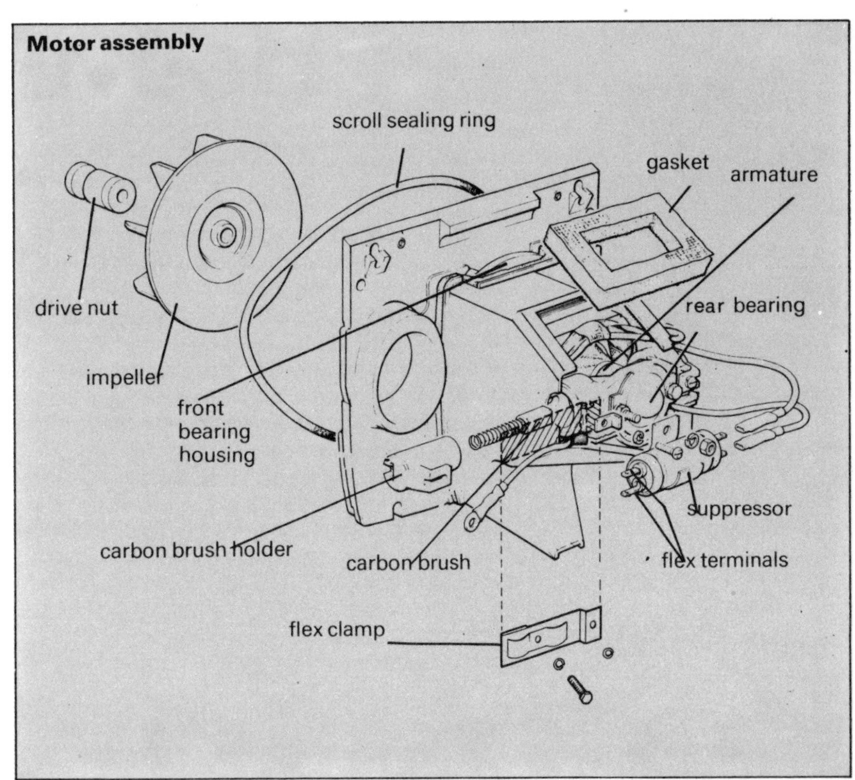

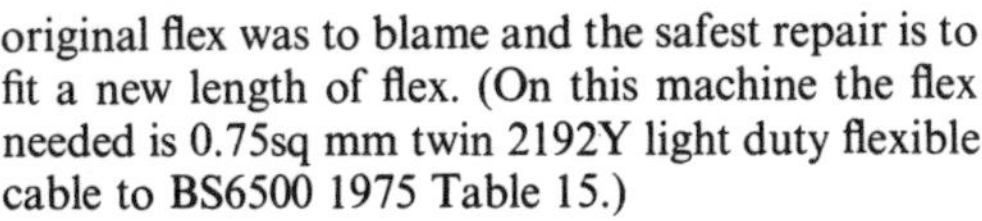

original flex was to blame and the safest repair is to fit a new length of flex. (On this machine the flex needed is 0.75sq mm twin 2192Y light duty flexible cable to BS6500 1975 Table 15.)

Motor assembly

Any major work on the motor itself should be undertaken by a recommended service dealer; your machine has already been tested for insulation. If the motor is stripped down, this may well upset the existing insulation and this must be checked on reassembly. You can, however, replace the carbon brushes and the suppressor without dismantling the motor. To gain access to the motor assembly, remove the undercover screws (**see 11**) and take off the undercover (**see 12**). Clean away any dirt with a small dry paint brush

Carbon brushes To check the carbon brushes, carefully unscrew the carbon brush holders (**see 13**), but make sure you do not pull the leads or you could break the soldered wire connection to the field coil. The brushes should be at least 6mm ($\frac{1}{4}$in) long with clean, unchipped surfaces. If they are worn or damaged, replace them with the recommended part. When refitting brushes, remember to match the curvature with that of the armature.

Suppressor You will see the suppressor fitted with four leads connected to it (**see 14**). Check these are tightly connected. To replace the suppressor, simply disconnect the four leads and release the retaining nut; the leads must be replaced in exactly the same order on the new suppressor.

Warning The drive nut and impeller (or outer fan) can be removed, but it is necessary to refit these to the correct torque otherwise you could damage the insulation. If you do remove the drive nut (left-hand thread), it must be unscrewed clockwise.

Bearings There is really no maintenance possible on the bearings. The front bearing is enclosed in its own housing and has to be replaced as a complete unit; the rear bearing, if removed, has to be centred on the armature when refitted.

Checking for faults

Fault	Cause	Remedy
Motor dead	No mains supply	Check plug, fuse, flex
	Loose suppressor leads	Reconnect
	Loose switch tag leads	Resolder
	Faulty switch	Replace handle front
	Faulty suppressor	Replace
	Faulty mains flex	Replace
	Dirty armature/brushes	Clean
Overheating	Loose or worn drive nut	Replace
	Roller seizure	Clean and oil, or replace
	Loose roller	Replace worn caps/ clips or replace
	Excessive armature sparking	Replace armature or motor
	Worn belt	Replace
Unusual noise	Loose or worn drive nut	Replace
	Worn bearings	Replace
	Broken impeller	Replace
	Loose motor screws	Tighten
	Worn roller and caps	Replace
Poor suction	Full paper bag	Empty or replace
	Blocked exhaust tube	Clear
	Twisted inner sleeve	Reposition
	Loose scroll sealing ring	Reposition or replace
	Loose front cover plate	Reposition or replace
Outer bag dusty	Split inner sleeve	Replace
	Split paper bag	Replace
	Loose paper bag	Reposition

Warning Check carefully which of the faults listed here you can tackle yourself before attempting any repair work.

Always fit genuine Hoover spare parts, obtainable from your local service centre – identified by this sign

Hoover Junior

We continue the section on servicing and maintaining appliances by looking at the Hoover Junior vacuum cleaner, taking the 1334/46/54 series as an example; you will find slight modifications on other Junior models. When replacing parts, always fit genuine spares, which can be obtained through your local authorised service dealer.

Take care of your vacuum cleaner and you will ensure the efficient operation and long life of the machine. This involves checking regularly there are no faults; worn or damaged parts should be replaced immediately before they cause problems to the rest of the cleaner.

Warning Before investigating the cause of any problem or attempting any repair work, you must always make sure the power is switched off and the plug removed from the socket. You should also check any job you do tackle does not invalidate any existing guarantee on the machine.

Some maintenance work can be done without the use of tools – and this is within the scope of any careful worker provided the instructions are followed and the necessary precautions taken. But before attempting work on the more complex areas of the machine, check you have the right equip-

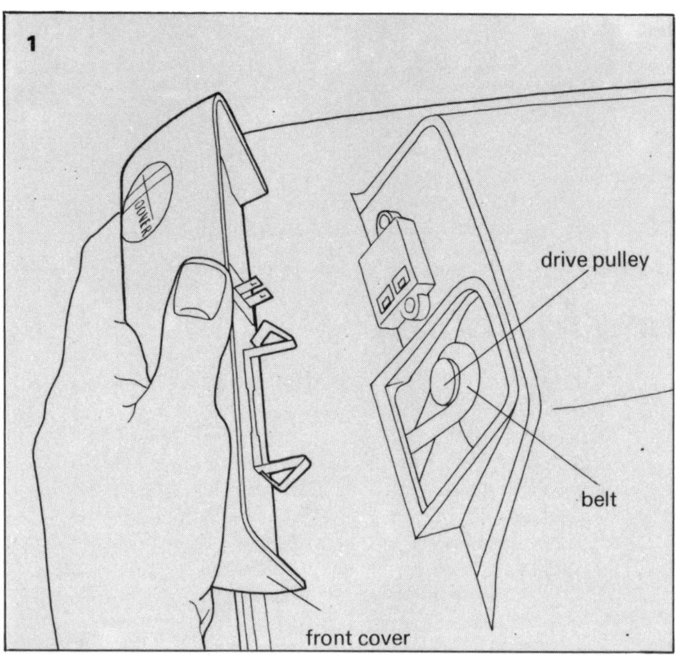

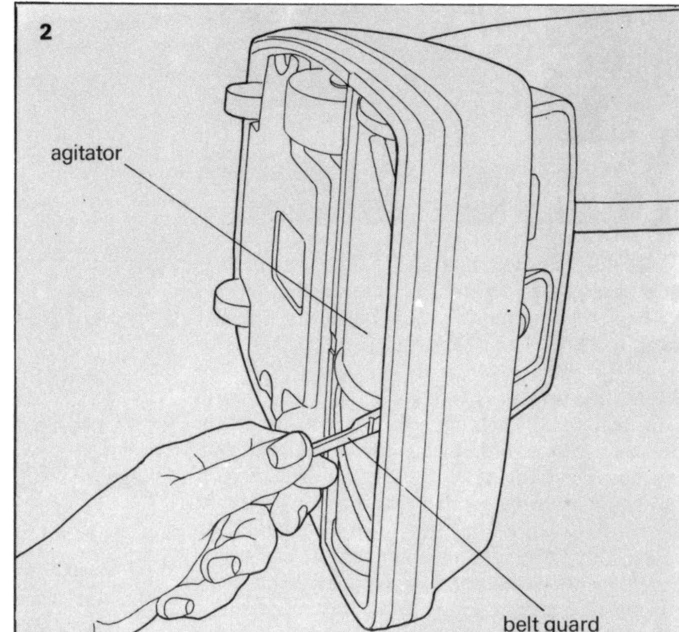

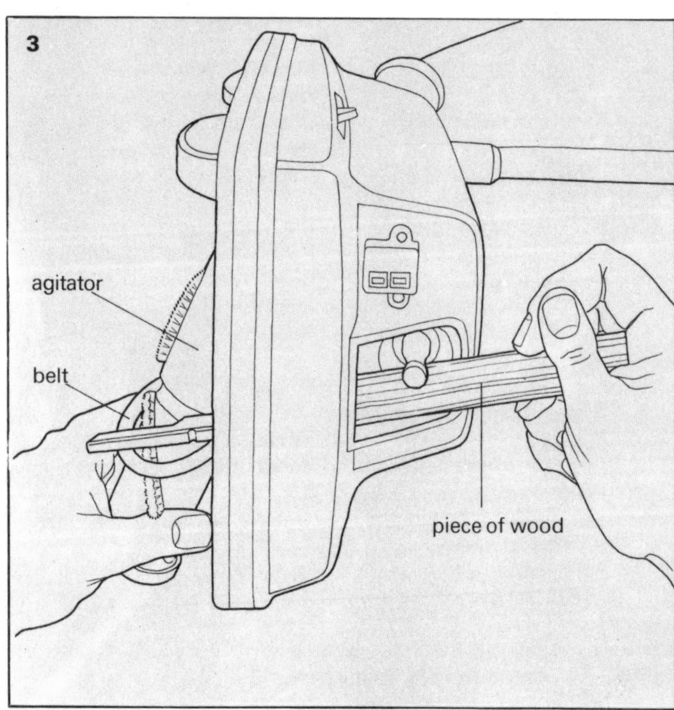

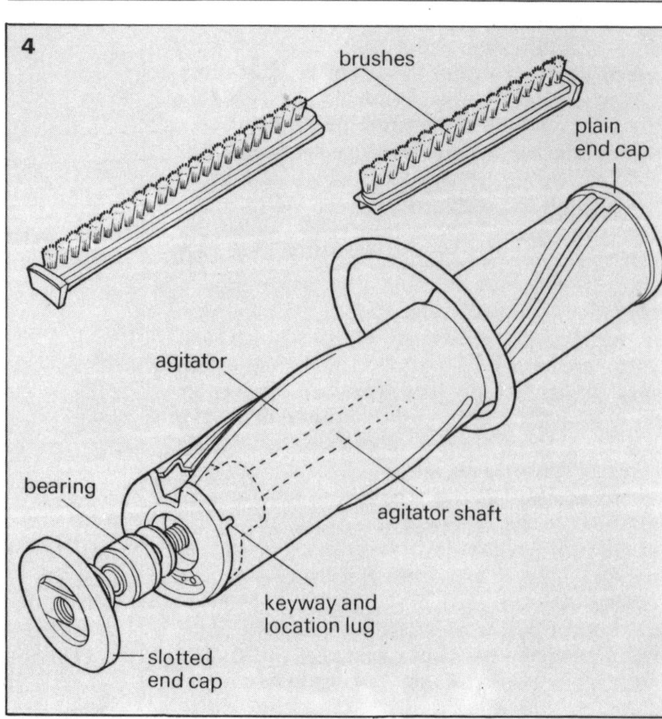

ment – if available. Remember also the machine has been tested for insulation; any major repair work will involve testing the machine again to make sure none of this has been affected and you should not attempt any such work unless you can get the machine tested for insulation by your local service dealer.

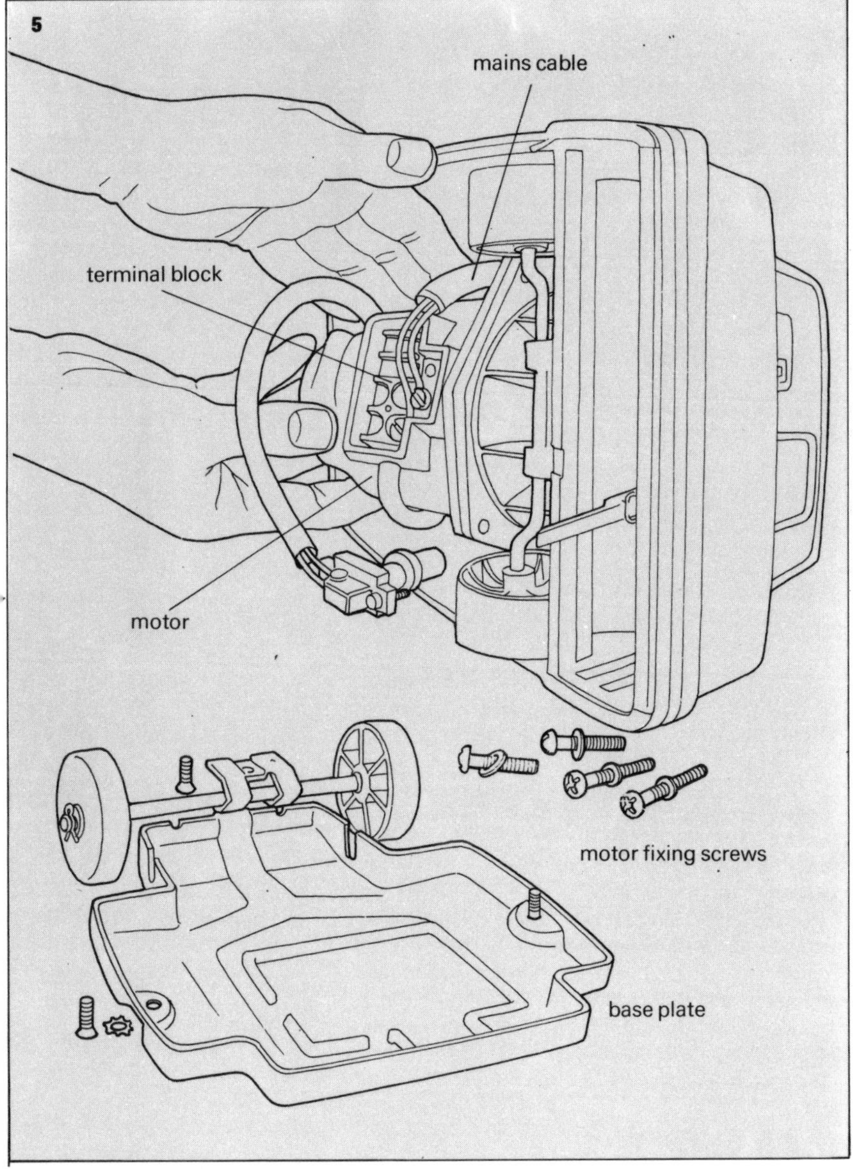

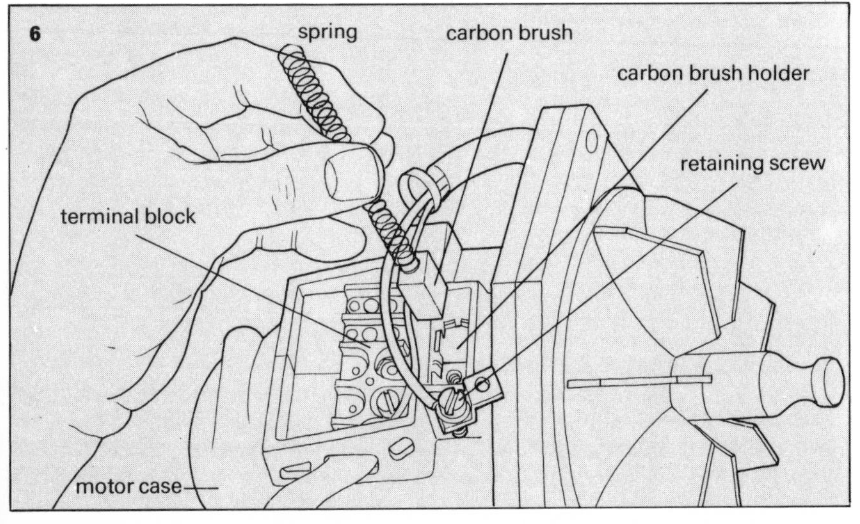

Checking for simple faults
If the machine is not picking up dust efficiently, first check whether the bag needs emptying. Excessive re-use of the same disposal bag will also reduce pick-up if the pores of the filter material become clogged with dirt. If you find excessive dust inside the appearance bag, check the bag and associated parts for faults.

If the machine does not start when switched on, this probably indicates an electrical fault. Check the mains supply and outlet, the plug and its wiring and fuse and the condition of the flex. If you detect any damage to the flex, don't be tempted to repair it; always renew the entire flex.

A change in the sound of the motor, which may seem to race, and a loss in the cleaning efficiency both indicate a worn belt. A further sign is the smell of burning rubber; the belt itself could burn through and break and the agitator stop completely. If the belt jams, it could stop the motor.

Fitting belt Take off the front cover to expose the drive pulley (**see 1**). Slip the belt off the pulley and turn the cleaner on its side so you can lift up the belt guard (**see 2**). Take out the agitator either by pulling on the belt or by gently tapping it through the front opening with a piece of wood (**see 3**).

Unscrew the thread guards on each end of the agitator shaft, noting from which end each was removed since they must be fitted back in the same position; remove any fluff or thread caught there. Replace the guards at their correct ends, making sure the agitator spins freely, and fit a new belt around the groove. Replace the agitator, twist the belt anticlockwise and stretch it over the pulley as indicated on the inside of the removable belt cover or on the front of the main housing. Put back the front cover.

Checking for major faults
Great care should be taken when checking for major faults. Before attempting any work, bear in mind the correct tools must be used and any repairs affecting the insulation must be checked for safety.

Agitator If the agitator does not spin freely after you have cleaned it, remove the aluminium agitator end caps and ball-bearings from the agitator body (**see 4**) to clean the agitator shaft. Make a note from which end of the shaft each end cap was removed so the caps are refitted in the correct position. The bearings can be cleaned and then greased or very lightly oiled. If they are worn, replace them with genuine spare parts and fit new washers. Check the bristles of the brush inserts are at least 13mm ($\frac{1}{2}$in) long. If they are worn, slot in new brush inserts.

Motor assembly A slow-running motor usually indicates a faulty armature. A noisy motor is caused by worn bearings or a broken fan. If your machine is still not working properly and you have ruled out the basic electrical faults already described, the motor can be examined by removing it from its case. You will need a very long Pozidriv-type screwdriver to remove the motor mounting screws; to reach these screws, remove the base-plate, rear wheel axle screws, handle socket screws and the switch.

Using the long screwdriver, remove the upper and lower motor fixing screws. Disconnect the mains flex from the terminal block (noting carefully the position of each lead so the flex is replaced correctly) and withdraw the motor (**see 5**). The motor case is in two halves held together by three

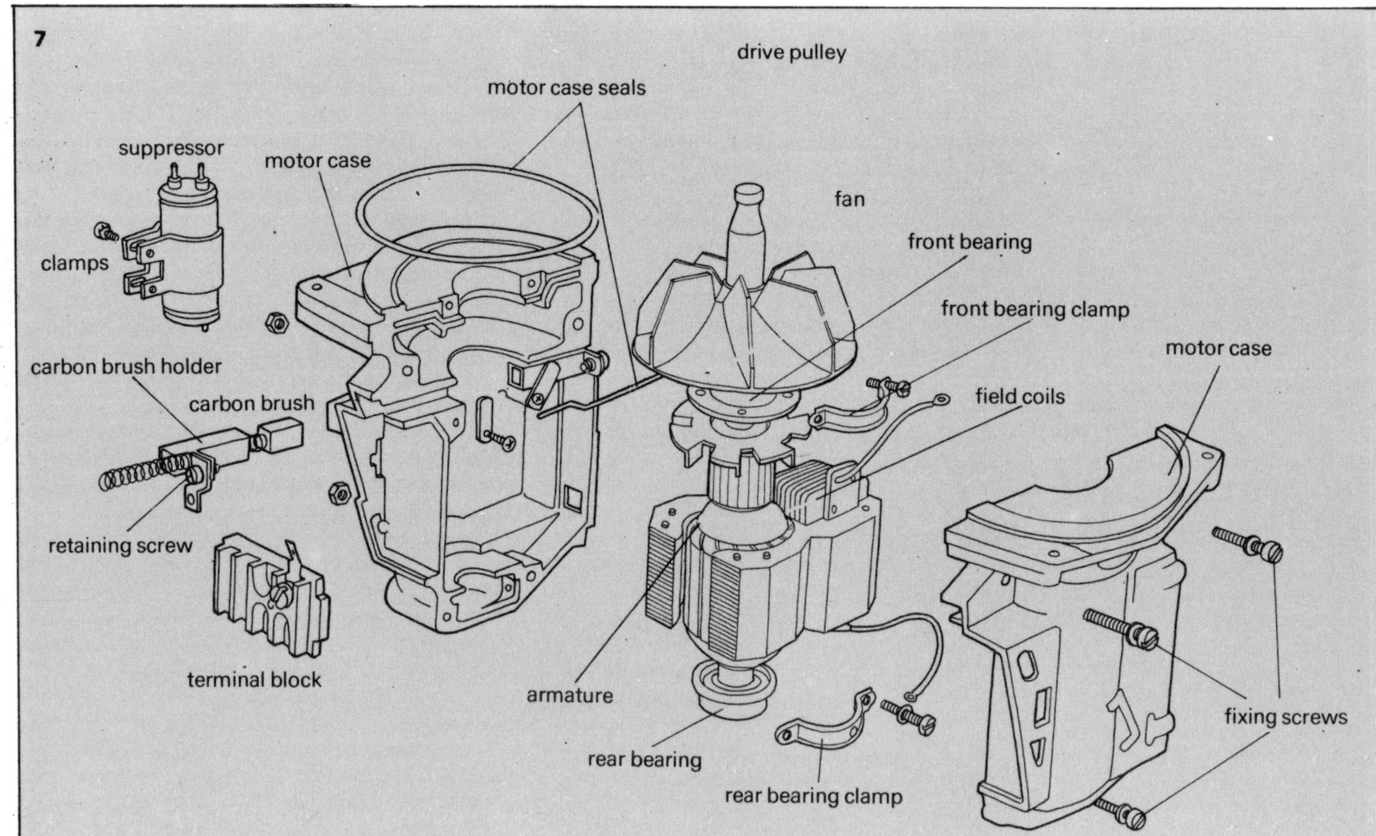

nuts and bolts. If you remove the single wire from the lower half (field coil) and a red wire from the terminal block, the two halves may be split apart. Again remember to note the position of the wires so each is replaced correctly.

Once the inside of the motor is exposed, the armature, field coils, bearings and carbon brushes can all be seen **(see 7)**. The carbon brushes, by use of their springs, bear upon the copper segments of the armature, so a clean contact is of paramount importance. Remove the brushes by unscrewing their holder **(see 6)**. Check the length of each brush is at least 6mm (¼in) and that the ends are not pitted or worn unevenly. If the brushes are worn, uneven or pitted, fit replacements. If the brushes do not need changing, make sure you replace the original brushes the same way round and in the same holders.

You can also remove the motor bearings from their clamps. Clean them with a small paint brush and check there is no sideways play or noise when they are revolved; if there is, they should be replaced. Before you put back original ball-bearings, grease or very lightly oil them; sleeve bearings do not require further lubrication. The field coils, held in position by the suppressor clamps, can also be brushed clean with a paint brush.

Warning The seal between the motor casing halves is vital to prevent dirt entering the motor; if you do undo the motor casing, make sure the seal is sound and replace it if necessary.

Looking after your cleaner

Your vacuum cleaner is less likely to go wrong if you use it carefully and observe a few simple rules.

- Empty the dust bag when it is about two-thirds full and replace it frequently with a new one; spare bags are available from the shop that supplied the cleaner. If the bag is overused, it will become clogged with dust and effect the picking-up of dirt.

- Keep the machine clean and store it safely with accessories when not in use; keep the flex neatly, but not tightly, wound.

- Lightly oil the machine according to the maker's instructions.

- When cleaning, avoid picking up sharp or large objects and items such as pins and hairgrips; large objects may cause obstruction in the cleaner or damage the fan.

- Replace parts when necessary. If there are jobs you cannot deal with, go to an authorised service dealer.

Hoover Senior

We continue with the Hoover Senior vacuum cleaner 625 series; other models may have slight modifications. Always fit genuine Hoover spare parts.

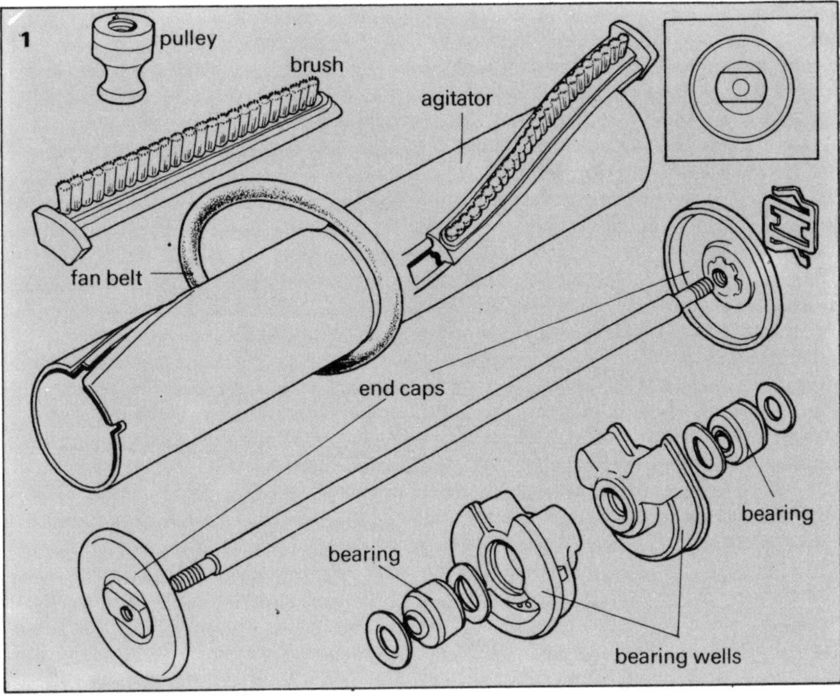

The Hoover Senior, with its high wattage motor, large agitator and high suction is a popular model for heavy duty carpet cleaning. As with the Junior, some maintenance can be done without special tools; this is within the scope of a careful worker provided the instructions are followed and the necessary precautions taken. The same warnings given for major work on the Junior apply to the Senior model, particularly as regards insulation. You should not tackle any work that affects the insulation until you have made sure you can have your machine tested for insulation.

Warning Before investigating the cause of any problem or attempting any repair work, you must always make sure the power is switched off and the plug removed from the socket. You should also check any job you do tackle does not invalidate any existing guarantee on the machine.

Checking for simple faults

There are several working parts of the Hoover Senior which should be checked regularly.

Agitator This can be pulled out after first removing the belt guard and releasing the belt from the pulley. To service the agitator, unscrew the end caps **(see 1)** and remove any fluff or threads caught there. Then

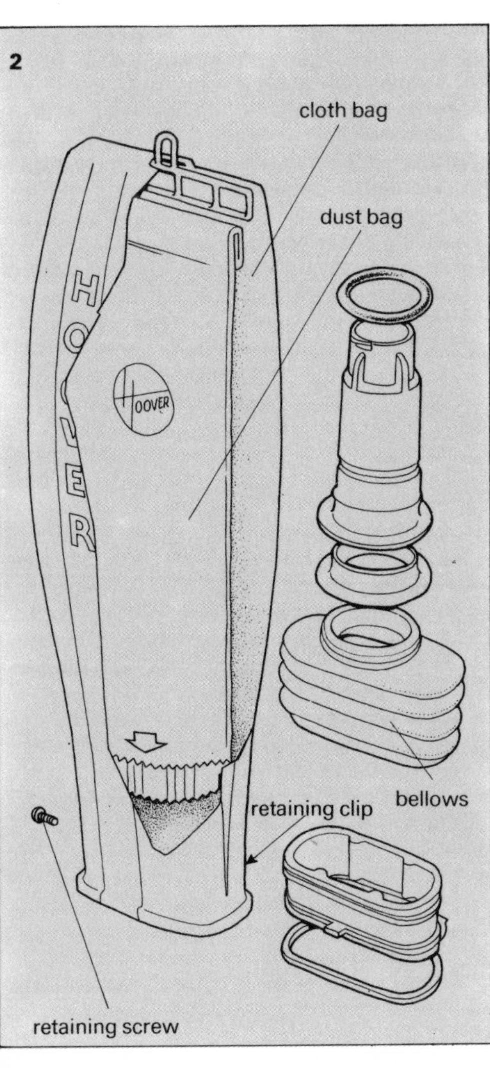

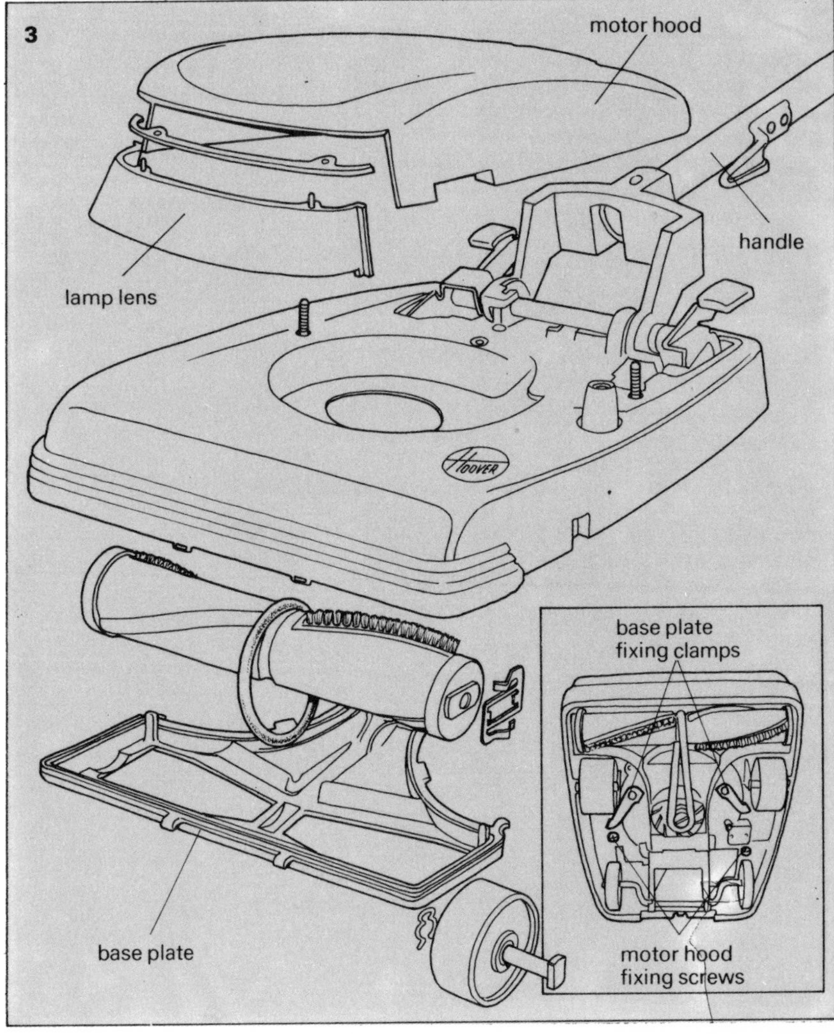

Always fit genuine Hoover spare parts, obtainable from your local service centre – identified by this sign

slide out the bearing wells, bearings and brushes. If the brushes are worn, they should be replaced. The bearings should be well greased; if they are worn, replace them and the washers.
Belt Make sure the belt is not cracked or unduly stretched. To fit a new belt, pass it round the agitator so it fits in the groove, replace the agitator and twist the belt anticlockwise round the pulley.
Wheels Check all the wheels turn freely; keep them dusted and lightly oiled to ensure quiet action.
Dust bag Look at the dust bag assembly to check the bellows are in good condition and not cracked or perished; otherwise dust will leak out and blow around the outer cloth bag. The bellows are held in place with a retaining clip and can therefore be easily removed and replaced (**see 2**).

Checking for major faults

Great care should be taken when checking for major faults. Before attempting any work, bear in mind the correct tools must be used and any repairs affecting the insulation must be checked for safety.
Pulley Make sure the pulley has a distinctive 'V' shape in it for the belt to run evenly. If the pulley is worn, unscrew it by gripping the shank with pliers while locking the fan with a block of wood; use padding to avoid damage. Remember the pulley has a left-hand thread, when unscrewing and refitting a new pulley.
Warning Great care must be taken not to damage the moulded insulation and belt groove with any tools used for loosening or tightening the pulley.

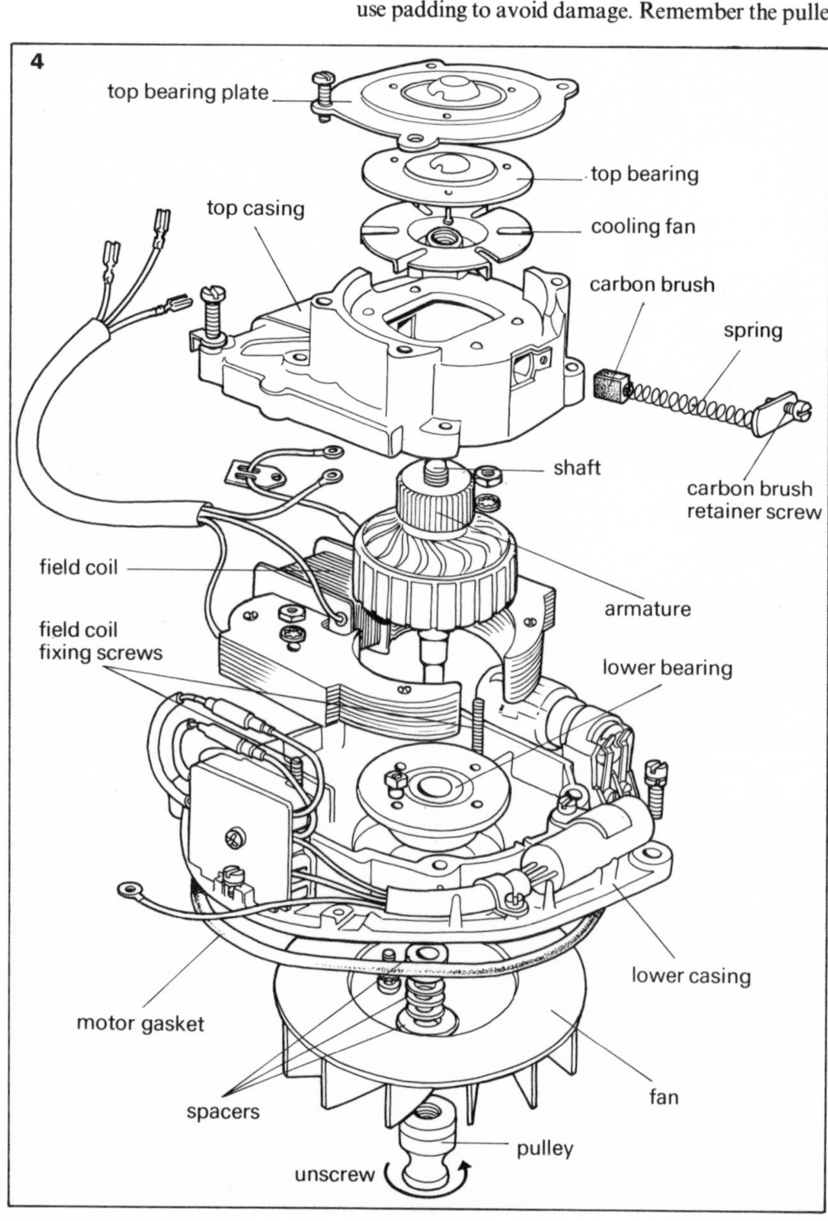

Removing the motor

You first need to remove the base plate and motor hood. Lay the cleaner on its side and release the base plate fixing clamps and remove the base plate. Look for the two cross-point screws, one on each side of the fan opening (**see 3**). Loosen the screws fully (they do not lift out), lower the handle assembly and stand the cleaner back on its base. Carefully lift the motor hood upwards away from the motor unit, removing it with the lamp lens. With the unit exposed, you can check components.
Carbon brushes Remove the carbon brushes by unscrewing the retainer screw and sliding it upwards (**see 4**). Carefully pull the spring and carbon brush outwards for inspection, noting which way round the brush faces since it must be replaced the same way round if there is still some life left in it. The carbon brush itself should not be chipped or unevenly worn on the motor armature end. Excessively worn carbon brushes should be replaced.
Bearings A worn bearing can cause 'armature wander', where the gap around the armature varies to such an extent the motor overheats while operating, resulting in total failure and a hefty repair bill. It is important, therefore, to check the armature bearings. Look at the top bearing, attached to the top bearing plate (**see 4**); if you unscrew this, you can see whether the bearing is worn internally or feel it by sliding it onto the armature shaft slightly and rocking it from side to side. A knock indicates excessive wear and you will probably have to replace either the top bearing plate assembly or the armature – or both; in which case you must replace with a complete, genuine part.

Replacing lower bearing

The lower bearing tends to be less troublesome since it is a caged ball-race type, compared to the top bearing which is simply a grease-impregnated bush. To check whether it is worn, spin the pulley; if this spins freely with no noise, the bearing is all right. If you need to replace the lower bearing, you will have to remove the motor unit. Take out the top bearing plate and unscrew the cooling fan. Remove the carbon brushes, undo the screws from the top motor case and lift off the case. The armature and field coil will now be exposed (**see 4**).

To extract the bearing, remove the screws from the lower casing and gently prise the casing upwards. As the motor assembly rises, the motor gasket, fan and pulley will be exposed. The pulley can be removed from the armature by unscrewing it (left-hand thread), but again great care should be taken not to damage the insulation moulded into the pulley. You can then remove the accompanying fan and spacers and pull out the armature. Once the armature has been removed, you will see the lower bearing. It will be riveted in place in the lower casing, unless the bearing has already been serviced, in which case it is screwed in. If riveted, you will have to replace the complete unit.
Field coil Should you need to remove and replace the field coil assembly due to a burn-out or breakage in wiring, undo the securing nuts and washers from the fixing screws, disconnect the wiring a fit a new unit.

Floor polishers

Electric floor polishers take a lot of the work out of polishing hard floors; some models are also suitable for scrubbing floors and shampooing carpets. The machines are heavy, but easily guided once in operation; because of its weight the machine will usually remove ingrained dirt and give the floor surface a bright, clean appearance.

A polisher has one, two or three rotary heads which are driven by an electric motor above them. The handle, which is telescopic in some cases, carries the controls and flex. Depending on the use to which the machine will be put, sets of stiff or soft brushes or polishing buffers can be clipped into the rotating heads. Some models have a detergent container fitted to the handle to convert the polisher into a carpet shampooer; detergent is fed to the brushes via a tube and controlled by a small lever.

A floor polisher should be kept clean and serviced regularly. Ensure the machine is dry before you put it away and hang it on a strong hook so it does not stand on its brushes. Wash the brushes and pads frequently.

Single head polisher
This type has a single rotary brush at least 300mm (12in) in diameter; it is generally used for commercial scrubbing and polishing. The machine has a single heavy duty motor which gives direct drive via a shaft to the head. This polisher is an extremely heavy piece of machinery, although two wheels are fitted to the rear so you can tip it backwards to improve mobility.

Switch The operating switch, which is built into the handle, has a dead man's action so the machine will work only when you apply pressure; once you release pressure, the circuit is broken and the motor stops. Because of its weight and powerful motor the polisher will continue under its own momentum; you will have to hold it back when you release the handle.

With the double-pole switch which is fitted, both the live and neutral supply are immediately broken when the switch is released. Even if one half of the switch contacts seize together, the other half will operate to cut the supply of electricity to the machine.

To check the switch connections, slacken the screw which holds the handle together and undo the set screw and sleeve which hold the handle to the machine. Once you have released the switch, check its connections and renew the flex as required. Check the earth connection is secure, if one is fitted. You can replace a seized switch, reversing the order of removal.

Remember . . .
Before starting work on any appliance
- Always make sure you will not invalidate any existing guarantee
- Always remove the plug from the socket and, where necessary, turn off the power at the mains
- Check availability and only fit genuine spare parts

1

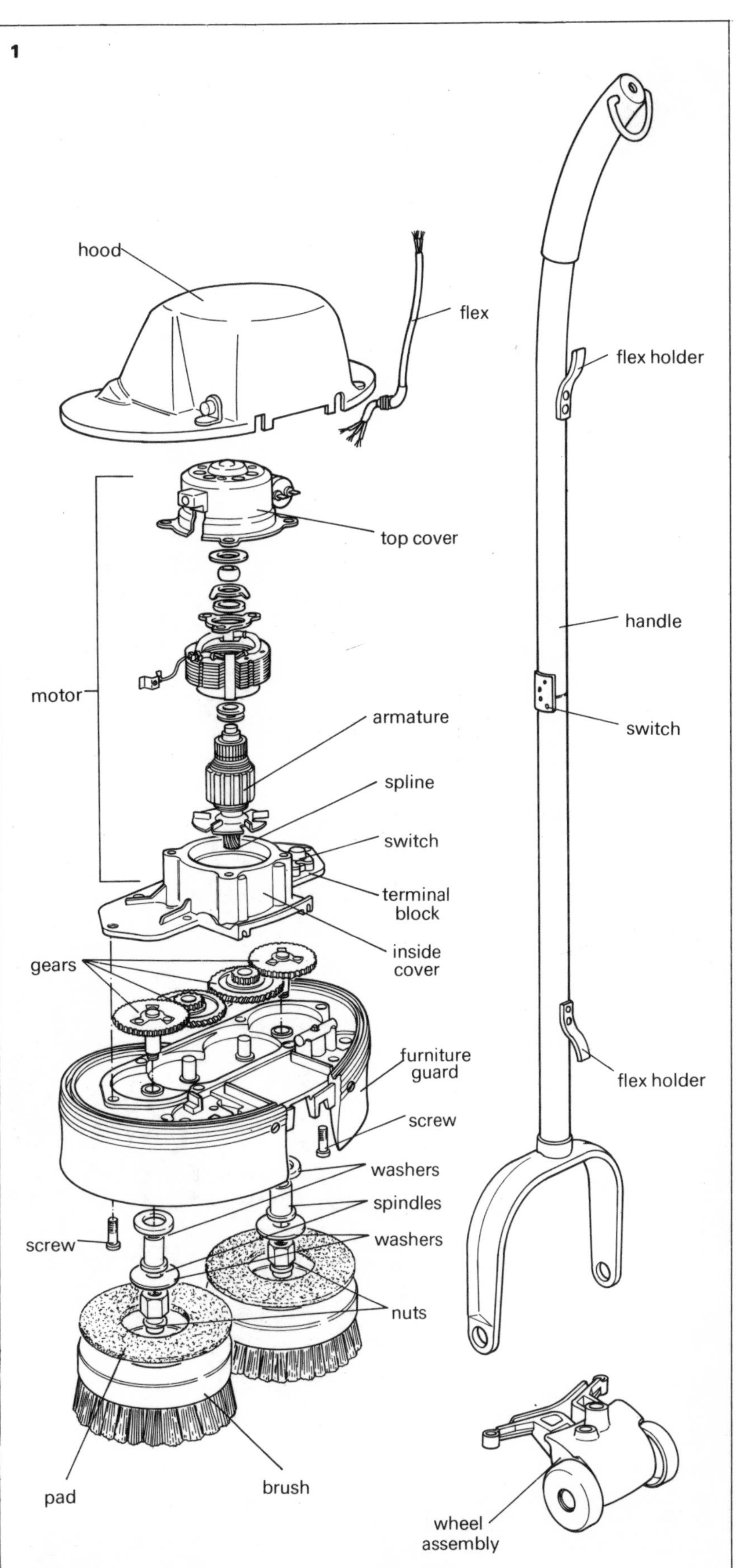

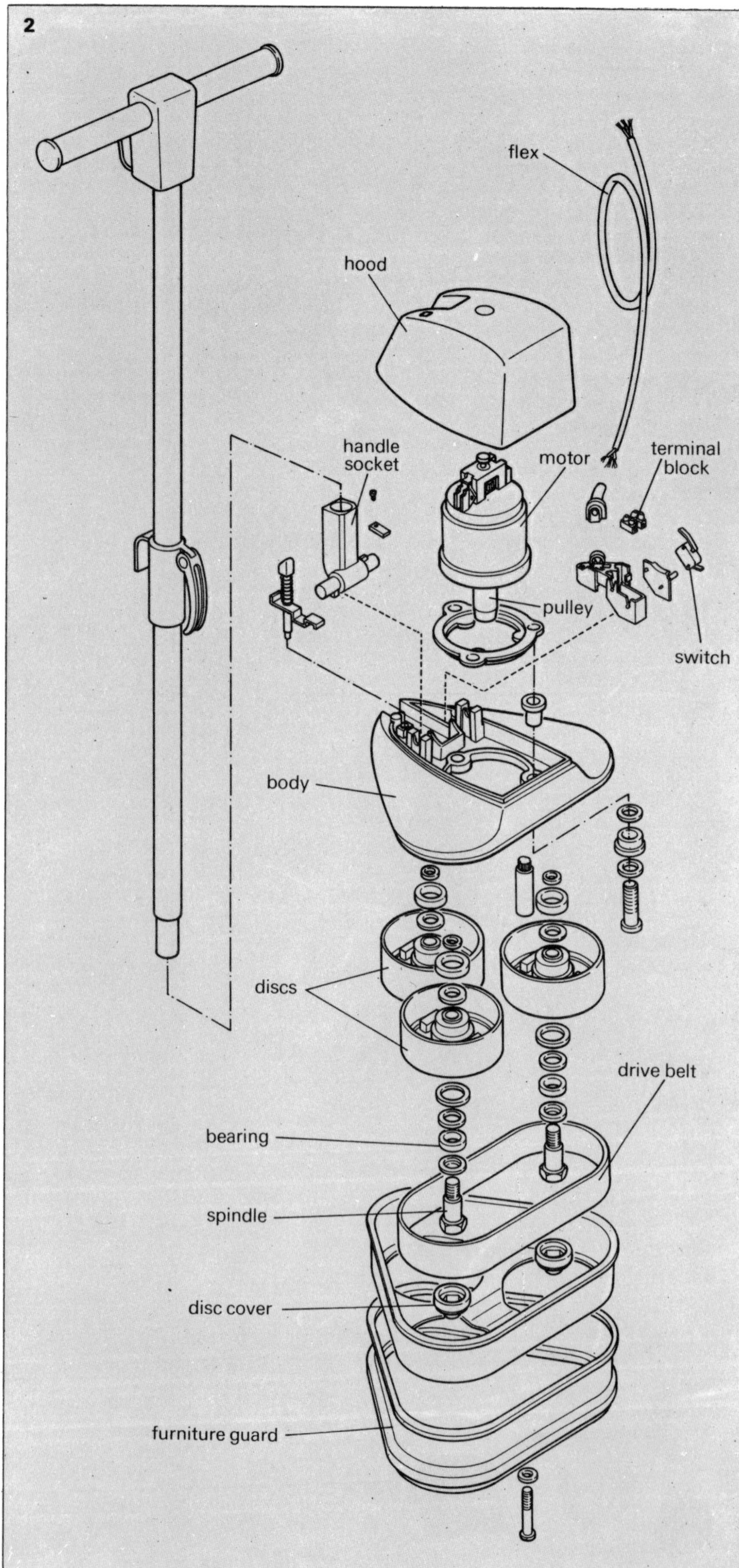

Double head polisher

This polisher, which is more suited to normal domestic use than the single head version, is powered by a much smaller motor; the drive is via gearing. The motor operates when you bring the handle into a working position; the lowering of the handle activates a switch inside to stop the motor and vice-versa.

Gears Beneath the polisher's hood, the small carbon brush-type motor has an armature with a spline built onto it. This spline drives a gear each side of it; one rotates in a clockwise direction and the other anti-clockwise. The two brush spindles each have matching gearwheels which interlock with the spline gears to drive the two heads.

If you find one head revolves and the other does not, it is likely one of the spline gears is damaged. These gears are normally made of nylon so their teeth can be stripped under pressure; this prevents them stopping the motor. A burnt-out motor is an expensive repair which must be tackled by a qualified engineer. Replacement gears, however, are quite cheap and simple to fit yourself. Remove the polisher pads and undo the screws underneath to remove the cover; lift off the inside cover and locate the four gears. Release them by holding one gear and undoing the nuts at the top of the brush spindles. Fit the replacement gear or gears in the reverse order of removal.

Most of the parts for the motor are available from your local service agent; these include the armature, field coils, carbon brushes and bearings.

Pads As already mentioned, brushes and pads should be washed frequently. When they are worn, replace them with spares from your local service agent.

Triple head polisher

The third type of floor polisher also has a single motor drive; this is to a belt which drives the three heads. The motor fitted to this type of polisher is fairly robust and unlikely to cause problems.

Belt Should the brushes slow down during operation, a worn or stretched belt is probably the cause. Before replacing the belt, make a careful note of the exact position of the worn one; it stretches round the discs which hold the brushes. The new belt should be a tight fit against these discs. It is very easy to fit a replacement belt incorrectly if you do not check the position of the worn one beforehand.

Bearings The discs which hold the brushes (or heads) are mounted on spindles which are fixed to the body of the polisher. You should check these from time to time for freedom of movement; there is a tendency for fluff and debris to build up in the bearings. The bearings should be cleaned of all fluff and dirt and lightly greased. To gain access to the bearings, unscrew the plastic cover which is located in the centre of each of the three discs.

Previous page

1 Cutaway of a typical double head floor polisher, showing the component parts; the wheel assembly is plastic and the complete unit can be replaced if necessary

2 Cutaway of a typical triple head floor polisher, showing the component parts

Washing machines

There are three basic types of domestic washing machine. The single tub is purely a washing machine, with possibly a wringer to extract excess moisture from the clothes; the twin tub is a combined washing machine and spin dryer; the automatic carries out washing and spinning in a single drum.

There are two main types of washing action – the central spindle agitator and the impeller or rotating wheel positioned at the side or bottom of the tub; the impeller provides a rather shorter washing time. Some machines have a tumble action, caused by horizontal drum rotation, and modern machines have a reversing tumble action in both directions.

The majority of machines have a 2–3kW heater positioned under the agitator on the floor of the tub; don't attempt to repair these elements.

Single tub machines

The servicing you can perform on this type of machine is limited. Inspect hoses and hose clips at least twice a year for wear and deterioration; they should be tightly fastened. Inspect the pump assembly for hose blockage, water leaks and excess wear; it should move freely, however. Some types of pump have an aluminium base and this may corrode through soapy water leaking. If there is a leak, you should replace the pump base. Leaks can also cause electrical faults; if water seeps out onto a moving part it will spray around the inside of the machine, damaging electrical components.

Gearbox Single tub machines which have a gearbox-driven washing action – usually identified by a large oscillating paddle inside the tub – need little or no maintenance. The gearbox will be a sealed unit; if a fault develops, you can have an exchange gearbox fitted. Check for oil leaks and excess wear on

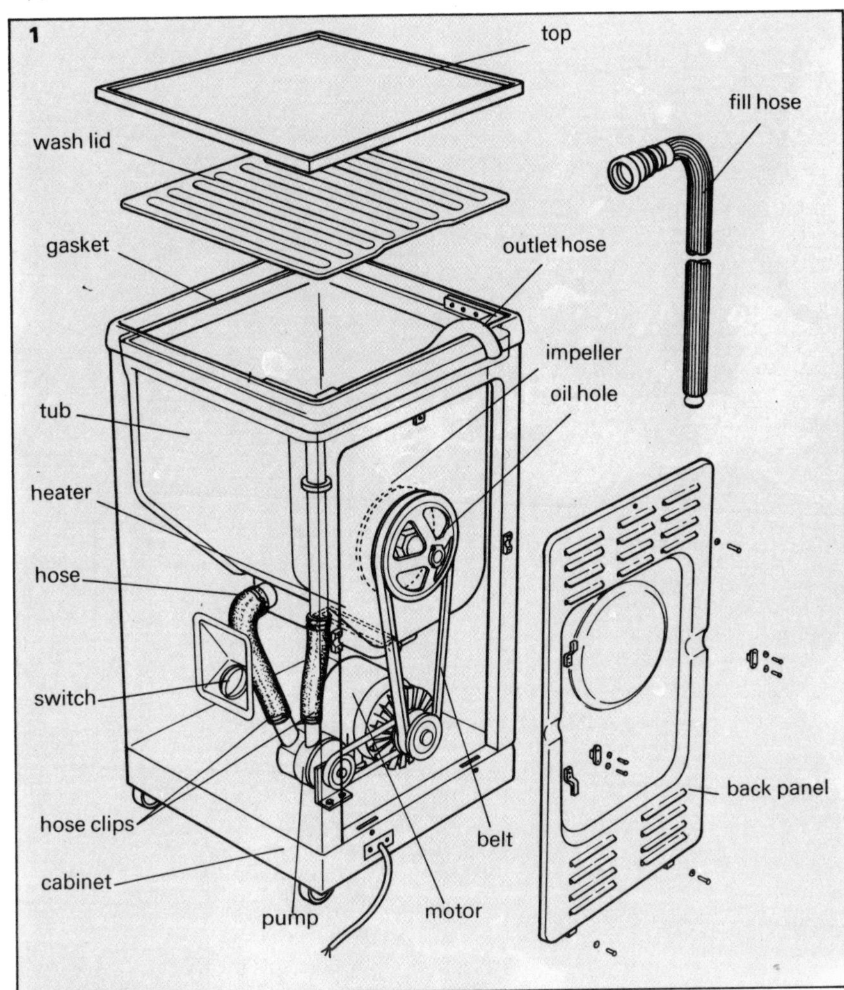

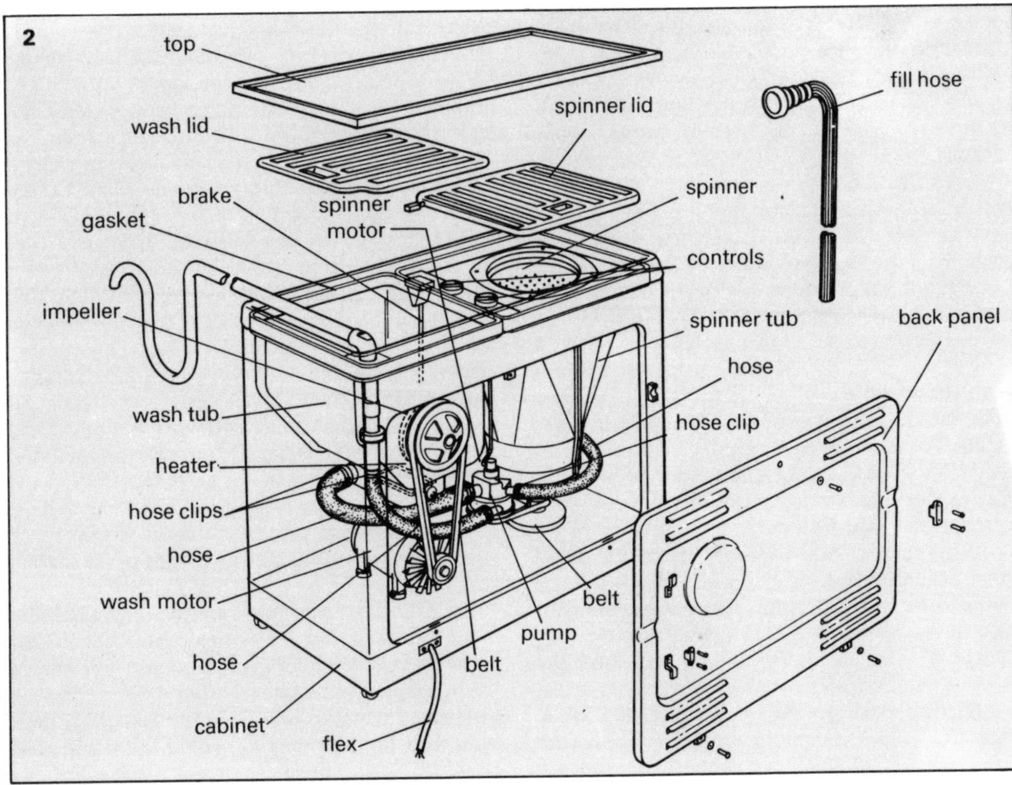

1 Cutaway of a typical single tub washing machine with impeller action, showing the component parts. This model is no longer made and spares may be difficult to find

2 Cutaway of a typical twin tub washing machine with impeller action and spin dryer. Few of these models are now left and you may have to search for spares

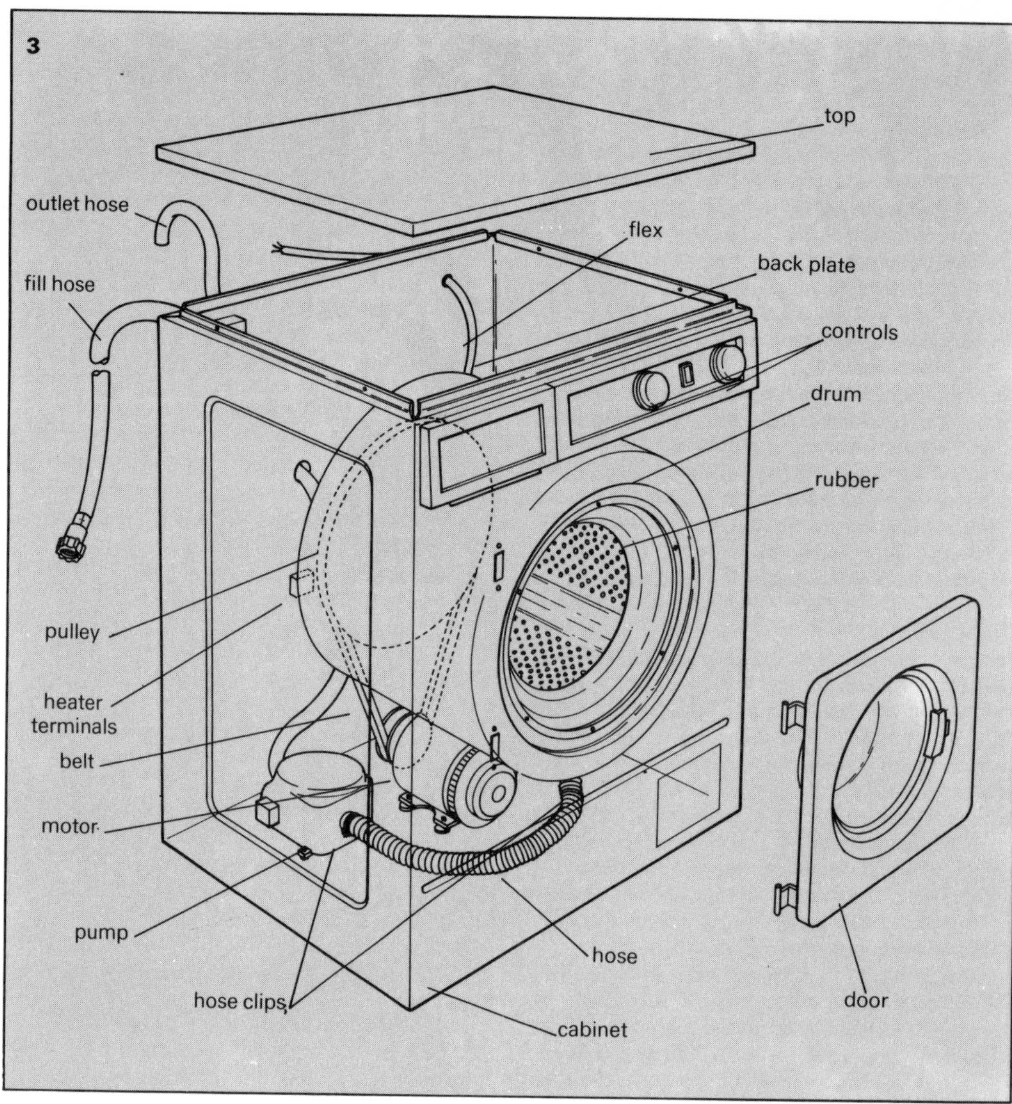

3 Cutaway of a typical front-loading automatic washing machine, showing the component parts

the moving driving parts; it may be possible to replace faulty oil seals and gyrator drive components. Remove the paddle frequently and clean the mounting surfaces.

Impeller If your single tub machine has an impeller which provides the washing action, maintenance is important. A belt-driven pulley provides power to the impeller, which is supported on its shaft by a phosphor bronze bearing. This bearing must be lubricated fairly regularly with light machine oil through the oil hole near the bearing. If this bearing is not oiled, the impeller shaft may seize; this could halt the motor and cause expensive and needless repair.

Twin tub machines

Twin tub washing machines have a spin dryer attached to the washing machine; its features and the servicing are basically similar to the single tub. The spinner side is usually belt-driven by its own motor; in this case the spinner is independent of the washing machine. Some spinners have a slipping clutch arrangement to offset the extra load imposed on the motor by wet clothing, which is spun at up to 3000 rpm.

Clutch The clutch for the spinner may take the form of two fibre shoes which move out at speed and grip the housing of the spinner assembly. Wear is inevitable, so you should periodically inspect the shoes and ensure the spinner assembly bearings are well lubricated at all times.

Brake Brake shoes and cables for the spinner should be checked for wear and adjustments should be made if necessary. As the cables stretch, the brake arm or band will engage; this will result in a lack of spinning speed and cause strain on the motor. Cable adjustments can be made via either a threaded portion of cable or a nut positioned at the end of the brake cable; if you turn this component to add tension, you should release the brake. But, for safety, repairs should be left to a specialist.

Belt You should check suspension mounting rubbers and spinner drive belts for deterioration and cracking. Vee-section drive belts should have reasonable tension – 13mm ($\frac{1}{2}$in) of play between the furthest pulleys. If the belt is stretched and there is no method of retensioning it, you should renew the belt; if it is not replaced, the belt will slip.

Motor The spinner may not have belts to drive the drum; if it has a motor giving direct drive, there is little maintenance possible. You can only check suspension mountings and adjust the brake cable if necessary.

Pump Spin dryer pumps are usually similar to those fitted to the washing machine. Inspect them for water leaks, loose hose clips, wear and tightness in the bearings. The pump belt is normally made of an elasticated material and deterioration of this will indicate a fault developing within the pump; this could be either a blockage or a dry bearing.

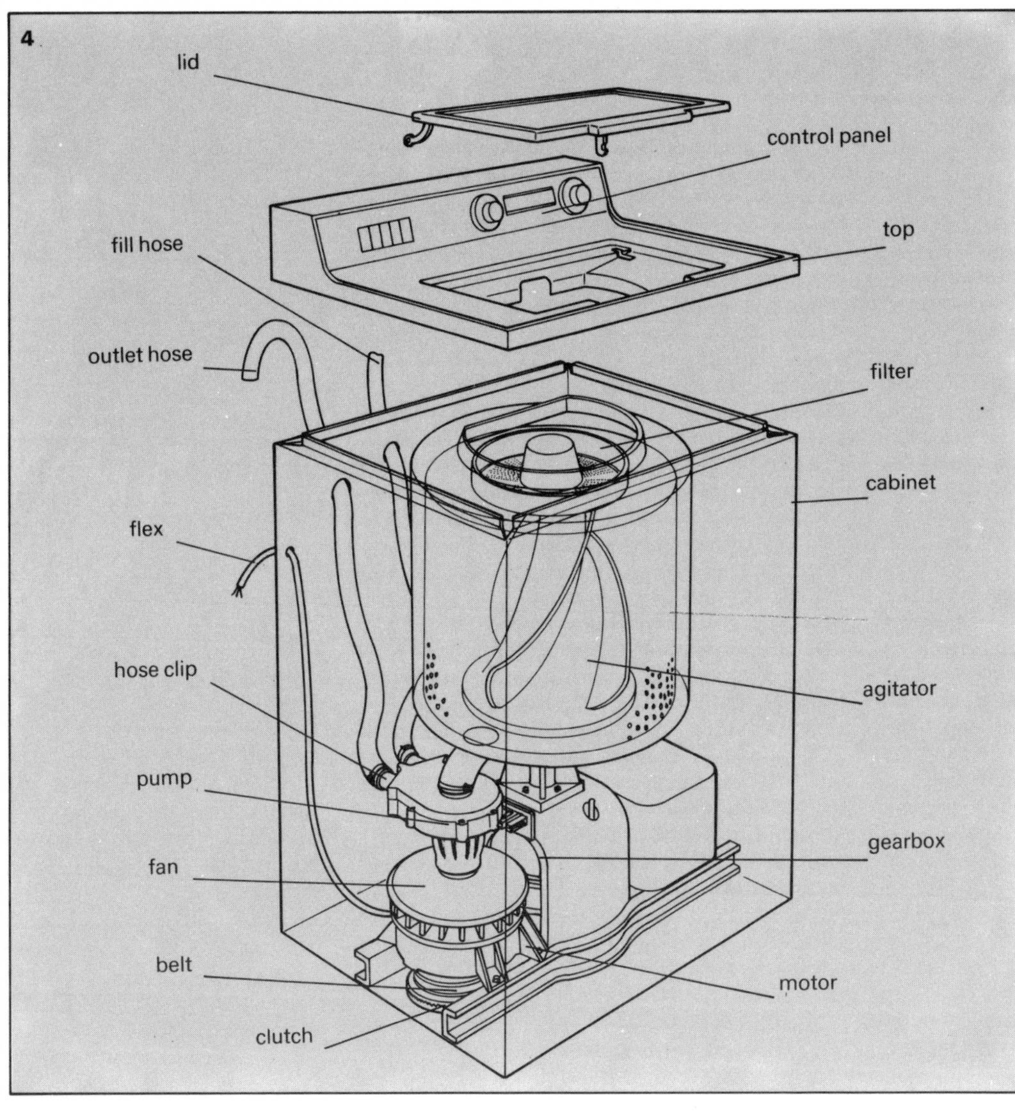

4 Cutaway of a typical top-loading automatic washing machine, showing the component parts

Automatic machines

These washing machines may be top-loading but front-loading versions are more common. Most people think of automatic washing machines as highly complex, sophisticated and expensive to maintain; there are however, several servicing jobs you can easily carry out if you are electrically minded and thorough.

Belt The effect of a broken drive belt on a front-loading automatic will be obvious; the machine will fill with water, heat and pump out, but the drum will not turn – even though you can hear the motor running. To replace the broken or worn belt, make sure you unplug the machine (as when working on any electrical appliance) and remove the back plate; you will now be able to see the belt. If you can turn the motor and drum pulley, you will be able to renew the belt. If, however, the drum is noisy and stiff to turn, it is likely the bearings have seized and the machine will require major repairs by a specialist.

Door rubber The rubbers which seal the door may split and begin to leak water; you can replace a defective door rubber. Remove the top of the machine, loosen the rubber from round the door and push the drum back into the machine; use a small piece of timber to wedge the drum away from the door of the machine. This should give you enough room to reach the thin band clamp which is normally held together by a nut and bolt. Once the nut and bolt have been loosened you can remove both the clamp and the rubber. The replacement rubber simply slots round the doorway and is clamped in the reverse order of removal.

Water pump The water pump will have a separate electric motor; you should inspect the pump from time to time for leakages, loose hose clips and dry bearings. Remove materials such as fluff from behind the impeller since it will collect there. To replace a defective pump, first drain water from the hoses and remove them. Note the positions of the wires (two or three) on the pump and remove them; once you have undone the bolts securing the pump to the base of the machine, you can lift out the pump for inspection. Remove the pump cover, which is secured with clips or screws, and inspect the impeller inside. The impeller is normally screwed onto the rotor shaft – and could have a left-hand thread so check before you force it. With the impeller removed, you can lightly oil and check the bearings for wear; they are positioned at each end of the pump body.

Hoses The hoses will deteriorate with age; inspect them regularly and replace them when necessary to avoid a flooded kitchen or laundry. All water leaks should be thoroughly checked because water could damage electrical components inside the machine.

Warning Electrical faults should be left to a specialist; never attempt to diagnose and repair them yourself.

Remember...

Before starting work on any appliance

- Always make sure you will not invalidate any existing guarantee
- Always remove the plug from the socket and, where necessary, turn off the power at the mains
- Check availability and only fit genuine spare parts

Tumble dryers

Along with the growing trend towards automatic washing machines away from twin tubs, there is an increased demand for tumble dryers. A tumble dryer is often purchased as a twin to an automatic washing machine; many manufacturers market the items as a matching pair and provide a stacking kit as an optional extra to enable the dryer to stand on top of the washing machine. This saves a considerable amount of space in your laundry area.

Apart from their obvious drying action, most modern tumble dryers are equipped to cool the clothing at the end of the drying cycle; this helps stop creasing and allows you to remove the clothes easily.

Dryer components

The usual features of a modern tumble dryer are a two-heat setting control and a clockwork timer which includes a cooling period as mentioned above. With all dryers it is very important to keep air circulating over the dryer heating element(s) clear and free from the dust and fluff which normally accumulates over a period of time. The filter, which collects lint and fluff, should be cleaned every week by removing the circular disc and peeling off the coating of fine, dry lint. One type blows air through its heater and into the drying drum; another has a motor fan which sucks air through the front of the drum and over its heating elements. In the latter case, the air is passed through the drum and filter and ejected through a vent at the front, top or rear of the machine. For most machines you can buy a flexible hose which fits over the vent to eject the warm, moist air away from the room to the outside through a window or through a permanent outlet in an outside wall. The belt-driven revolving drum is powered by an electric motor; the fan may also be belt-driven on some models.

Element cut-out Tumble dryer heating elements have thermal overload cut-out units (TOCs) positioned close by; these are designed to prevent the element overheating when in use and to provide a constant drying temperature. One model has an auxiliary cut-out fitted in addition to the TOC; if the drum temperature rises above a safe working limit, it will stop the machine.

Rear element One type has its heating element and TOC mounted on the rear panel; this is convenient for servicing and repair work, since access is easy.

Front element Another type has the heating elements mounted above and below the door; the TOC is also fitted here. The spiral elements are fitted on the inside of the heat shield and are spaced with porcelain insulators.

Timer Most machines are fitted with a clockwork timer switch; this usually gives a 12-minute cold tumble before stopping.

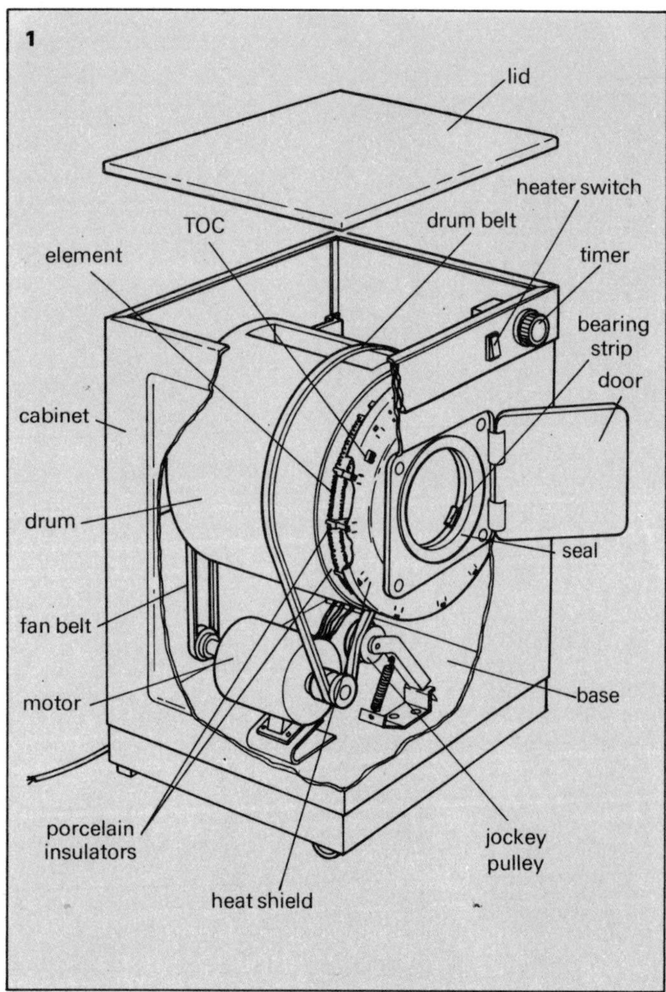

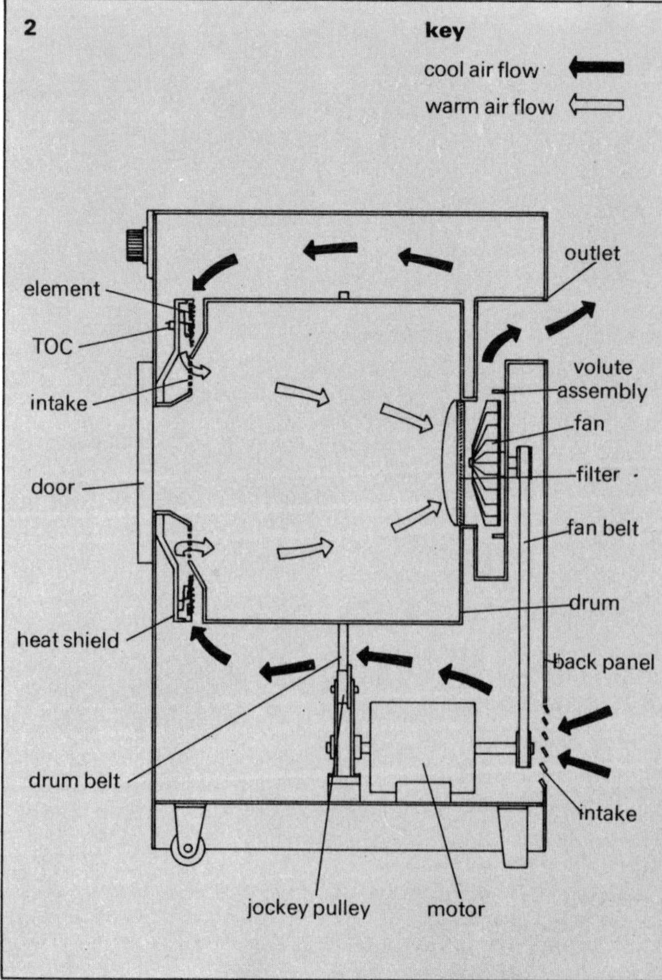

1 Cutaway of a typical front-mounted element tumble dryer
2 Direction of air flow through a front element dryer; the fan sucks air through the drum via the heating element and expels it through the outlet at the back

Heater switch This is a simple rocker action switch which usually provides two-heat selection from the element(s) by means of a thermostat.

Bearing strip This strip is located on the lip of the drum inside the machine; it is lubricated with a heatproof silicone PTFE fluid and usually consists of a braided tape glued onto the lip. If the tape runs dry, it could cause a rumbling noise as the dryer operates; see below for the necessary repairs.

Dryer repairs

Regularly check the condition of the filter, belts and drum. The drum should swing freely; lightly grease its bearings to ensure it does. You can oil the door hinges lightly, but not too much since any component behind or above the door could be affected. Any belts fitted should be correctly in line with their pulleys; they should not be overstretched or cracked. The jockey pulley (found on dryers which have one belt for the drum and one for the fan) should have spring tension; a little light oil on the wheel spindle will keep it free. Don't forget to put a drop of oil on the wheels; if the machine is on the floor and you have not fitted a venting kit, you may have to move it to an airy position before you use it.

Warning If you are in any doubt about carrying out repairs on your tumble dryer, refer to the manufacturer or call in a recognized service agent.

Replacing belts The belt used to drive the drum – and the fan as well on some machines – is made of elasticated material. The cabinet will probably have to be removed if you need to replace the belt which drives the drum. Take out the lower front panel screws, lift the panel off and remove the screws from the rear of the cabinet. Undo the screws from the front of the cabinet, some of which you will find behind the door and others on the lower panel. Pull the bottom sides of the cabinet slightly out of position and lift them upwards; take care not to scrape the drum. Undo the screws in the back panel, remove it and release the belt from the jockey pulley. Slacken the clamp around the fan and slide the fan assembly off the motor shaft. Take out the nuts from the tie rod (remembering to note their positions for reassembly) and unscrew the nut which secures the drum shaft through the ball race bearing. Remove the nuts and bolts holding the side struts to the machine from the back panel, hold the tub in position with one hand and pull slightly on the back panel with the other; this should create enough space to slide the old belt out and the new one in. Always fit replacement belts as recommended by the manufacturer. Reverse the procedure for reassembly.

Another type of dryer has separate fan and drum belts. To replace the fan belt, which is elasticated, remove the back panel and substitute the belts. The drum belt on this type of dryer is more complicated to replace. Remove the back panel and fan belt and disconnect the drum belt from the tensioning jockey pulley; you can make access to this part easier by removing the cover on the base of the dryer. The base cover is held in place with plastic rivets in two pieces; prise the centre out first and then the outer portion. The base cover can now be removed. The next step is to remove the volute assembly. This is a metal plate upon which the fan assembly is mounted; the fan itself is held with screws. Before you remove the volute, hold the drum in a horizontal position so the front bearing face is not disturbed. Holding the drum in one hand, slip off the old belt and slide on the new one; slide the volute assembly back on and secure the parts you have removed.

Remember...
Before starting work on any appliance
- Always make sure you will not invalidate any existing guarantee
- Always remove the plug from the socket and, where necessary, turn off the power at the mains
- Check availability and only fit genuine spare parts

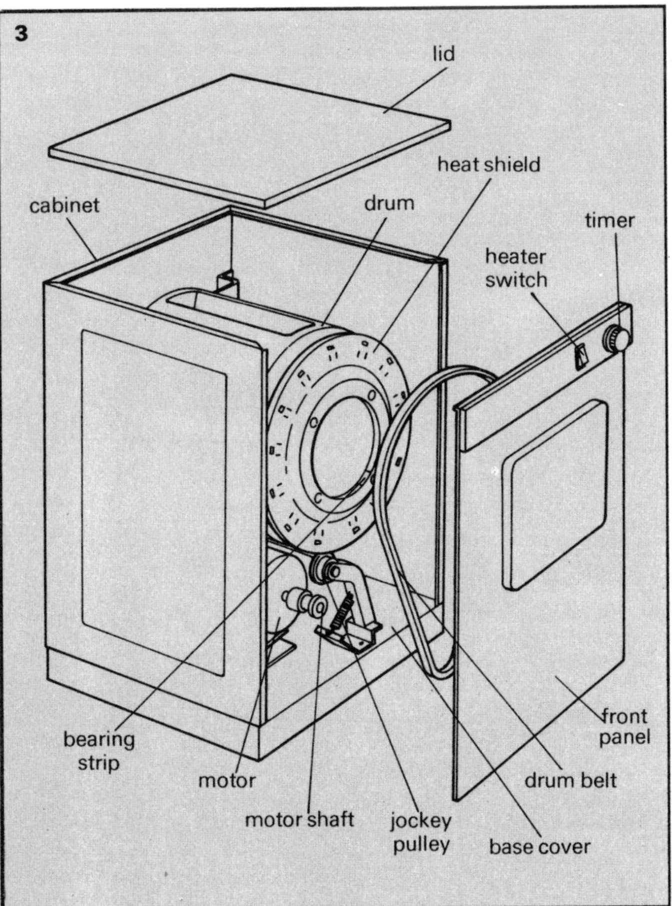

3 Replacing the drum belt on a front element tumble dryer; pull the jockey pulley against the spring to release the tension and remove the belt

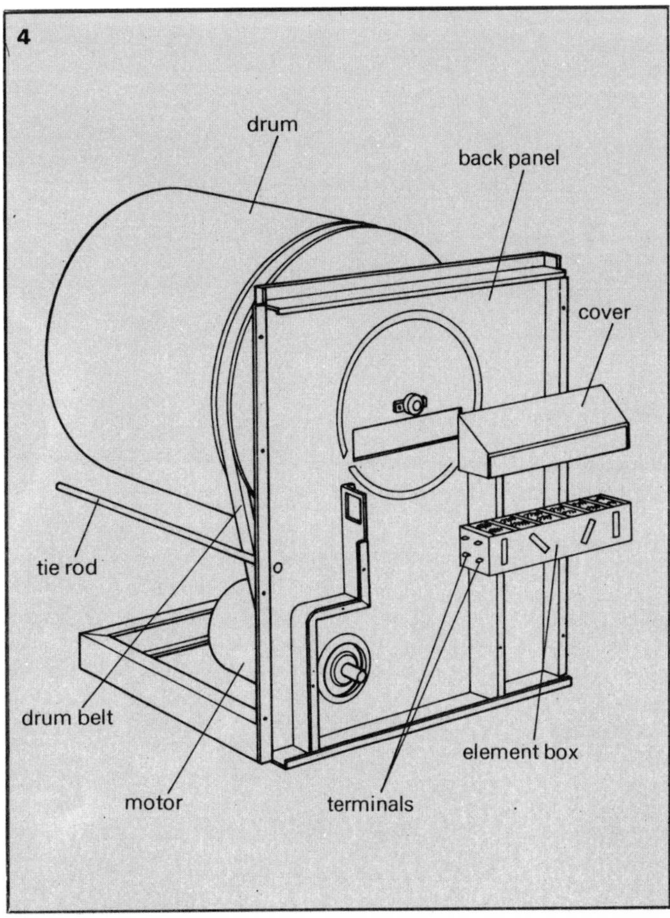

4 Typical rear-mounted element tumble dryer; to remove the element, simply disconnect the terminals and lift the element from its mounting brackets

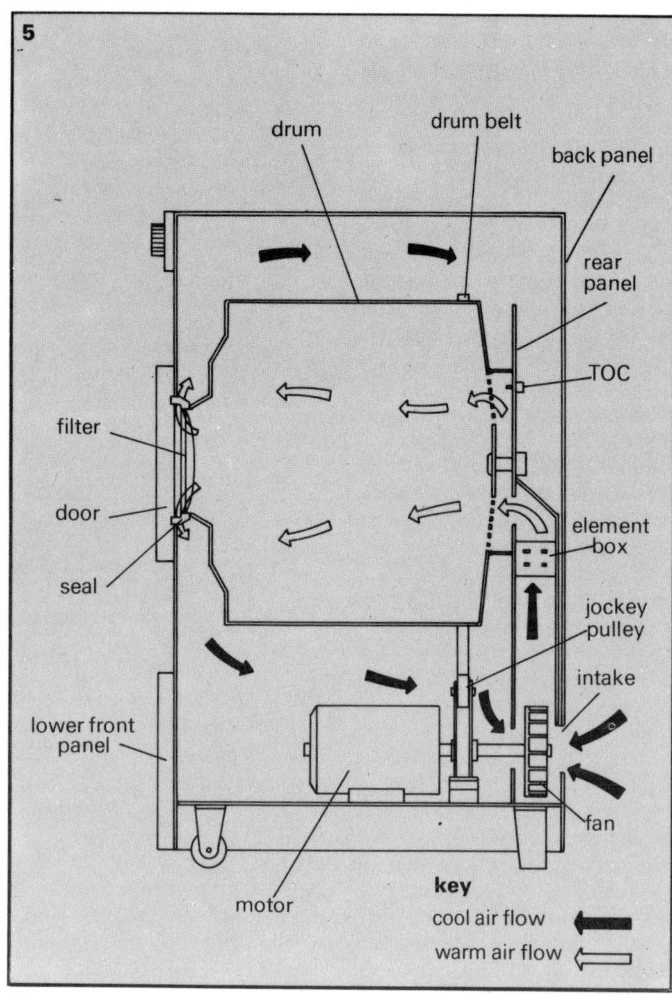

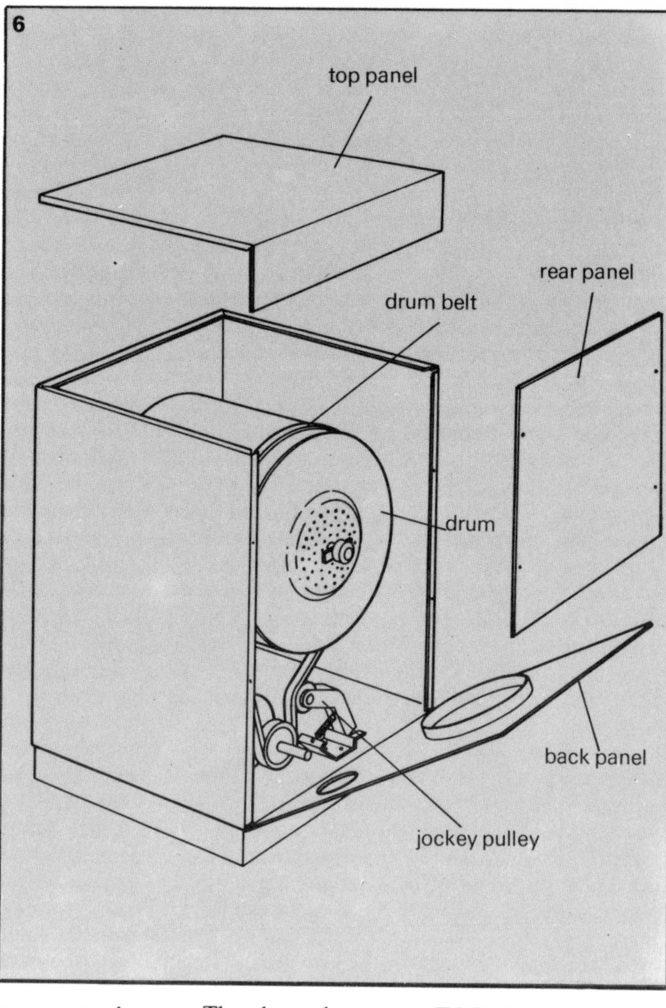

5 Air flow through a rear element dryer; the fan blows the air through the drum via the element and into a filter at the front, expelling it through the outlet in the back panel
6 Replacing drum/fan belt on a rear element dryer; pull the jockey pulley against the spring to release the tension and remove the belt

Removing drum Should you need to remove the drum because the bearings are worn, the procedure is similar to replacing belts. You will have to remove the lid since the drum must be lifted out through the top of the dryer. The front bearing felts often become worn; this is indicated by a rumbling noise from the front of the dryer. Bearing felts have now been superseded by plastic bearings which are fitted on the heat shield assembly of modern tumble dryers; you can adapt your machine to accept plastic bearings. Two front and two rear bearings, clips and an instruction sheet are available in the form of a kit for this purpose.
Replacing timer If the dryer does not stop at the end of its cycle, the timer switch is faulty and you will have to replace it. On one model you remove the lid of the dryer, pull off the timer knob and remove two screws which hold the switch to the cabinet. Carefully note the wiring connections and fit the replacement timer, reversing the procedure for removing the faulty one.

Another model also requires the removal of the cabinet before you can replace the timer; lift off the top of the dryer, pull off the knob and remove the two screws and washers. Be careful not to drop these spacer washers or screws into the body of the dryer; change over the wires and fit the replacement timer.
Replacing cut-out If your dryer is fitted with an auxiliary cut-out which fails, it will usually stop the feed to the heater; it is a preset unit and you will have to replace it. Two screws hold the unit in position; simply push the leads over the correct terminals of the replacement.

The thermal cut-out (TOC) is working constantly and it is therefore likely it will need replacement at some time. If it fails, there will be a total lack of heat when the dryer is operating; the contacts of the TOC soften and a gap forms between them which prevents power reaching the heater. The TOC is usually secured to the heater with two screws; loosen the unit and detach the leads. Be careful not to damage the TOC as you do this, since it is a complete item; if you break one of the spirals, you will have to buy a new element. Remember to replace the sealing compound round the edges of the TOC unit since this prevents air leaks.
Replacing heater switch This is held in position with spring clips; by squeezing the clips you can withdraw the switch from the front of the dryer. Make a note of the wiring and replace the new switch in the reverse order of removal. On some models, you have to remove the top of the dryer; the leads are replaced in the same way and the switch is also mounted on fixing lugs.
Renewing front bearing strip If the front bearing strip runs dry of lubricant, this could cause a rumbling noise when the machine is working. To replace this strip you have to remove the drum; if you remove the cabinet and strut, you will have enough room to lift the drum carefully out. You may need to spring out the front and rear cabinet panels slightly to do this. Strip off the old adhesive after removing the tape; if you leave a lump of adhesive, a knock may develop. Make sure you replace the recommended braided tape or strip and check it is soaked with silicone PTFE fluid; this is heatproof and also acts as a lubricant.

Electric irons

There are two basic types of electric iron – dry and steam. Some repairs are simply a matter of maintenance involving no special tools, while others are complicated and best left to a qualified person. Bear in mind if you embark on a complicated repair and find you cannot put the pieces back together properly, the cost of a replacement or repair by a professional will be much greater than if you took it to an expert originally. Before you attempt any work on this type of appliance, check carefully to ensure you will not invalidate any guarantee.

If your iron is not working properly, check first whether the plug fuse has blown or if there is a faulty connection at the plug. Check also the socket outlet is working, using another appliance. Before starting work on your iron always remove the plug from the socket outlet.

Dry irons

A common problem with dry irons is wear on the flex – due to age and usage. This occurs as the flex is wound round the iron and as it rubs against the ironing board. As soon as any wear on the outer covering is apparent the flex should be replaced. If the flex covering is allowed to wear through, it will expose the plastic or rubber-covered inner wires. This is a dangerous state; once the insulating cover breaks, the bare live and neutral wires will be exposed. Should these wires touch, a dead short will blow the fuse or give a shock to the person using the iron – and electric shocks can cause death. Even getting the flex kinked or knotted can cause the internal wires or conductors to break.

Replacing the flex When buying replacement flex, take the old length with you to make sure you get a replacement of the correct type and rating. It must be of the cloth-covered, braided sort; don't use PVC flex (should this flex touch the hot iron it will melt). Check the flex is long enough; too short a flex can cause stress on the flex clamp in the handle and on the plug and socket outlet.

To remove the flex, undo the screw securing the back plate to the handle and lift off the back plate to expose the terminal connections. The terminals may be of the clamp or ring type. For clamp terminals slacken off the terminal screw to release the cores; for ring terminals, remove the securing nuts and washers to release the cores. Slide off the three heatproof sleeves which protect the rubber-covered wires from the internal heat of the iron. If these sleeves are in good condition, they can be used again; if they are cracked or worn, you should fit new ones. The old flex can now be pulled through the rubber grommet. You will find a clamp securing the flex to the handle; this is for safety so the flex cannot pull loose from the terminals and short the power supply. Note the position of this clamp in relation to the flex and its tightness and remove it to free the flex.

Remove the braided covering from one end of the new flex to a distance equal to the length of the

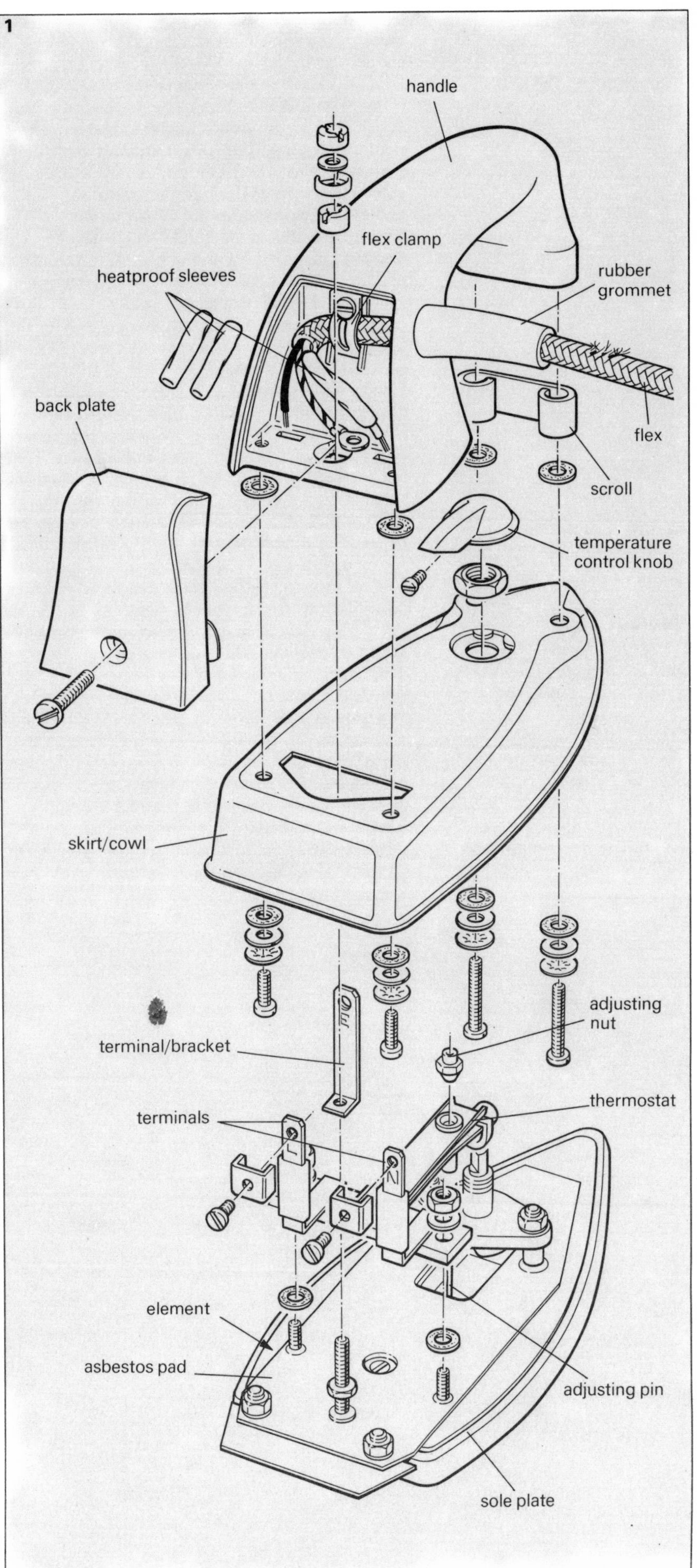

heatproof sleeves plus 13mm (½in). Thread this end through the rubber grommet and secure the flex clamp, leaving about 100mm (4in) of flex free – enough to reach the terminal connections. For clamp terminals bare 10mm (⅜in) at the end of each core and twist the strands tightly to ensure a clean, tight connection. For ring terminals bare 6mm (¼in) at the end of each core and crimp on new rings before connecting. Replace the heatproof sleeves and make the connections to the terminals. The brown core should be connected to the live (L) terminal, the blue core to the neutral (N) terminal and the green/yellow core to the earth (E) terminal. Finally replace the back plate and screw it down firmly. Connect the plug to the other end of the flex and protect it with a 13amp fuse, if it is of the fused type.

Handle replacement To replace the handle (if it is cracked, broken or burnt), first remove the flex. Remember to set out all screws and other parts in order of removal to make reassembly easier. Take out the earth bracket and, if present, slacken the small screw securing the temperature control knob. Prise or pull off this knob and loosen the large nut or hexagonal bolt beneath it; use either a small socket spanner or long-nosed pliers. You should now be able to lift the handle and metal skirt (or cowl) clear of the base plate assembly.

Turn over the handle assembly and remove the fixing screws and their accompanying washers. The handle and cowl can now be separated; you may find a loose metal spacer called a scroll, which you should keep carefully. Replace any asbestos washers not in good condition (or the heat may damage the handle). Refit your new handle carefully in the reverse order, making sure you replace all screws and washers in the correct position.

Thermostat assembly If the thermostat assembly needs replacing because of temperature irregularity or worn contacts, strip the iron down to the base plate assembly (as for handle replacement); then remove the screws securing the thermostat to the base plate and disconnect the wires from the thermostat to the element terminals. On some irons you will have to remove the adjusting nut from the pin at the front of the thermostat assembly; note very carefully the position of this nut before removing it and make sure you replace it in the same position, otherwise the thermostat setting will be affected. Always replace the asbestos washers used beneath the thermostat.

Completely reassemble the iron and test it on pieces of scrap material at the different heat ranges. If the results are not satisfactory, take the iron to an electrician to test on a pyrometer.

Element replacement To replace the element, strip the iron down to the sole plate and remove the clamp plate, the asbestos pad and the element. As before, lay out all screws, nuts and washers in the correct order to make reassembly easier. Fit the new element in place by reversing the procedure you used to remove the old one. When refitting, ensure all surfaces are clean and tightly clamped.

If in any doubt about the right procedure for any work on your iron, seek advice from your local spares or service agent.

Steam irons

All types of steam iron need certain routine checks for internal cleanliness. The most important of these concerns the type of water you use. Lime and fur from tap water or other impure sources build up a deposit in the steam channels; this causes poor performance and corrosion. Even water saved from a defrosted fridge can be slightly contaminated and present problems. The best water to use is distilled, usually available from a chemist or good hardware shop. Don't use battery topping-up water since it may contain ingredients other than

Previous page

1 Exploded view of a typical dry iron, showing the component parts

2 Details of flex connections and different types of terminal (**inset**). When replacing ring terminals on the flex, refit the heatproof sleeves before crimping on the new rings

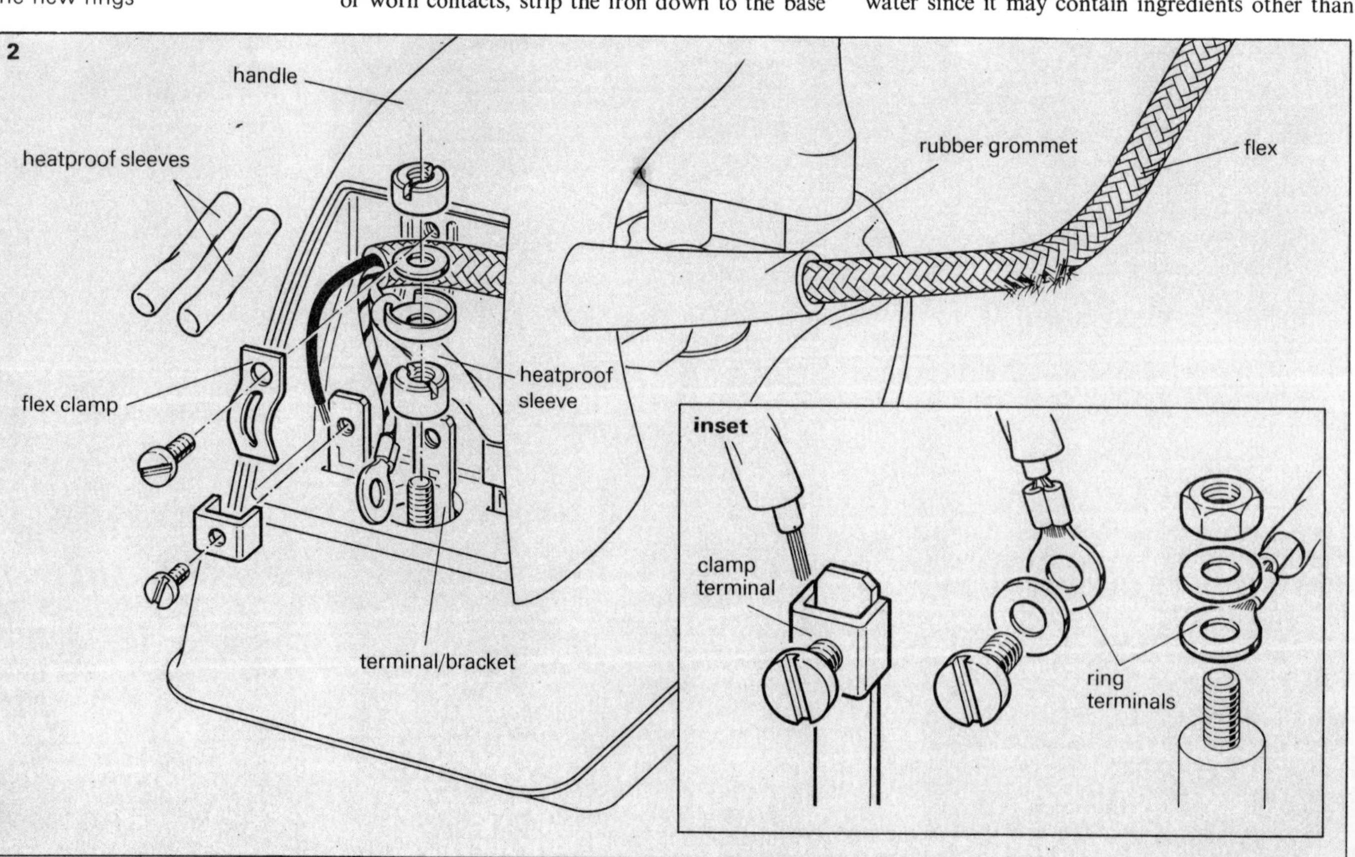

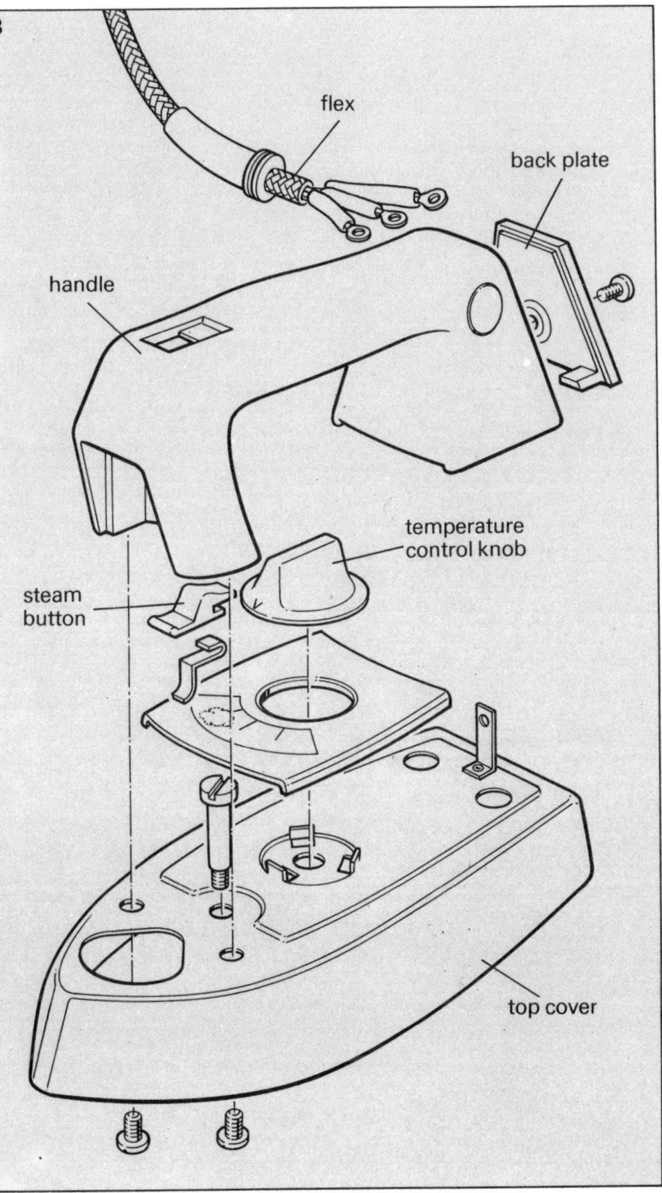

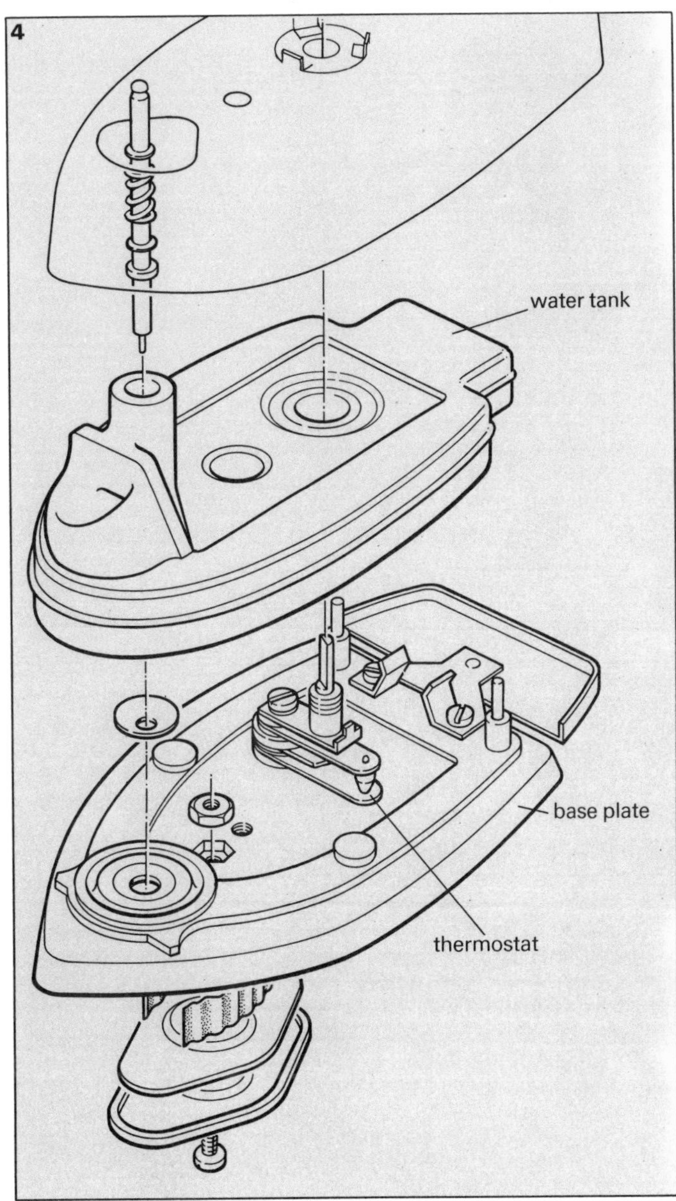

3 Handle assembly of a typical steam iron
4 Base plate assembly of a typical steam iron

distilled water. It is possible to buy a demineralizing agent – crystals which, when dissolved in water, purify it and last for up to 200 fillings of an iron. If you do not have distilled water or a demineralizer, use cooled boiled water rather than tap water.

If a routine cleaning of steam vents, channels or holes does not clear the blockages, you can use a steam iron cleaner. This is a mild acid type of cleaning mixture specially prepared for such a job. No other form of fluid should be tried; it may damage seals or jointing compounds used inside the iron.

Stains on the base plate need not mean impure water but simply the iron has been stored away after use, with a slight amount of water still in it, not standing up on its heel rest but on its base plate. Since the base plate is made of aluminium, dampness caused by water seepage will discolour it and, over a prolonged period, cause corrosion. Therefore, always empty your iron thoroughly after use while it is still hot and make sure the steam button or knob is in the closed position before putting the iron away – on its heel rest. To remove any stains or rough patches from the base, polish it lightly with fine wet and dry emery paper and wipe it clean with a soft cloth.

Sometimes white spots appear on coloured articles being ironed. This usually happens when the iron has been used for long periods as a dry iron and particles of lint or soap powder have become wedged inside the steam channels or holes. A thorough steam cleaning with clean water may be all that is needed to clear away these particles.

Flex renewal Remove the screw covering the back plate and lift the plate off to expose the internal flex connections. Renew the flex in the same way as for a dry iron and replace the back plate firmly.

Handle replacement Remove the back cover and loosen the wires. Prise off the temperature control knob and remove the cover fixing bolt. Lift the handle and top cover clear of the rest of the iron and remove the handle fixing screws. Reverse this operation to refit the new handle. As before, lay out all the components in the right order to ensure easy refitting.

Warning The base plate assembly, water tank and thermostat will be visible when the handle is removed; but alteration or removal of some of these parts is best left to a qualified service agent since some screws rust or deteriorate with age and inexperienced handling can cause more harm than good.

Hair dryers

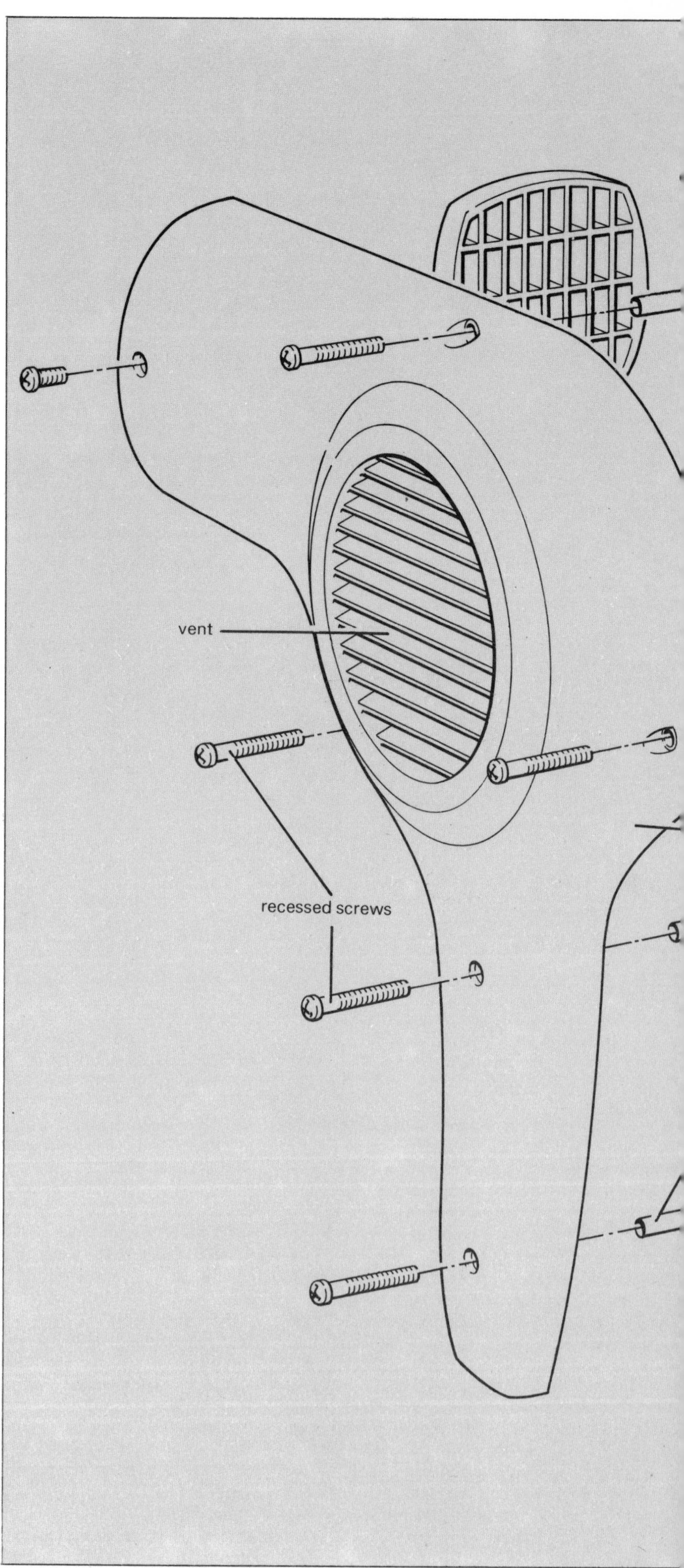

There are many makes and models of hair dryer on the market from which to choose; while looks and price will influence your choice of dryer there are other factors you should consider when buying. For example, it is worth enquiring about servicing both in and out of guarantee, since you may not want to own an appliance which has to be sent away for repair. Check the availability of spare parts; there are many foreign-made appliances which perform extremely well but for which parts are difficult to obtain.

The various models of hair dryer can be categorized into three basic groups: hand-held, shoulder-hung and salon types.

Hand-held dryer

This is probably the most popular type of dryer because of its price, ease of use and speed of drying. Hand-held dryers do differ internally in the shape and size of motors, fans and elements. The motor is usually of an induction type, which does not use the armature and carbon-brushes which vacuum cleaner motors have. This type is usually very reliable in an enclosed space provided the bearings on which the motor revolves remain lubricated and there is no build-up of dust and fine particles of hair within the confined space inside the casing; if there is, the motor will tend to slow down. You should oil the bearings (if they are not of the long-life grease-packed type) and clean the inside of the dryer once a year as described below.

A slow motor is usually indicated by an increase in the heat given off by the element – so it can be seen to glow more brightly than before. If fitted, a cut-out should operate once the element overheats to prevent the element being damaged or the plastic casing of the dryer melting. The reason for the overheating is the motor is not blowing enough air over the element. To correct this you will first have to gain access to the inside of the dryer by removing the screws securing the two halves of the casing. Remove the fan and use a fine, clean paintbrush to dust the motor clean; where relevant, apply a small amount of thin oil to the bearing at each end of the motor. Revolve the motor spindle by hand slowly in both clockwise and anticlockwise directions to ensure the oil works well into each bearing; wipe away all traces of excess oil from the motor and surrounding areas.

If you drop your dryer, don't shake it to see if anything inside appears loose; because of the delicate nature of the interior any loose objects such as nuts, screws or pieces of plastic from the casing may foul the element wire or jam the motor and fan. Carefully check the inside of the dryer; if part of the fan is broken, don't continue to use the dryer since the balance of the fan will be affected and cause wear on the motor bearings as well as becoming noisy. If part of the element is damaged, don't be tempted to join element wire together; such a repair is potentially dangerous.

Flex should be regularly inspected for signs of

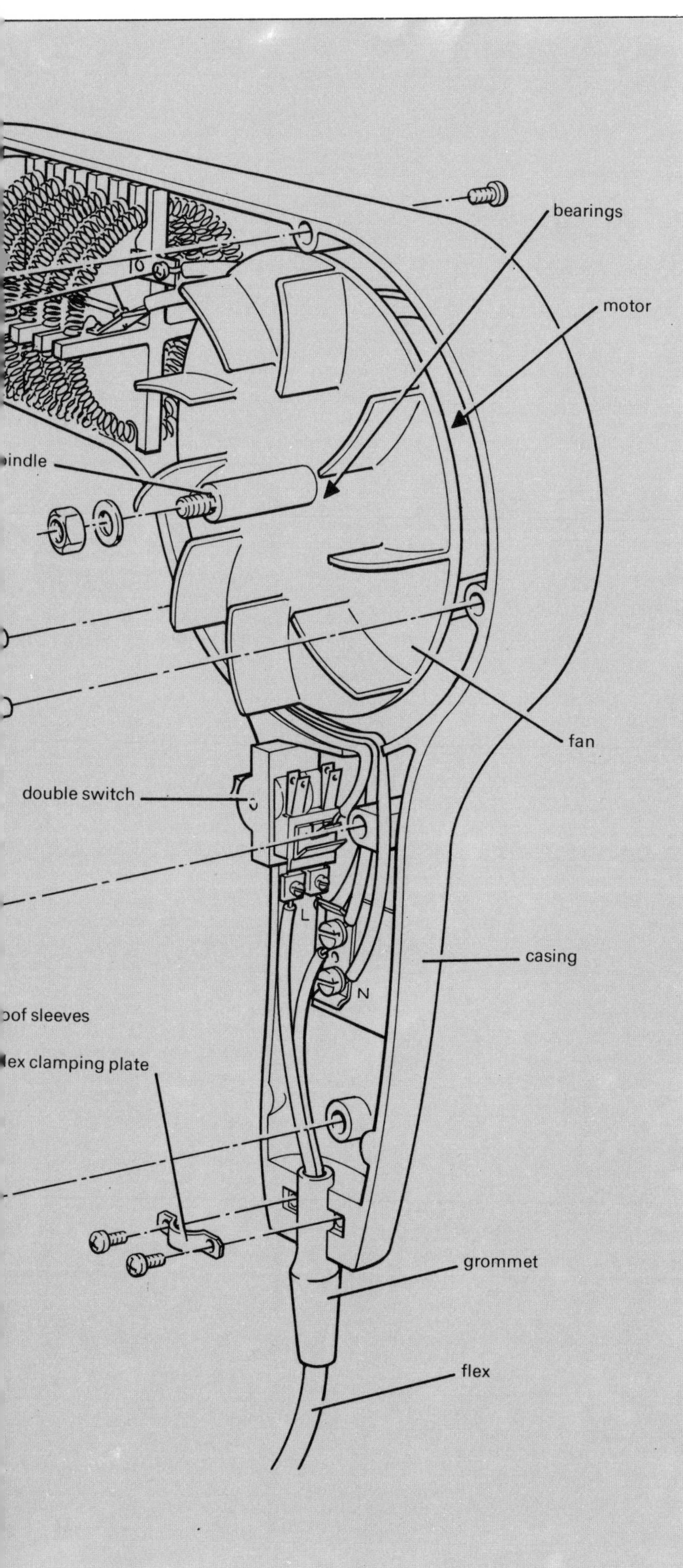

wear and cracks. To replace damaged flex, separate the casing of the dryer and locate the flex clamping plate and screws; remove the screws, lift off the clamping plate, slacken the terminal screws and pull out the flex. Before removing the flex note the length of bared flex for connection purposes and check whether the ends have been soldered or have had ring terminals crimped to them.

If sparking occurs at the switch while the dryer is running, separate the casing and clean the switch contacts (if accessible) by pulling a strip of fine emery cloth between them. If the contacts are not accessible or the sparking continues after cleaning, you will have to replace the switch. Disconnect the wires from the switch terminals, noting the position of each wire on the switch, release any fixing screws and remove the switch. Fit the replacement switch in reverse order, making sure you connect the wires to the correct terminals.

Cold air blowing from the dryer when the temperature switch is in the hot position indicates the element has probably broken. To replace the element, separate the casing, disconnect the element from its terminals and release any fixing screws. Insert the new element and former in reverse order, taking care not to damage the coiled element wire.

Shoulder-hung dryer

Dryers of this type are similar in basic layout to hand-held dryers, but may have a variable heat switch to cope with varying styles and trends of hair dressing. Also, since heat needs to be transferred along a pipe to the hood, a shoulder-hung dryer has a larger element, motor and fan. The condition of the flex and fan motor is very important; you should also check the hose, hose end connections and hood since deterioration will affect the amount of heat transferred to the hood and cracks and loose fits will cause leakage of hot air – thus increasing drying time.

Salon dryer

This type has the motor and element built into the headpiece and is normally attached to a floor stand to allow height adjustment. Most models have three heat settings, with the element and assembly having three sets of spiral heaters to give this variation. Some have remote control switches on the end of a cable, giving a setting from cool to very hot; in these cases the motor and element are combined, with the speed of air blown and the degree of heat being designed to work together (for example, slow speed and low heat, fast speed and maximum heat). These dryers are more expensive to repair than other types, but carrying out simple maintenance as described for the hand-held dryer will ensure longer life.

Left Typical assembly of hand-held dryer showing double switch and element

Remember . . .

Before starting work on any appliance

- Always make sure you will not invalidate any existing guarantee
- Always remove the plug from the socket and, where necessary, turn off the power at the mains
- Check availability and only fit genuine spare parts

Electric fires

There are two main types of electric fire: radiant heaters which give off reflected heat from the front of the fire and convector heaters which give off convected heat from the top of the casing, supplying background heat to an area. Some heaters combine the two types, with radiant elements for instant heat and a convector for background warmth.

Electric fan heaters are also available; these work by forced convection, where air is warmed by being blown over a heated element. With this type of heater, the warm air is distributed more quickly through the room than by natural convection.

Changing mains lead
Because of age, heat deterioration or damage from feet, the mains lead on any electric fire is subject to cracks in the outer covering – and this can be dangerous. You should change the lead at the first sign of wear; don't patch it up with tape and try to disguise the need for replacement. The lead usually passes through the back of the heater and is clamped. Remove the cover to expose the clamp; from here the lead divides to a terminal block, where the switch wires join up. Once these terminal screws are loosened the leads may be withdrawn and replaced. Make sure you buy a replacement lead of the correct rating and with the correct covering to withstand wear and give maximum protection.

Convector heaters

These types of heater are particularly useful in areas where constant warmth is required, such as a sickroom, baby's bedroom or hall. They avoid the risk of burning or fire due to direct concentrated heat, associated with a red-hot bar type of heater; but for safety they should not be installed in bathrooms, airing cupboards or greenhouses where conditions are damp – unless the heater is specifically designed for these conditions. Never place clothing on or near the hot air vent to aid drying; this can lead to overheating and eventual element failure.

It is best to choose a model with a built-in thermostat since this provides control over the amount of heat given and regulates a steady and constant temperature over the required area to give efficiency in terms of comfort and cost.

Parts for most convector heaters are available from the manufacturer by post, together with instructions for fitting them; this is usually the best way of obtaining spares since not many heaters are identical internally and elements and thermostats are made and preset to suit a particular model.

Radiant heaters

These types of electric fires come in many shapes, sizes and designs and with two types of element – pencil-bar and silica-glass tube.

Pencil-bars are the traditional fire elements. Element wire is closely wound along a length of

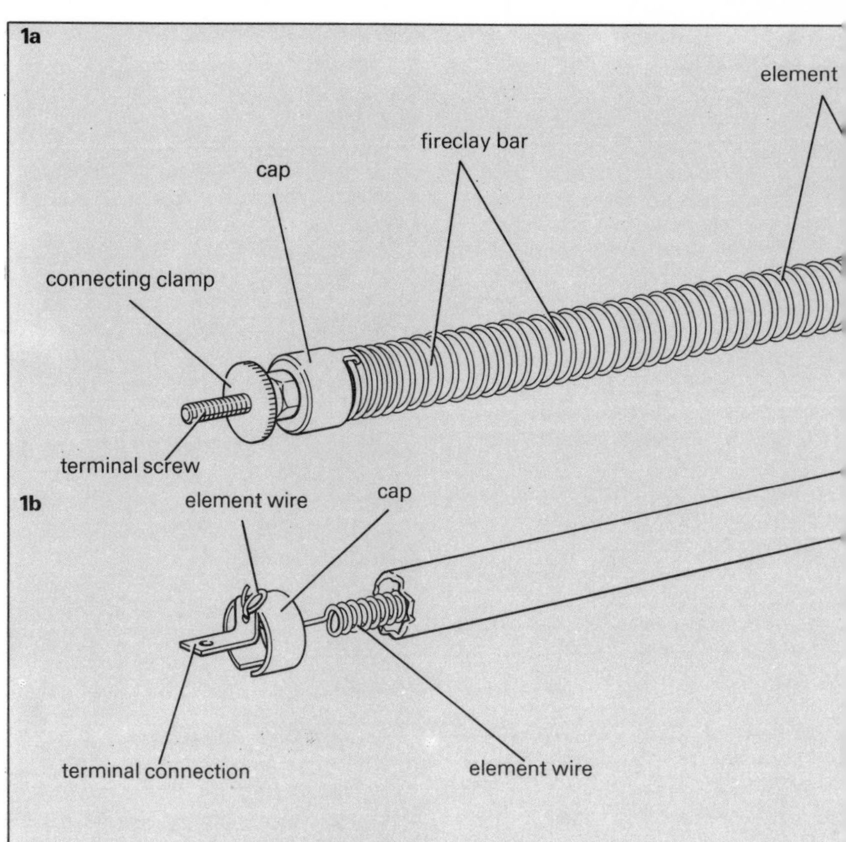

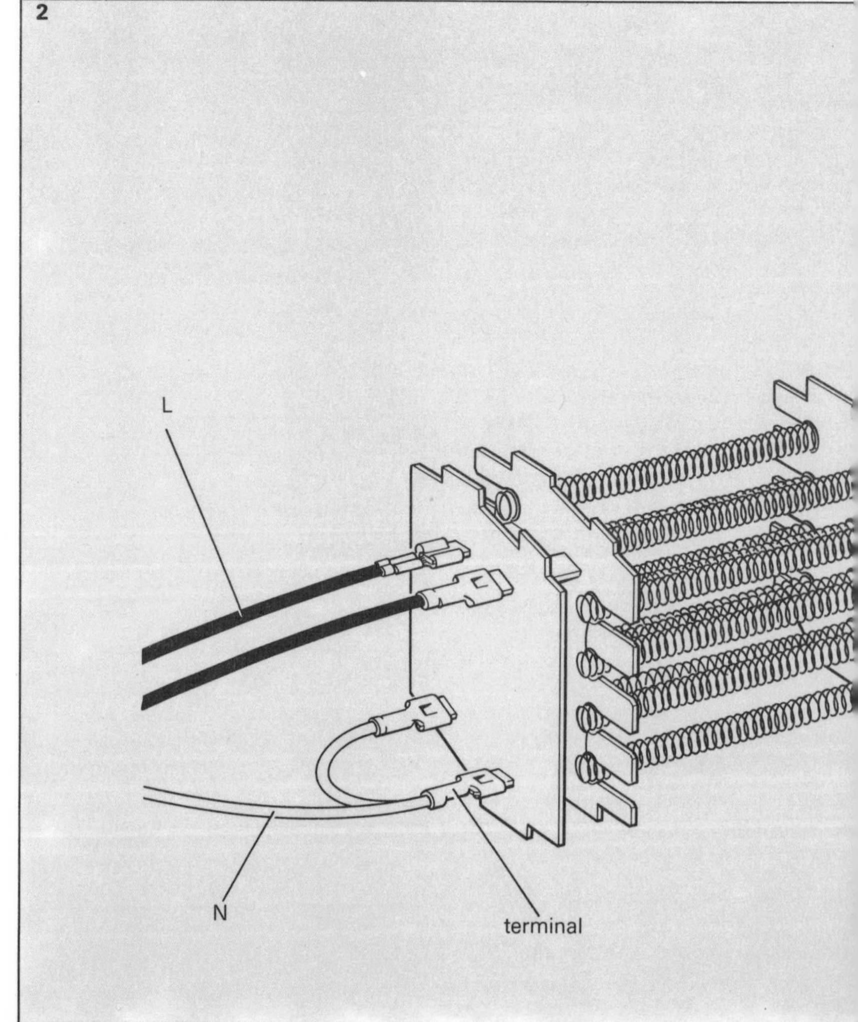

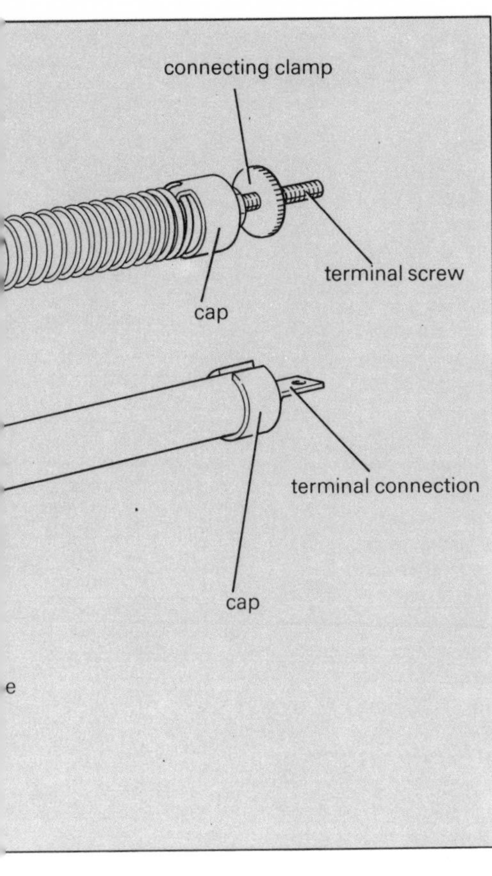

Remember . . .
Before starting work on any appliance
- Always make sure you will not invalidate any existing guarantee
- Always remove the plug from the socket and, where necessary, turn off the power at the mains
- Check availability and only fit genuine spare parts

1a Pencil bar element usually found in older radiant heaters
1b Most modern radiant fires have a silica-glass tube element
2 Rear view of a fan heater element

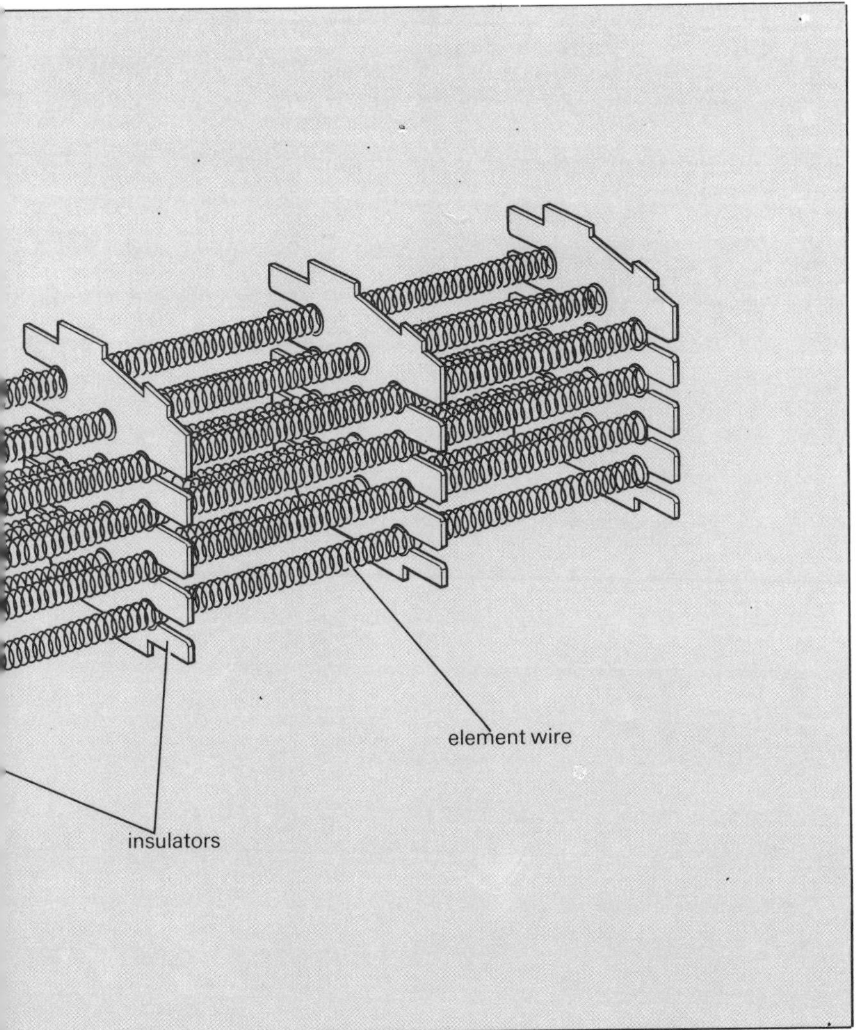

fireclay bar with either wire-round connections round a nut and bolt fixing to the internal wiring or, more commonly, caps on each end with built-in terminal connections. Pencil-bars are very reliable and strong, but can take time to give a red glow.

Silica-glass elements, which are generally more expensive than the pencil-bar type, are used in most modern radiant fires. They have an attractive appearance, give out plenty of heat in a short space of time and are easy to change; they are also easily spoilt. The appearance of the element depends on the cleanliness of the glass tube; never use a dampened cloth or polish to clean the glass since, because of its composition, smudges and smears will appear which cannot be removed. Instead you should lightly dust the glass frequently with a clean lint-free cloth. If the elements need to be removed to make it easier to clean the reflector, remember to protect and handle the glass with cloth since fingerprints on a silica tube are unsightly and once the heat has 'burnt' them on they are impossible to remove. If tubes are accidentally touched during cleaning or handling, use a liquid solvent to remove the grease from the fingerprint marks.

Many elements often fail at the end connections and show signs of burning on these terminals, usually because dirty or loose and badly fitting connections have been sparking slightly and creating heat, a process known as 'arcing'. The heat causes burning of the connections and you should on no account fit a new element to bad connectors or terminals; if they are only slightly worn, clean the terminal connections with fine emery cloth until all traces of burning and corrosion have been removed. Make sure the element connections are firm since a loose fit will cause burning of the ends.

If you are buying a replacement element, first measure the exact length of the failed element so you can ask for one of the right size. It is also important to remember the exact make and model number of the heating appliance; on some fires the number can only be seen once the coal-effect is removed since it is stamped on the inside of the base. If a model number is not available, the fixing centres of the element will be needed and also the wattage of the element, if this is known.

Warning When you need to change an element make sure the fire is disconnected from the power supply. Many accidents occur because people start to loosen the terminal screws or remove supposedly 'dead' elements while the fire is connected.

Fan heaters

It is important the inside of a fan heater is kept free from dust and fluff; besides increasing the risk of fire, a build-up of this type of material can find its way into the motor and its bearings, causing the motor to slow down and possibly fail. A slowly running motor will cause the element to overheat and an overload cut-out to operate so the heater will not function.

To gain access to the inside of the heater, undo the screws which hold the casing in place underneath and remove the casing. Using a clean long-bristled paint brush, carefully dust the motor and fan assembly, the element, overload cut-out and switches. Apply a small drop of light oil to the motor bearings (if not of the permanently sealed grease type) and slowly revolve the spindle by hand to allow the oil to penetrate; wipe off any excess oil.

Refrigerators and freezers

Refrigerators and freezers are designed to keep perishable foods for varying lengths of time by storing them under suitable conditions and at the right temperature. The appliances work by means of a liquid refrigerant flowing through tubes which vapourizes into a gas and absorbs the heat from its surroundings – the freezing unit and refrigerator; on passing through a condenser, it liquefies again and releases its heat from the condenser.

Although you cannot carry out any major repairs on these appliances, you can prolong their life by careful maintenance and by being on the lookout for any malfunction.

Maintaining refrigerators

There are two types of refrigerator, the most common being the compressor type; this compresses the vapour and changes it back into liquid by passing it through a condenser. Some small domestic refrigerators use the absorption method and have an electric element or a gas or oil burner instead of a compressor.

The temperature inside both types of refrigerator is controlled and kept constant by a thermostat. Domestic refrigerators maintain a temperature of below 7°C (or 44°F). Manufacturers usually indicate a normal setting and this should only need to be adjusted in very hot weather or in an exceptionally hot kitchen.

The evaporator is the compartment formed by the tubes containing the refrigerant and is at the top of the refrigerator. It is the coldest part and the star markings on the door of the evaporator indicate the length of time frozen foods can be stored in the evaporator; corresponding markings are put on frozen food packages.

Your refrigerator should run trouble free for a fair number of years. The power unit – the compressor and motor – is sealed into a welded steel casing and needs no attention. If thermostats fail, they can be replaced; but this and other major faults which might eventually occur can only be repaired by trained servicing engineers.

Defrosting Unless your refrigerator is of the automatic defrosting type, it should be defrosted once a week. Defrost regularly and don't wait until you have to; a layer of ice means the unit has to work harder and so costs more to run. Around the outside of the freezer box there is a sensor tube from the thermostat; if the tube has a covering of ice on it, this can make a great deal of difference to the temperature of the refrigerator. You may have to raise the setting on the thermostat to maintain adequate cooling of the interior, which means the compressor motor of the refrigerator (if fitted) or the heating element is working overtime to create normal conditions. This will use up a great deal of energy needlessly. Moisture drawn from the air in the cabinet freezes on the surface of the evaporator and should be removed when it reaches a thickness of about 6mm (¼in). Remember to switch the thermostat off when you defrost.

There are three ways of defrosting: by setting the control dial to off, by depressing the defrost button which switches off the refrigeration system or through a fully automatic defrosting system where fitted. With the first two methods you will have to empty the refrigerator first and you can speed up defrosting by placing a bowl of hot water on the top shelf. On models with the fully automatic system defrosting takes place at regular intervals; there is therefore no build-up of ice and no need to remove food from inside the refrigerator.

Remember not to use a hard, sharp instrument to remove ice when defrosting the freezer compartment; the evaporator is made of thin aluminium with pipes attached and a crack in the lining of the evaporator can damage the cooling system.

Over-freezing This is usually caused by a badly fitting door, a faulty thermostat or a worn or damaged main door seal which allows the warmer air into the refrigerator; this creates a false temperature and makes the thermostat or heater work harder than usual. If the points inside the thermostat stick because of age or wear, the motor will not receive the signal to switch off and over-freezing will result; this may cause the motor and system to overheat and eventually fail. If you find the evaporator quickly becomes covered with a deep coating of frost, the cause is probably not in the machine but because vegetables, salads and other foods with a high moisture content are packed in the refrigerator without being put into polythene bags; it may also mean the door seal is faulty.

Malfunctions Although gas leaks are difficult to detect, they are indicated by a lack of freezing

1 Typical domestic refrigerator showing component parts
2 Cycle of compression-type refrigerator
3 Cycle of absorption-type refrigerator

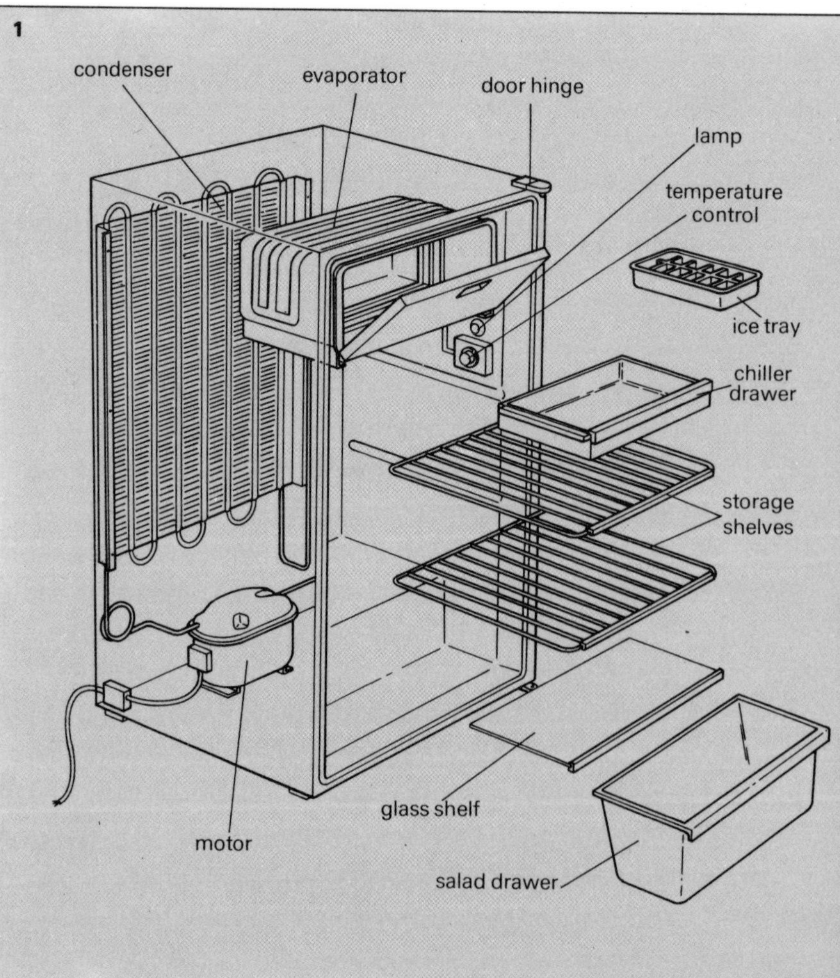

despite the thermostat being set on maximum. To replace the refrigerant you will have to call in a service engineer, who has the necessary equipment. If the interior light fails, fit a new lamp; if that does not work, check whether the door switch controlling the light is faulty. If the power fails, check the plug fuse and wiring and check the socket outlet by plugging in another appliance. Also check the flex is not damaged or broken.

If the light works but the motor does not run, leave the door open till the frost on the evaporator begins to melt. If the motor does not start then, the fault is either in the thermostat or in the motor. If the motor is running but there is no frost in the refrigerator, select the coldest temperature setting, shut the refrigerator door and check whether the condenser is getting hot; if it is not, the fault is in the refrigerating system and needs expert attention. Excess cooling when the motor is running and the temperature selector is at the lowest setting means either the thermostat has failed or the refrigerating system is faulty.

To stop your refrigerator smelling, wash it out from time to time with warm water and a little bicarbonate of soda. Wash the outside with soapy water and give it an occasional rub with a silicone polish to keep the surface in good condition. Never use soap or detergent inside the refrigerator.

If you are going away for any length of time and you switch your refrigerator off, remember to turn the thermostat off as well, otherwise the bellows inside the switch will expand as the temperature in the refrigerator rises and possibly damage the contacts. Also leave the door open, otherwise dampness will cause mould to form inside.

Spare parts You can obtain spare parts such as door seals, hinges and shelves for most makes of refrigerator from the manufacturers or service dealers. These parts are usually held on with self-tapping screws which are easy to remove when replacing a damaged part. Remember to quote the correct model and serial numbers when you want a spare part. The lamps, which are activated by the automatic light switch when the door opens, can be either screw or bayonet fittings. The switch and lamp are both replaceable. Don't attempt to repair the motor or the thermostat; call in an engineer.

Maintaining freezers

Freezers operate in a similar way to refrigerators, but they have a more powerful compressor motor since they have more work to carry out. There are three types of freezer: the chest type which has the lid on top, the upright type which has a door in front and the combination type which comprises a freezer and refrigerator in one cabinet with separate doors. A freezer can be kept almost anywhere, provided there is adequate air circulation around the cabinet to prevent overheating.

Defrosting A chest freezer should be defrosted once or twice a year and an upright model two to three times a year. As with a refrigerator, don't let frost build up to more than 6mm (¼in) otherwise the performance of the freezer will be impaired.

Malfunctions It is important the freezer is not out of action for a long period of time since any food in it would soon be defrosted; a number of warning devices are therefore fitted to appliances. These include an electricity supply light, a temperature safety light, a fast freezing indicator light and on some models an alarm plug which makes a loud buzzing if the power fails.

If the freezer is not operating and there is no glow at the pilot light, check the plug or connector to see if the unit fuse has blown or whether the switch has been turned off by mistake. Serious rises or drops in temperature are usually caused by a faulty thermostat and you should call in a service engineer to rectify the problem.

If your freezer cuts out, there is no need to panic. The contents, depending on the quantity of food, are usually safe for between six and 12 hours, provided you keep the door or lid shut. This should be long enough for a simple fault such as a blown fuse, loose connection or faulty socket, to be diagnosed or for a service engineer to arrive.

Remember...

Before starting work on any appliance

- Always make sure you will not invalidate any existing guarantee
- Always remove the plug from the socket and, where necessary, turn off the power at the mains
- Check availability and only fit genuine spare parts

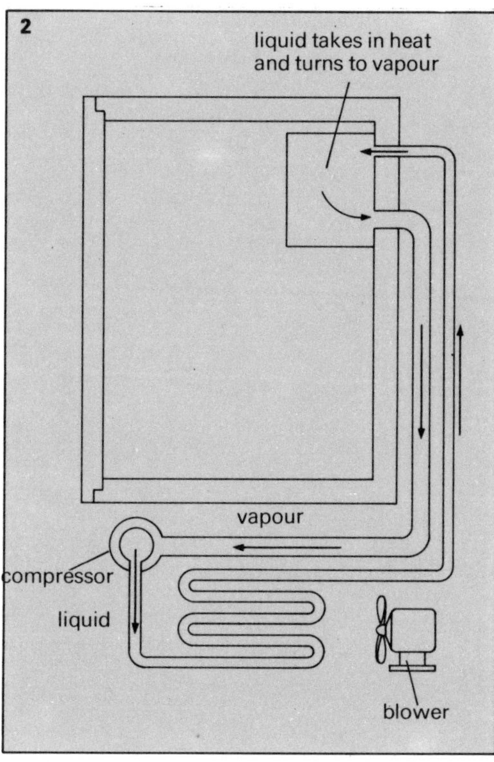

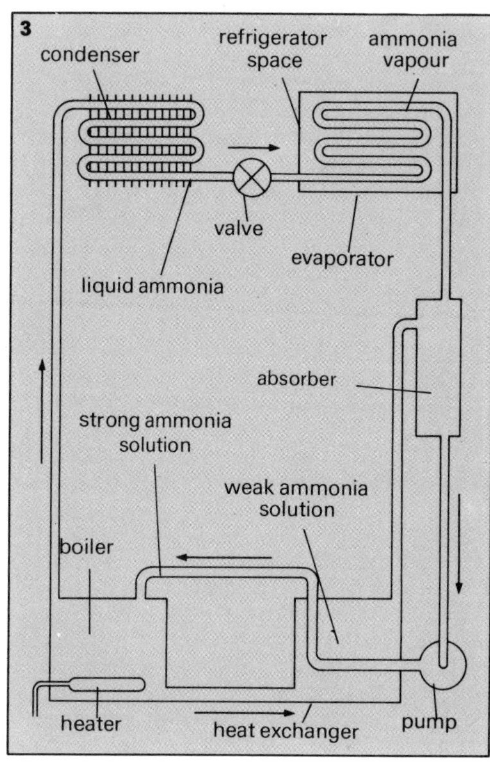

Mixers and blenders

Food mixers and blenders are two of the most labour-saving appliances available for the kitchen. There is a wide range of models and your choice will be determined – apart from appearance and price – by the number of jobs the appliance can perform using the variety of attachments available with each model.

Some food mixers may be uneconomical to repair if the motor fails; many manufacturers, however, have service agents who carry spare parts and in most cases a replacement motor can be fitted at a reasonable cost. Always check to see if a repair is possible and worthwhile.

Mixers can be divided into two groups – large food preparation machines and hand mixers; blenders are either an attachment to a mixer or a separate unit. Food preparation machines are large and powerful; they can tackle a wide variety of cookery tasks and will cope easily with large quantities and heavy mixtures. They usually have a wide range of optional attachments, including primarily a blender, which are for specialized food preparation.

Hand mixers are smaller and less powerful than food preparation machines; they are also less expensive and more commonly used. They can tackle most of the tasks performed by the larger type of machine, but in smaller quantities and with lighter mixtures; they are flexible since you can use them in a saucepan or mixing bowl.

Hand mixers

This type of mixer should be used only for light work; it tends to become overloaded if used for heavy work such as making dough. When choosing a mixer decide to which uses it will most often be put; if you have to overload a hand mixer, you really require a food preparation machine.

Replacing gears One of the results of overloading the mixer is damage to the gears which drive the two beaters. The gears are normally made of plastic or nylon; in the event of overloading they are designed to strip and lose the drive from the motor, preventing the motor seizing up and burning itself out. To renew the gears, separate the two halves of the mixer body; these are usually held together with nuts and bolts. Once you can see the gears, you will find they are held in position by a frame, which also connects the motor drive shaft to the gears.

Determine whether the gears are different from each other (that is moving to the left or right); some mixers use identical gears and some use opposites. Note which type you have and how they fit together before you remove them. Ensure you buy the correct replacement gears and ask the supplier which grease you should use with them; the gears must be coated with the recommended grease before you reassemble them inside the appliance.

Once greased and replaced, insert the two beaters in place and slowly rotate the motor shaft by hand. This will turn the beaters; if they scrape against one another, you will have to reposition the gears so the inserts for the beaters are in the correct relative positions. Beaters knocking against one another while the appliance is running will cause serious damage and could be dangerous.

Food preparation machines

These machines may at first sight appear very enclosed and sealed; there are, however, several small repairs and simple maintenance jobs you can perform.

Belt and pulleys If the drive belt needs to be replaced because it has frayed, cracked or stretched, you can do this yourself. Remove the mixing bowl and take off the top cover, usually held with three screws. This cover will usually have an anti-vibration seal on the front of the gearbox assembly; this should also be removed. You can now remove the drive belt; check whether the large pulley is metal or nylon since each type requires a different belt. The correct replacement belt can be obtained from the supplier of the mixer. The small pulley is held to the motor shaft by a pin driven through it. If it should need replacing, remove the pin by lifting off the loose sleeve and tapping it out with a drift. Support the back of the pulley with one hand to avoid damage to the motor shaft or motor as you tap the drift. Once the pin is out you can remove the pulley and replace it with the correct component.

To replace the large pulley you have to remove the clutch dog which holds it in place; this is screwed to a drive pinion assembly. Hold the gear

1 Exploded view of a typical electric hand mixer, showing the component parts
2 Exploded view of a typical food preparation machine, with the mixing bowl removed for clarity, and detail of the gearbox (**inset**)
3 Exploded view of a typical blender attachment, showing the component parts

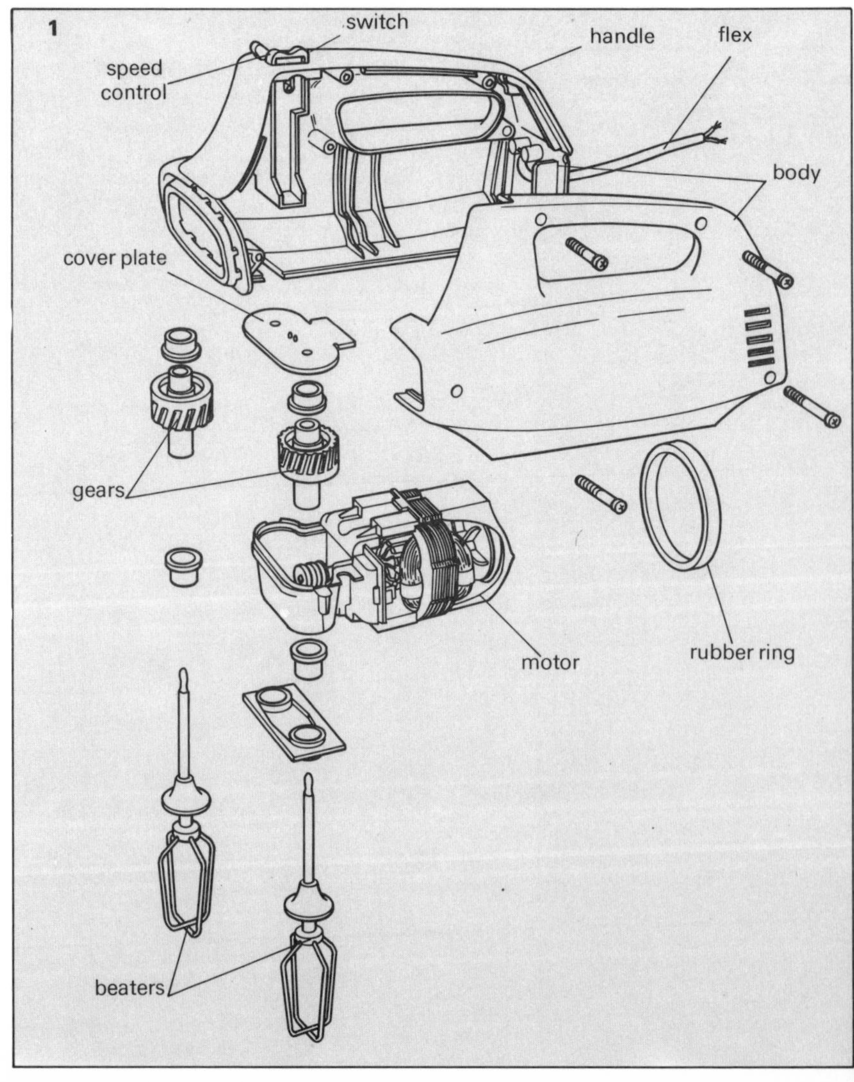

inside the slow speed connection as you remove the dog with the correct size spanner. Be very careful not to damage the gear mechanism. You may be able to borrow or hire the correct removing tool from the manufacturer; if not, try to lock the gear with a large flat-bladed screwdriver.

Planet hub and gear Inside the moving hub gear is a smaller gear, which may be metal or nylon. This gear may fail, therefore nylon versions are now replaced with their metal counterpart since it is much stronger. You will have to remove the planet hub to replace the gear; lift the head of the mixer backwards and secure it in position. The hub is held by a nut and washer; once removed you can free the hub by tapping the spindle with a mallet. With the hub free you should see the gear attached to its drive shaft with a push-on clip. If the gear is broken, you will see the pieces loose inside the hub. Prise off the hub clip with two small flat-bladed screwdrivers and fit a replacement gear; it is worth fitting a new hub clip to ensure the new gear is completely secure on the drive shaft.

Blenders

A blender or liquidizer may be an attachment to a food mixer or a separate self-contained unit. These machines vary in power, design and price.

Drive coupling wear If you disregard the correct quantities and thicknesses to use in the blender, the drive coupling inside its base will tend to wear very quickly. The coupling is made of a flimsy material so if the blender seizes up during use, the coupling will break or melt. This prevents the motor stopping and causing greater damage to the appliance.

Bearing wear Another reason the blender may seize up is if the bronze bearing in which the cutter blade rotates dries up because of lack of lubrication; in this case heat is created which will cause the shaft to seize. When lubricating this bearing, grip the nut securing the cutter blades with pliers and unscrew the drive coupling; on some blenders the blades spin in a clockwise direction while on others they spin anti-clockwise. Lubricate the bearing with vegetable oil and clean the shaft so there is a smooth running fit. Replace the cutter blade in the reverse order of removal.

Motor wear Adjustment to the speed variation control and the motor of these appliances should be left to your local service agent; they are complex and require fine adjustment.

Remember . . .

Before starting work on any appliance

- Always make sure you will not invalidate any existing guarantee
- Always remove the plug from the socket and, where necessary, turn off the power at the mains
- Check availability and only fit genuine spare parts

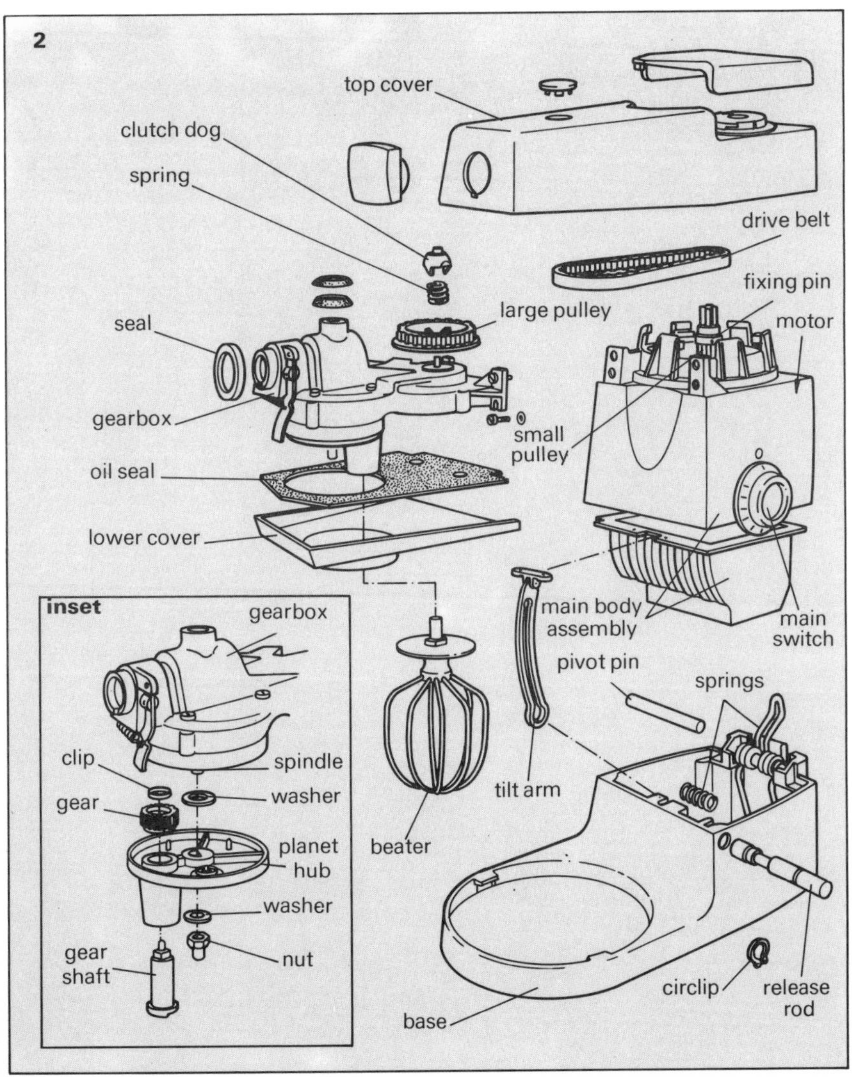

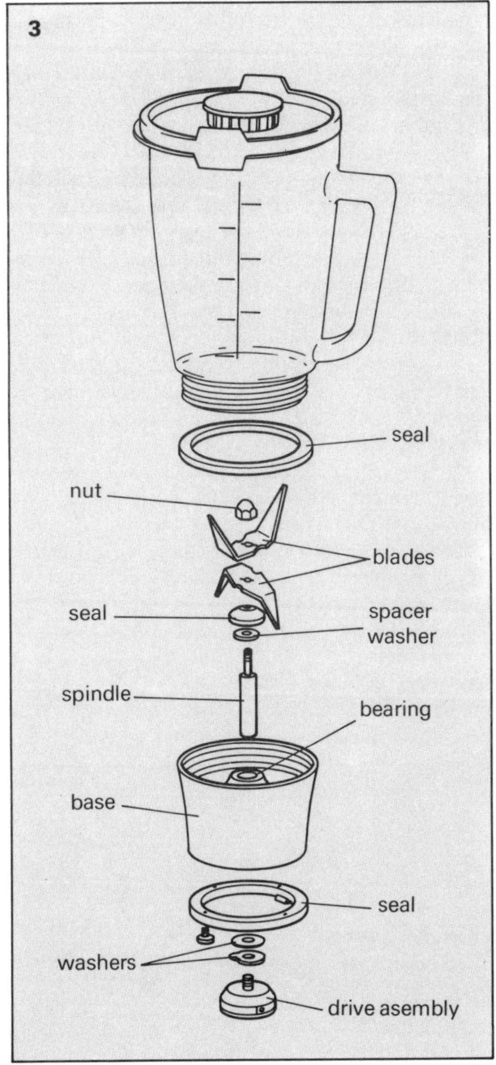

Electric kettles

The electric kettle is a very useful appliance and worth looking after, since you will only realize how much you rely on it when it breaks down. A regular check takes only a matter of minutes, while the length of time it takes to boil a pan of water on a cooker compared with the high speed electric kettle is quite enormous.

The working part of the kettle – the element – is available in different sizes, both in wattage and means of fitting. The higher the wattage, the faster the kettle boils – and the less electricity you use to boil the water. You will need to know the make and model number of your kettle as well as the diameter of the element fitting hole when buying replacements to ensure you get the right type, although adaptable elements are available.

Most spare parts can be readily obtained from electrical shops, although handles, lids and knobs may need to be ordered from individual manufacturers.

Wiring Inspect the plug for loose connections and the kettle connector for evidence of overheating. Regularly check the flex for wear; at the first sign of deterioration, such as cracking or melting of the outer insulation, replace the flex with a new one of the correct rating.

Looking at the connector end of a standard kettle you will see a recessed screw. If you remove the screw, the outer part of the connector will slide down the flex and expose all the terminal screws and the clamping screws. Loosen all the screws so the flex can be withdrawn and replaced. Make sure the new flex is correctly fitted; if in any doubt, have it checked by an expert.

Connector When replacing the flex, check for signs of burning or wear on the connector contacts. If the connector is worn, replace it at the same time; you can buy ready made-up leads with the connector attached. Burning on the live terminal of the connector is sometimes caused by the connector being removed from the kettle when the power is turned on. Every time this is done, a spark jumps between the live connection and the pin on the kettle element; this cannot usually be seen, but it does cause overheating to both the pin and connector. If you notice burning on the element pin, the element must be replaced before serious damage occurs.

Element To change the element, first unscrew the shroud; behind this you will find a fibre washer. Remove both, lift off the lid and grasp the element from the inside; you will now be able to move and withdraw it from the inside of the body. Fit a rubber washer on the new element to provide a seal between the element and the kettle body; clean all traces of old washers and fur from the kettle, especially round the element hole. Place the fibre washer on the outside of the element before tightening the shroud. Test the kettle for leaks before using it again and, after one or two boilings which will slightly soften the rubber washer, tighten the shroud again. Repeat this operation whenever you have to change element washers or descale the kettle.

Feet Feet are often damaged by placing the kettle on a hot surface such as a cooker. Most kettles have 'push-on' type feet which are easy to replace; if, however, a foot is knocked off along with its fixing stud, this is more difficult to replace. One company does make a foot repair kit; all you need to do is drill a small hole in the kettle base where the stud was fixed, insert a screw and washers from the inside of the kettle and onto this screw a new plastic foot with a threaded insert inside.

Spout Leaks around the kettle spout are a serious problem since most adhesives do not form a permanent seal on chromium plating or aluminium:

Remember...
Before starting work on any appliance
- Always make sure you will not invalidate any existing guarantee
- Always remove the plug from the socket and, where necessary, turn off the power at the mains.
- Check availability and only fit genuine spare parts

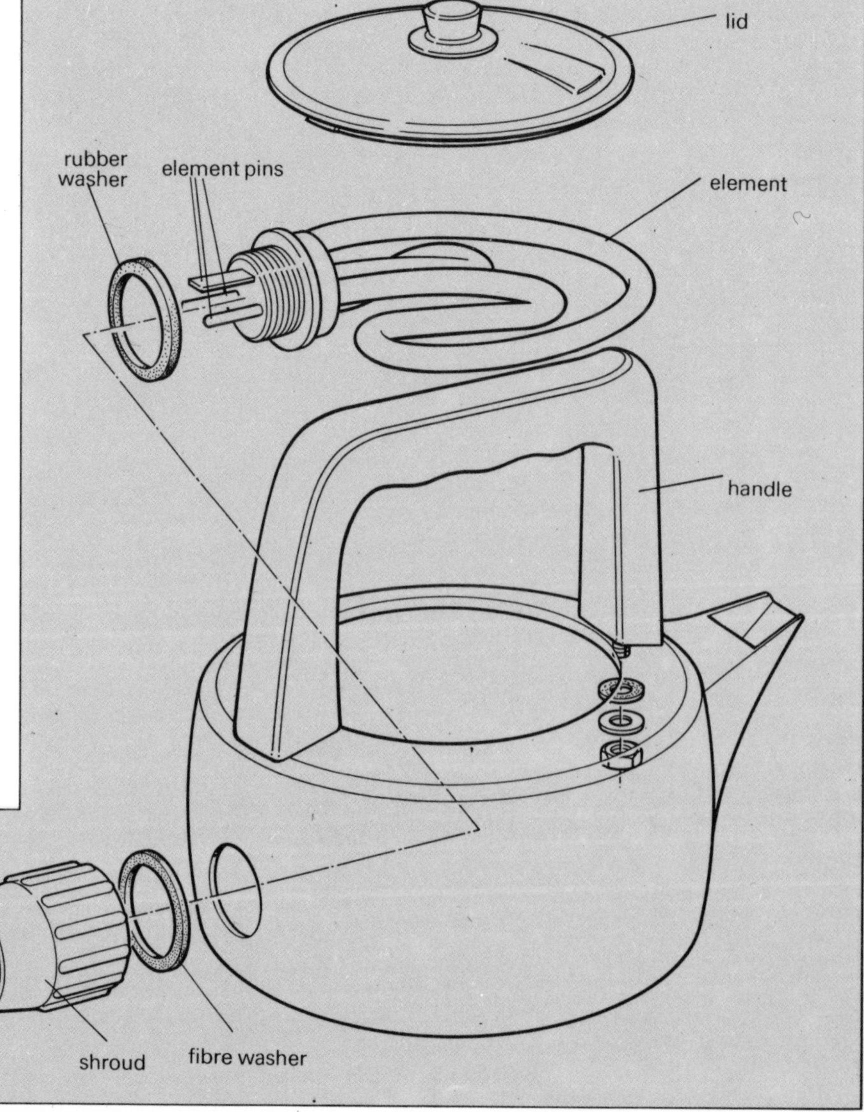

nor are they able to withstand the high temperatures of boiling water. The only sure remedy is to buy a new kettle or a new body.

Descaling kettle All types of water heater are subject to furring. In the case of kettles, fur will increase the boiling time, cause automatic kettles (see below) to switch off prematurely due to excessive heat transference to the switch and could lead to failure of the switch unit as it melts from overheating. The kettle should be regularly descaled with a proprietary descaler which will dissolve the lime and fur; you can also try using a defurring device to prevent build-up of lime on the element.

Automatic types

Automatic kettles, which switch themselves off once the water has boiled, work on the principle that heat or steam from boiling water activates a cut-out or trips the switch to off. This avoids accidentally leaving the kettle to boil dry.

Heat-operated Some kettles use temperature controlled devices in which the switch is activated by heat passing through the element. The preset thermal cut-outs work on pins or studs attached to the inside of the element: heat passing through these pins bends the thermal contact and shuts off power to the element. Although this is a safer mechanism than the steam-operated cut-outs, since steam does not enter the switch contact area, furring around the sensing area of the element can lead to overheating of the contacts and a reduction in the life of the kettle. If this happens you will have to replace the element as previously described.

Steam operated With some kettles the steam travels along a tube to the bi-metal cut-out; care must be taken not to overfill the kettle since large amounts of water passing down the tube can damage the switch assembly. This type of kettle is usually identifiable by a small black switch unit with a neon light and a red button on top to activate the unit. The switch assemblies are preset and cannot be adjusted once fitted.

Changing switches

To change the switch you simply remove the single self-tapping screw and gently lift the switch, along with its sealing washer, away from the kettle. You will see the moving point or contact; as the switch button is pressed, the contact springs into position and pushes a glass rod down onto the leaf of the bi-metal strip. Extreme damp may cause the rod to seize up, which can result in the contact failing to reach the element pin and therefore not switch on; or the rod may stick in the downward position and so hold the switch to 'on'. These defects cause overheating and the element may burn out. Should they occur, try to free the mechanism very carefully until, by pushing both button and bi-metal strip, the contact moves smoothly. If the kettle does not boil, check the condition and tension of the contact and bi-metal strip. If they are too slack, the slightest amount of steam will activate the mechanism and cause it to switch off prematurely; in this case you will have to replace the switch assembly.

Changing element seals

The element on an automatic kettle has a rubber seal inside the body and a fibre one on the outside. Instead of a shroud securing the element, as with standard kettles, a locking ring is used. This is a threaded collar with slots in it to take a special spanner; you can use a blunt screwdriver to tighten or loosen it, provided you are careful. If there is a cover tube over the steam pipe, take out the single screw which holds it in place before removing the element.

Don't forget to test the kettle for leaks before fitting the switch assembly and check the condition of the element contact before reconnecting to the power. The element contact is small and must be kept clean and unpitted. Above the contact is a small bent contact for the neon light; if slightly displaced, the light will not work. In this case a slight repositioning of the neon light contact should correct the fault.

Below left Typical assembly of standard electric kettle
Below Typical assembly of automatic electric kettle

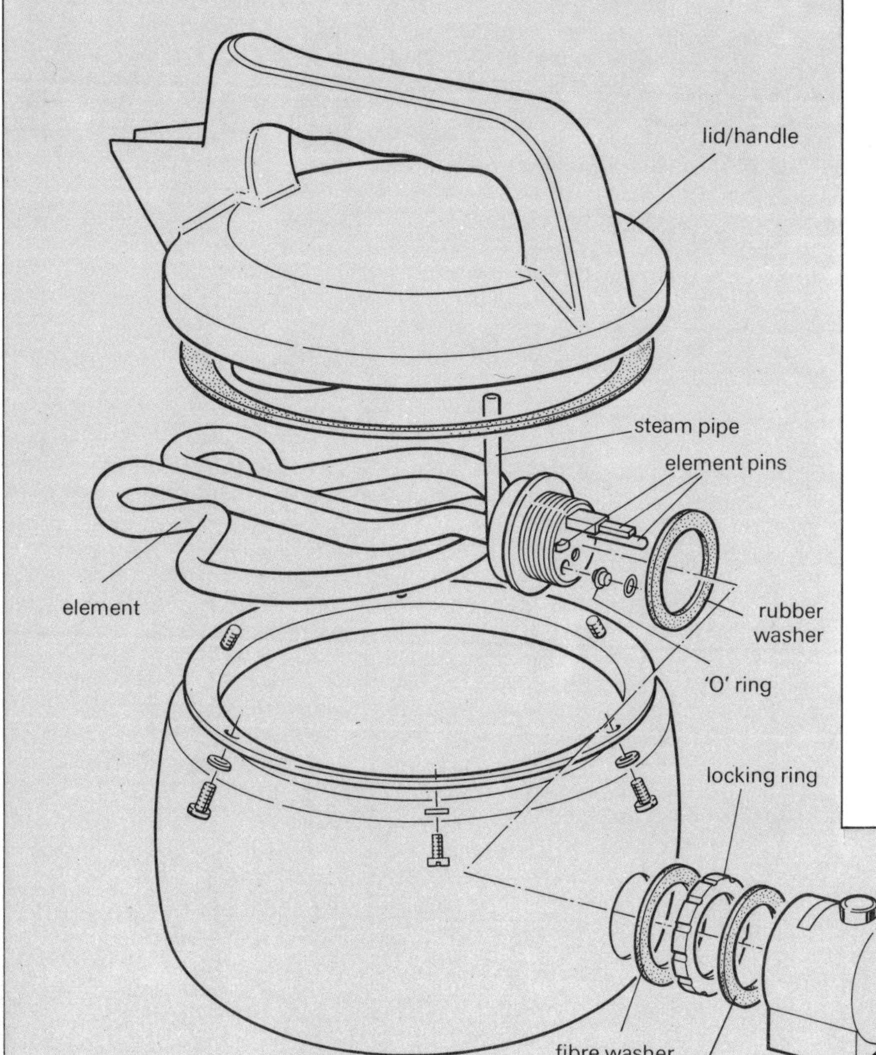

Electric toasters

As with most domestic appliances there are various makes and models of toaster which work in much the same way. A bi-metallic type of thermostat bends with the heat and operates a solenoid cell which trips the pop-up mechanism. There is a certain amount of basic maintenance and repair work you can do yourself, although for some jobs you will need a qualified electrician. To replace the element, thermostat or the latch-release solenoid, special tools are necessary and settings have to be precise; this work should be left to a professional.

Renewing flex Flex renewal is necessary if the outer covering deteriorates or if the flex has 'blown'. Place the toaster upside down on a protective surface, remove the screw(s) which secures the base cover and lift it off. This exposes the lead terminals and their screws; note their positions and remove the screws. The leads from the flex clamp to the terminals are covered with heatproof sleeving which protects them from the extreme heat inside the toaster. Loosen the flex clamp and pull out the flex. When refitting the new flex, it is important the leads are bared back and cut to the correct length. The three cores, when exposed beneath the outer sheathing or braided covering, should be the same length as those on the original flex, and the bared ends of the cores should be 9–12mm ($\frac{3}{8}$–$\frac{1}{2}$in) long. If the heatproof sleeving requires changing, cut it into the same lengths as the original sleeving. You can buy this sleeving by the length and it is worth keeping any left over to use in the future.

Cleaning linkage mechanism From time to time it is important to remove the base and give the linkage mechanism and associated parts a good cleaning. A build-up of crumbs not only impedes the pop-up assembly, but also fouls the thermostat bi-metal, causing burning, and attracts flies and insects. Remove the screw(s) at the opposite end of the toaster from the flex entry, which secures the base and crumb tray. Clean out any pieces of food with a long, narrow, soft bristle brush. Remember the element wires are very fragile; if caught by a sharp instrument and broken, they cannot be repaired. If you need to get at the inside of the toaster, remove the screws – usually one in each corner – which secure the body to the base and ease off the body.

Remember...

Before starting work on any appliance

- Always make sure you will not invalidate any existing guarantee
- Always remove the plug from the socket and, where necessary, turn off the power at the mains
- Check availability and only fit genuine spare parts

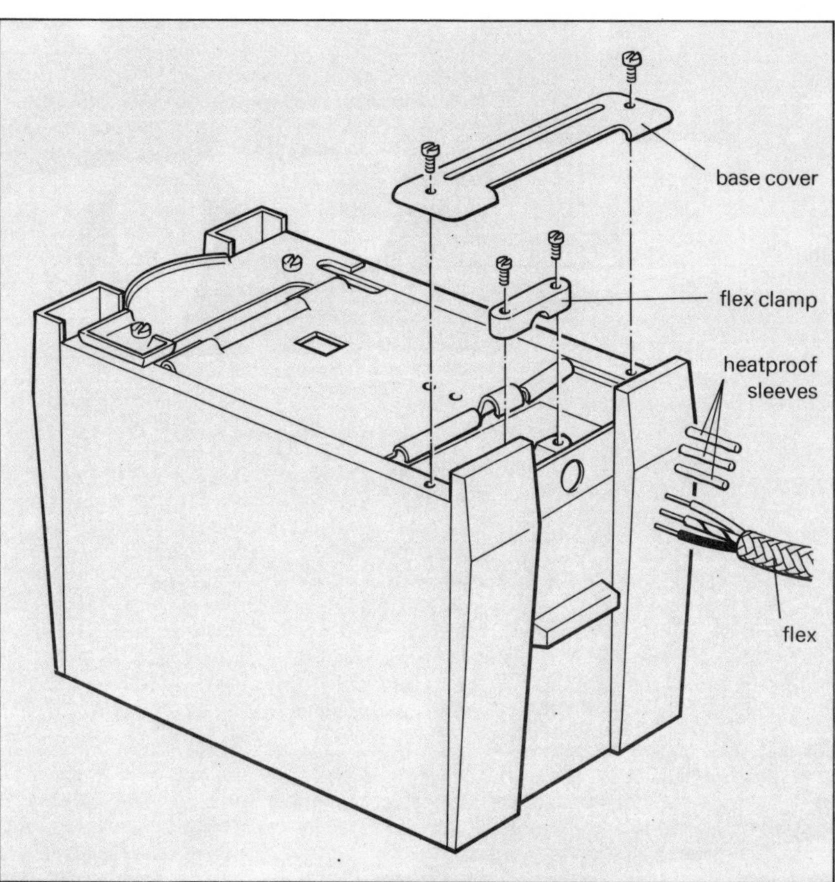

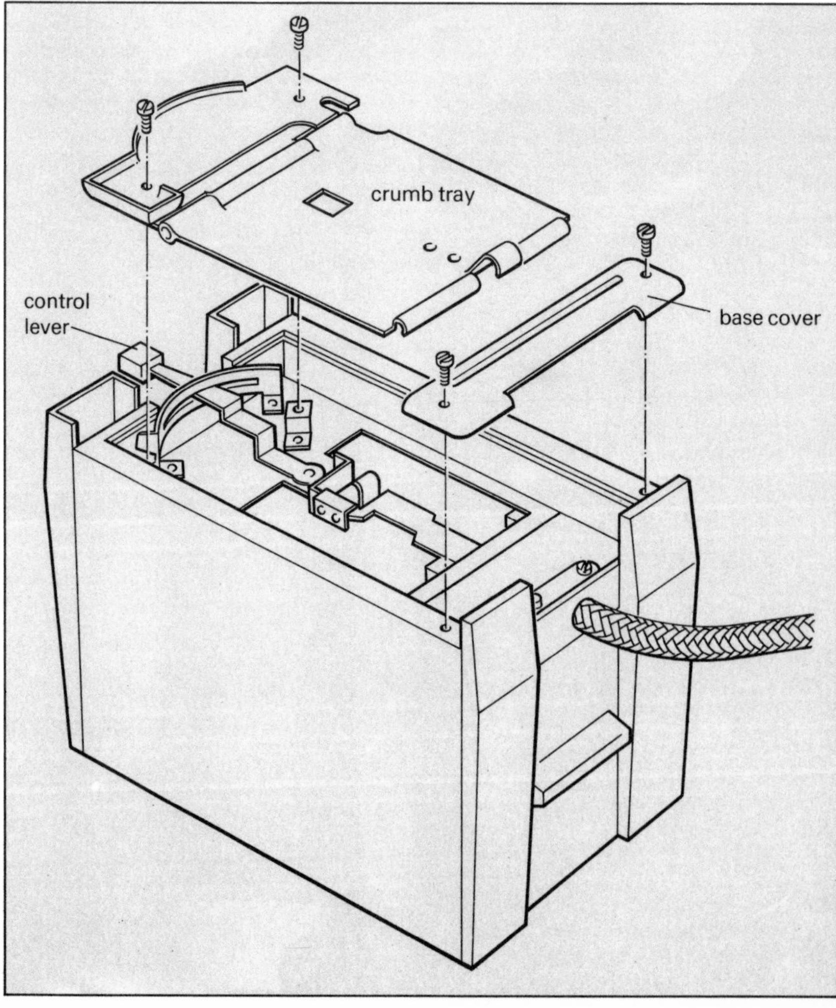

Above right Renewing the flex on a toaster
Right Removing the crumb tray to gain access to the linkage mechanism

Index